Sylvia walked ahead of me toward the enormous stage with its orchestra, a backdrop of manhigh Oscars, amid a sea of flowers. The applause was overpowering. She stood in front of the microphones.

"Ladies and . . ." she stopped, smiled happily. I smiled happily. "Ladies and gentlemen, and my dear friends. I thank you with all my heart for the great honor you have bestowed on me . . ." The Oscar slipped from her hands, fell on the floor, and rolled to one side, as she collapsed. I was just able to prevent her from falling on the floor. Shrieks from the audience!

Now Sylvia was lying on her back, her eyes open wide, unseeing. Her dress was torn at the shoulder.

Was this yet again one of her "performances," or had something truly terrifying thrown her into shock?

NO MAN
IS AN
ISLAND

a novel by

Johannes Mario Simmel

translated by

Catherine Hutter

FAWCETT POPULAR LIBRARY • NEW YORK

NO MAN IS AN ISLAND

Original German title: NIEMAND IST EINE INSEL

Published by Fawcett Popular Library, CBS Educational and Professional Publishing, a division of CBS Inc., by arrangement with Droemersche Verlagsanstalt Th. Knaur Nachf. Copyright © 1975 by Droemersche Verlagsanstalt Th. Knaur Nachf., Munich/Zurich.

English translation copyright © 1982 by Catherine Hutter

ISBN: 0-445-04699-6

Printed in the United States of America

First Fawcett Popular Library printing: February 1982

10 9 8 7 6 5 4 3 2 1

The author was inspired to write this book by the passionate struggle being waged by specialists and laymen in every country on earth, by church and state and by the mass media, to resolve a problem that illustrates the helplessness of mankind to master a situation, and the blindness when faced with the dangers to which he is exposed.

All events and characters in this book are fictitious, with the exception of a few people and events that belong to history. In such cases, names, places and dates have occasionally been changed.

True to fact, however, are the descriptions of setting, examinations, treatment and working methods. Experts were consulted whenever necessary; the author was familiar with the film industry by experience.

Sonderschule Garatshausen on Lake Starnberg in Bavaria served as a model for Remedial School Heroldsheid, which does not exist. But no living child or adult—whatever connection there may be between them and Garatshausen—is depicted psychologically or physiologically, directly or as a key figure, in this book.

It is insupportable—I would go so far as to say it is criminal arrogance—when someone says of another person's life that it is meaningful or senseless. Confused and helpless creatures like ourselves can never decide this. And we will never know what importance a human life can have, what extraordinary meaning—just in its profound misery.

CRIMINAL INFORMATION

THE PEOPLE	MURDER
vs.	File No: 5 Js 422/73

SUSANNE MANKOV, aka Sylvia Moran

Date of birth: May 25, 1935
Residence: 705 Mandeville Canyon
      Beverly Hills, California, USA

Parents: Eric Mankov (deceased)
      Olga (Oster) Mankov (deceased)

VICTIM Romero Rettland, born August 9, 1912, Myrtle Creek, Oregon, USA

* * *

The Prosecuting Attorney alleges the following facts based on information and investigation.

The Defendant arranged to meet the victim Rettland, motion picture actor whom she had known for years, at 5:00 P.M. at the Hotel Zum Weissen Rad, in Nürnberg, on October 8, 1973.

The Defendant refuses to state the reason for this meeting with the victim or to reveal any conversation that might have taken place between them.

Due to the fact that the Hotel Zum Weissen Rad has a reputation as a "hot sheet hotel" because it rents rooms by the hour, and because the Defendant went there disguised with a wig and dark glasses, it must be assumed that their meeting was of a highly private nature.

As a result of the investigation it was learned that in 1961 the victim was hired to act in a film to be shot in Berlin,

6

together with the Defendant, who at the time was an "unknown" and still acting under her true name of Mankov. The victim is reported to have made repeated claims that he was the father of the Defendant's eleven-year-old daughter Barbara (Babs), who, according to witnesses' statements and newspaper reports, is now in a boarding school in Norristown, approximately twenty-five kilometers northwest of Philadelphia, Pennsylvania, USA.

The Defendant has presented documentary evidence that categorically excludes the victim as the father of her illegitimate daughter but persists in refusing to discuss her relationship with the victim or the nature of their conversation on October 8, 1973, all of which leads to the assumption that the Defendant is concealing the motive for the alleged offense.

The Prosecutor charges that the Defendant on the eighth day of October 1973 was carrying a 6.35mm Walther automatic pistol, Model TPH, Serial No. 128467. The Defendant was found in Room 39 of the Hotel Zum Weissen Rad with the above described pistol in her hand, from which one shot had apparently been fired because an expended shell casing ejected by this pistol was found on the floor. The victim received one bullet wound. Ballistic tests of the bullet removed from the victim's body prove it was fired by the pistol found in the Defendant's possession. There is therefore strong circumstantial evidence that the Defendant fired the one shot.

According to the Medical Examiner's autopsy report, the victim died instantly of the one bullet wound.

The victim was not carrying a weapon and had no identification on his person. He was identified through distinguishing physical characteristics. A keyring with three keys, $85.30 (U.S.) in cash and two travelers checks were found in the victim's possession. Room 39, in which the alleged offense took place, was rented by the Defendant.

According to all evidence, the victim Romero Rettland was unsuspecting and defenseless.

The Defendant SUSANNE MANKOV is therefore charged with the willful, wanton and premeditated killing of ROMERO RETTLAND, contrary to Section 211 of the Penal Code and against the Peace and Dignity of the people of Bundesland Bavaria.

The Prosecutor proposes to call the following witnesses on behalf of the People:

7

(1) Joseph KUNZINGER, doorman at the Hotel Zum Weissen Rad, Nürnberg

(2) Elfie KRAKE, prostitute, Nürnberg

(3) Joe GINTZBURGER, President of the American film company, Seven Stars, Hollywood, California, U.S.A.

(4) Rod BRACKEN, agent of the Defendant, Hollywood, California, U.S.A.

(5) Dr. Ruth REINHARDT, Sophienkrankenhaus, Nürnberg

(6) Philip KAVEN, at present unemployed, in jail as material witness, no permanent residence

(7) Vigbert SONDERSEN, Police Commissioner, Nürnberg

(8) Dr. Elliot KASSNER, Chief of staff of the Psychiatric Clinic, Santa Monica Hospital, Beverly Hills, California, U.S.A.

(9) Dr. Robert SIGRAND, Chief of staff of Hôpital Sainte-Bernadette, Paris, France

(10) Dr. Clemens HOLLOWAY, Director of the Norristown School, Norristown, Pennsylvania, U.S.A.

(11) Alexandre DROUANT, Chief of Security Police, Monte Carlo, Monaco

(12) Julio DA CAVA, film director, Madrid, Spain

(13) Carlo MARONE, film distributor, Rome, Italy

(14) Frédéric GÉRARD, anchorman and commentator, Radio and Television Monte Carlo, Monaco

(15) Steve COMMING, associate producer, Syran Productions, Hollywood, California, U.S.A.

(16) Carmen CRUZEIRO, foreign language secretary, Madrid, Spain

(17) Gerhard VOGEL, Police Captain, Nürnberg

Experts:

(1) Dr. Walter LANGENHORST, ballistics, Berlin

(2) Prof. Hans PRINNER, Pathologist, Court Medical Institute, Nürnberg

(3) Prof. Wilhelm ESCHENBACH, University Psychiatric Clinic, Erlangen

Exhibits:

(1) Walther pistol, model TPH, 6.35 mm, Serial No. 128467

(2) One pair of dark glasses

(3) One blond wig

8

(4) Gold locket containing a color photo of the Defendant's daughter

In compliance with Court Rule 80 and Sections 7 and 9 of the Penal Code, the offense charged is cognizable before the County Court of Nürnberg-Fürth, and I herewith file this Criminal Information with the Court and pray that the Court order

    (a) that this matter be brought for trial before the Assizes Court, Nürnberg-Fürth

    (b) that an early date be set for the trial

    (c) that no bail be allowed because of the gravity of the offense charged.

Submitted to the Presiding Judge of the Criminal Court, Nürnberg-Fürth, this 20th day of December, 1973

Dr. Guido Wenger

Prosecuting Attorney
Office of the Public Prosecutor
District of Nürnberg-Fürth

COPY TO DEFENDANT'S COUNSEL

Dr. Otto Nielsen
Nürnberg, Loblerstrasse 126A

PART
ONE

Symptom

SABINA: We're all just as wicked as we can be, and that's the God's truth.

—Thornton Wilder, *The Skin of Our Teeth*

1

"Good evening. Please step in front of the window on your left. Make sure your face is directly in front of the window and that you are standing approximately ten centimeters from it."

The deep metallic voice of a woman, issuing from the speaker in a chrome panel, was in all probability a recording. It responded when you rang the bell at the gate. I'd been through this whole performance before.

So I walked over to the window on my left. As I positioned myself at the correct distance I had to stoop a little, because I am six foot four. It was very cold and raining hard that evening, November 24, 1971, a Wednesday, and a high wind was raging over Paris. The rain was running off my coat and down my collar, and seeping into my shoes. That was all we needed at this point—that I get sick. Actually, in my state of utter disgust, I wished I were drunk. But for what lay ahead I had to be cold sober. . . .

A bright light went on above me. I knew what that meant. So did everybody who had the right to enter here. There was a closed-circuit television system in the villa at the rear of the park. The stolid gentleman on duty had a set in his room. On it he could see my face. Everybody who came here and had permission to come again was photographed. I presumed there were stacks of photo albums in the gateman's room. He was probably looking for mine right now.

The metallic voice again. "State your name, please, slowly and clearly." The first request was always in French, then it was followed by German, English and Italian. ". . . *Adesso dica il suo nome, per favore.*" A cultured voice.

I had taken off my hat. The rain was running down my hair into my eyes. "Philip Kaven."

The voice: "And your number, please. . . . *Ed il suo numero, per favore.*"

For a change I answered in French. *"Treize."*

Thirteen. That was the number they had given me last night when I had come here the first time. Two employees of the establishment, huge fellows, had picked us up at Orly in a big Buick. One of them had also been asked to step in front of the opaque glass window before the gate was opened. When I had left, they had told me my number was thirteen. "Don't forget your number, please, Monsieur Kaven. Without it we can't let you in."

An elegant place, probably *the* most elegant and certainly the most expensive of its kind in the world. Not a soul could have climbed over the high picket fence that surrounded the park, with its electrified wiring on top and alarm signals all over the place—at least that's what they said. For all practical purposes the place was as secure as the Bank of England.

"Merci," said the metallic voice. And she proceeded to say thank you in the other three languages. Then the bright light above me went out; the two sides of the gate were on a track and parted. I walked out onto a gravel path and the gate closed behind me. I was impressed.

No lights in the park, but on both sides of the gravel path, obscured occasionally by low-hanging shrubs, illuminated honey-colored small arrows indicated the way to the villa.

The wind was sighing in the treetops. I had my hat on again and was following the arrows. I looked at my watch: 6:36 P.M. I'd left the Hotel Le Monde at four, of course not in Sylvia's Rolls and not in my Maserati Ghibli, and of course not in one of the taxis parked in front of the hotel. I had walked over to a stand on the Champs Élysées, taken a taxi there and told the driver where to go, in the wrong direction, naturally. "Place de la Concorde, please," and as usual the driver had taken off like a madman.

Have you ever driven through Paris in a taxi, your honor? With a French driver? Yes? Then you know how I felt. You know there was no point in suggesting that he drive carefully. He wouldn't do it. All he'd do is suggest that I take the wheel and drive his goddam cab myself or, more probably, that I go fuck my mother.

I had experienced Parisian cabs so many times that I no longer paid much attention. Besides, there were other things on my mind. I kept looking through the back window. Were any of the fellows following me? If so, I'd have to shake them off. Until now I'd managed to do so. Yesterday too, in Zürich, after the press conference at the Dolder Hotel. I hadn't arrived at Le Monde until 1:30 A.M., but by then disaster had already struck.

Governess Clarissa and Rod Bracken were waiting for

me—the latter fairly drunk—in the brilliantly lit salon. A small, baldheaded man with thick glasses and a sad, infinitely kind face was also present. I knew him. "Dr. Lévy! What are you doing here?" And then he told me.

That was this morning at 1:30, and now, on the evening of the same day, I was tearing around Paris in taxis. I got out of the first one at the Place de la Concorde, changed to another that drove me along the Quai d'Orsay on the left bank of the Seine, after that on the Quai Branly west and across the Pont de Jena back to the other side. Changed taxis again. He had to detour to get from the Place du Trocadéro to the Avenue Poincaré, and from there north. At the Avenue Foch, another taxi, and now through the Bois de Boulogne to Porte de Madrid. I had traveled an almost complete circle, and I was sure no one had followed me. I walked the rest of the way in the pouring rain, braced against the wind. Only a short distance, but the rain was so heavy that in ten minutes my shoes were muddy and my trousers soaked. When I finally reached the Rue Cavé, I was filthy. My fur-lined coat was shiny wet and water was dripping from my hat. I kept slipping. But at last I was standing in front of the high iron gate, and a metallic-erotic voice was saying in four languages, "Good evening. Please step in front of the window . . ."

2

Now I had the park behind me and was facing a mansion, built around 1880 or 1890, a time when I had always wished I had lived. I walked up a broad stone staircase, stone amorettes on both sides of the banister. A brilliant light flashed on over me and the entrance door opened as if by magic. I walked in. I knew what to expect, but last night it had startled me—a beautiful *fin de siècle palais* on the outside, and inside, an ultramodern clinic. Everything in steel and chrome. Corridors. Doors labeled Lab I; EKG; Lab II; Chief of Staff; OR I; X-Ray; OR II; Resident Doctor; OR III. Medicinal smell in the corridors. I met nobody, I didn't hear a sound. It had been the same the first time around, as if the place were uninhabited.

I reached the two elevators. One was large, for the trans-

14

portation of patients, the other was normal size. I got into the latter and pressed the button for the third floor. As the elevator hummed its way up, I looked in the small mirror hanging in it. My face was wet. Rain and sweat. Rings of exhaustion under my eyes. I took off my hat. The water was still dripping from it. Third floor. A long corridor, dimly lit. Numbers on the doors, nothing else. I hadn't been here before, but I knew where I had to go; they'd told me in the afternoon when I'd called up from Le Monde. Room 11. I opened the door. A dark antechamber. I couldn't find the light. Unfortunately I'd closed the door behind me and now I couldn't find my way back either. I couldn't find the damn door! You must know the feeling, your honor. But I felt my way along the walls until I found a second door, which I opened. It led into a large room.

I couldn't find the light switch here either, but I could see a little because a bulb with a thick yellow shade was plugged in just above the floor. By its light I could see a hospital bed in the middle of the room. I walked over to the bed and almost fell over a chair. Then I saw the ghastly sight.

Her head, completely bandaged, only nose and mouth left free. Bandages over the eyes. It looked dreadful, that head swathed in white; it looked bigger than life. A big white ball. Everything else hidden under the bedclothes. Here there was a strong smell of hospital. I can't stand the smell. It makes me sick.

"Sylvia!"

No answer.

"Sylvia!" Louder this time. Still no answer.

I called her name three times; the last time I was shouting. No response. She might have been dead.

I slipped my hand under the covers, tried to find her hand, found it. Ice cold. I pressed her hand, pinched it—no reaction. Then I saw plastic tubes protruding from under the bandages where her ears must have been and from the nape of her neck, running down to the floor and ending in a glass bottle. Since I could barely see anything, I knelt down. There was some blood in the glass bottle.

I got up. The sweat was trickling down my body. I took off my wet coat and threw it and my hat behind me. I opened my jacket, took off my tie, opened my shirt and stared at the horrible white ball that contained Sylvia's head. Sylvia, who lay there as if dead. I was horrified. What if something had gone wrong?

15

3

All right, let's face it—women are crazy about me. I'm one of those men women dream of. So, let's have it: I'm a playboy.

Here, in the jail I happen to be in, everything's in tip-top shape. The cells are homey, the mattresses are good, the conditions are fine. The food's all right; the same can be said of the sympathetic-polite attitude of inmates and wardens. Sports, if you want them; a good library—the collected works of the classic writers of many countries, and not only practically every modern book—fiction, nonfiction—that happens to be a bestseller, but also the most modern reference books. For instance, the fourth and latest edition of Brockhaus dictionary (Wiesbaden 1971). In Volume IV, Page 201, you'll find "*playboy* (Engl.) an elegant, worldly, usually wealthy idler. A woman's hero . . ."

Whoever the editor may nave been, I'd like to shake his hand. I am grateful for the word "usually." But—and this is not to be construed as criticism, much less as a reprimand— the ideal word would have been "sometimes."

A playboy is not always wealthy, and I wish the general public would recognize the fact. I, for instance, am not wealthy; in fact, I don't have a cent to my name. You shake your head, your honor, you have your doubts. You're thinking of my brother and the famous cable factory we inherited from our father. This drama, which you have encouraged me to write, was a worldwide sensation, and you know that's no exaggeration. My family name has been bandied around in every mass-media forum. My poor courageous brother, Karl-Ludwig . . . how I wish I could have spared him the whole mess. Was that ever possible? Certainly not.

But if you think it's a fine thing to be a playboy, an impoverished playboy, you're making a big mistake. It's just as shitty to be a wealthy one. A goddam shitty job, my way of life, if you want to call it that. I wish to God I hadn't been a playboy, but what can I do about it now? Nothing. You know, your honor, there were times, as a matter of fact quite frequently, when I would have liked to kick myself in the teeth for hours on end for the things I was doing, fine character that I was. But then I thought of the beautiful carefree existence I was leading. . . .

Once upon a time it wasn't the worst thing in the world to be loved by Greta Garbo, right? And you will have to agree, your honor, that the lady who happens to love me is even greater than Greta Garbo. You'll agree with me also, I'm sure, when I say that in our industry she is the tops—Sylvia Moran.

Naturally—and I'll say this fast before you get there ahead of me—we are living in an age when the idea of the great female star is becoming obsolete. There are only a few left—Taylor, Cardinale, Loren, Streisand, Schneider, Minelli, and several others, right? Because the international film industry demands more and more male stars as the subject matter of motion pictures becomes increasingly masculine. Movies centered around a great *actress* have become increasingly rare. But famous women haven't become entirely obsolete. There may be more and more international films with men for heroes who barely know how to run, yes, yes, I mean it—but there are still worldwide productions with female stars, and of the few I have mentioned, Sylvia Moran is the most remarkable. Looking back to the very beginning of the motion picture industry—she *is* the greatest, past, present and future!

And now, there's nothing I can do about it—I have to be indiscreet. Soon I shall have to be worse than that in this, my confession. This great star, Sylvia Moran, took possession of me, to be her beloved forever and ever. I was to be her flesh and blood. That's what she thought. I would have liked to think differently, but I was never able to get out of this squirrel cage. So I went along with it. I only want you to understand, your honor, right from the start, that I never had any intention of clothing what I did in an ethical gown. I got over that long ago. I don't play the hero I never was any more. A nauseating fink who is about to tell you his story—that's what I am! A bastard called Philip Kaven.

I was twenty-seven years old when I met Sylvia Moran, she was thirty-three. That was five years ago. Next week, in this cozy cell, I shall celebrate my thirty-second birthday, and Sylvia is thirty-eight and *the* most divine woman in the international film industry, and at the same time the most extravagant, insatiable and craziest . . . what the hell else? It's November, 1973. Since 1968 I have lived on her, on her alone. Before that, playboy Philip Kaven was a fucking mess,

17

and with that, your honor, I am expressing myself euphemistically.

Yes, for five years Sylvia Moran has been supporting me. It's all going to come out anyway. I'm sorry only for my brother, Karl-Ludwig, such a good fellow, and for the cable factory. But everything has changed radically, especially after this man was shot, on top of everything else. Yes, I lived off Sylvia Moran, and not exactly frugally. Tailor-made suits, real silk shirts, platinum wristwatch, everything I wore, and the Maserati Ghibli (cost: 130,000 francs, *new* francs!). All this and more she bought for me and paid for. Because . . . and how I hate to brag about it now . . . because she was in love with me. I did everything I possibly could to satisfy her. I was there for her, day and night. I ran errands for her and fulfilled her every wish, and she had a lot of wishes, you may take my word for that, your honor.

During the last five years I have visited many countries and many cities with Sylvia Moran. I have spent a great deal of time with her in luxury hotels, traveled with her on more transatlantic flights than I can keep track of to wherever she was making a picture, all of which I only partially remember. On the other hand, there were certain experiences and impressions in these five years that are indelibly impressed on my memory. I have met men and women of whose existence I had no previous knowledge, of whose existence very few people are aware, nameless men and women. Nobody makes a fuss over them as they do over the bloody seducers and destroyers of mankind; they get no medals; their lives consist of sacrifice, self-denial and work to the point of collapse. Over and over again they experience disappointment and despair, but also frequently revived hope and renewed courage, all nourished, it seems, by sources that never dry up. These men and women were so far removed from anything I had ever experienced that when I met them first I had the feeling I had been moved to another planet.

"Some are in the dark, and others in the light. We see the ones that are in the light but not the ones in the dark." Brecht, your honor. And I'm about to contradict that genius too, with all due respect, *because I have seen them,* the ones in the dark.

My encounter with them was one of the most deeply moving experiences of my entire life, and I shall never be able to forget the smallest detail, not even in these pages. I feel it is my duty to describe the good things I experienced among them, which, paradoxically, mysteriously, and one might say perversely, arose out of the most dreadful circumstances and the greatest evil, to report it all as something that has to be conveyed to mankind; to report it in these pages to you alone, your honor, but later, at the trial, to as many people as possible. As a matter of fact, your honor, I feel that I have been *chosen* to play this part. By whom? Me, of all people, the most unworthy one! I have therefore decided—and I am sure this will reassure you, your honor—never to lie. What happened to me, with these nameless feeble creatures in the dark, and with the strongest of the strong by way of integrity and infinite humaneness, makes it impossible for me to lie. I must bear witness through the truth and nothing but the truth. Ridiculous, isn't it, your honor? That at this point I should dare to insist on the luxury of truth!

4

To continue: Sylvia gave me everything. *Almost* everything. She never gave me a checkbook or power of attorney. And no cash. Pocket money, yes, but pretty meager. She was convinced that otherwise I would deceive her, or decamp with the money, or both. She was a woman, your honor, with indescribably fine perception. And then there was her daughter, Babs. I wasn't the girl's father, but I was on duty for Babs like three fathers! She is almost eleven now, six when I saw her for the first time. On her part it was love at first sight. She took to me and stuck to me like a leech. Right from the start, I couldn't stand the child. Altogether, I never liked children. I hated them, if that isn't too strong a word. But there was Babs and here was I—broke. And by now?

What has been dished out to you and to the rest of the world for so many years, and has been believed, is: The divine Sylvia Moran had a daughter without the grace of marriage. She always refused to name the father and got away with it. You know, your honor, how the gossip columns feasted on the fairy tale: Babs, the love child. A doll, even as a baby, and getting prettier every year. The World's Greatest Little Sunshine Girl—that's how they labeled her. Still do. Rod Bracken, Sylvia's agent, dreamed it up. I'm sure he also thought up the "love child" bit, and the secret concerning the father. Some people thought he might be the father. But all that's beside the point now.

Five years ago Sylvia Moran found the great love of her life—me. We were made for each other. (Text courtesy Rod Bracken.) Sylvia Moran is an emancipated woman who has fought for and gained her freedom. Sylvia Moran has spoken the following words of wisdom, probably hundreds of times: "I love Phil and he loves me. We shall never marry, just *because* we love each other so much and because ours is such a perfect love. Because marriage, even under the most perfect circumstances, leads to the death of love." Sylvia Moran really believes those words!

As I look around me, there may be some truth in her viewpoint, in spite of the fact that she's slightly crazy. *I* would have married her right away. Consider the fact, your honor—we're growing older, we're not as spirited as we used to be, we begin to think of the future, of aging—right? And of security. Security above everything else. But nothing doing. Sylvia was of the just-mentioned opinion, and to keep the peace, I made it mine.

So . . . we were the dream couple of the twentieth century, a truly modern couple, incredible how we managed go on loving each other in spite of the fact that we'd decided to do without that damn ring on the finger and all the documents to be signed, and the until death do us part bit. Wild, no? And even wilder than our love *à deux* was our love *à trois!* Both of us adored Babs. Especially me, Philip Kaven!

Can you follow me, your honor? Always on the go, facing cameras and microphones, always in the spotlight—and however difficult for me, always a perfect front, as if I loved the brat as much as she loved me. And all this with reporters and photographers ever present. Because this was Bracken's most devilish and successful publicity stunt, as you know only too well, your honor. Babs and I accompanied Sylvia wherever she went to make a picture. Always the three of us, and ever new stories of the great love that kept us so happily together!

I'll spare you an account of the number of times in the past five years when I felt like killing Babs. Plus her mother. Had several good ideas. The perfect crime. To be free again. Free!

Pure hysteria. First of all, I'm too much of a coward to bring off anything like that. And then, when someone like me has a fish on the hook, he doesn't kill her. He doesn't kill anybody. Instead, he swears that he loves her. And her little daughter.

I beg your pardon, your honor. I know that my soul searching is the last thing you're after right now. What you need is the truth concerning all the circumstances that finally put a bullet into a man's heart.

The truth is not pretty, in fact it is hideous. But before I could tell the truth that is going to be so horrifying, I had to get rid of what I've just written or I'd have choked on it!

Well yes, that's how it all began, on a stormy, rainy evening in Paris, November 24, 1971, a Wednesday, as I stood beside the hospital bed in Room 11, third floor, facing that dreadful sight: her head completely bandaged, only nose and mouth free, plastic tubes hanging down to the floor from under the bandages, ending in a glass bottle that was slowly, slowly, collecting her blood; as I received no answer from Sylvia, who was lying in front of me, motionless, the room almost dark, the storm howling outside, the rain beating against the windows.

5

I crept out, leaving the door to the room open so that some light could fall into the small anteroom, and went into the dimly lit hall and down to one of the nurses' stations. I pushed aside the curtain in front of it. Brilliant light! A young nun, all in white, wearing hornrimmed glasses, was sitting at a desk, surrounded by medication in little paper cups, above her head a shelf with various clinical packs, beside her a sterilization apparatus for hypodermics. A nun? Here? Why not? I suppose one could expect to find such religious ladies in a place like this.

"Bon soir, chère soeur . . ."

She looked up and—was very pretty! A nun! What a shame! What a waste of sweetness.

"Good evening, monsieur." She looked at me questioningly.

"Thirteen," I said.

"Oh, thirteen." She looked at the room plan. "You must

excuse me, I didn't recognize you at first." She got up. A black cross on a thin chain dangled over her breast. "I don't usually work in this section, monsieur. Two of the regular nurses couldn't come in today. I'm substituting for them. My name is Hélène."

"I'm very pleased to meet you, Sister Hélène."

"I'm usually on the ground floor. Injuries, burns, disfigurement after accidents—poor souls like that, never up here."

I nodded.

"I . . . I am against this plastic surgery for beautification. I know it's not my place to say anything like this, but God gave us a face and features according to His unfathomable wisdom, and . . ."

"And here we are interfering with His handiwork. I understand."

"What can I do for you, monsieur?"

"In Room Eleven. I was just there. She doesn't move, she doesn't respond. She lies there as if dead."

"Oh no, monsieur. Madame is all right. I was told that they had difficulty in OR, getting her to calm down. It was hard to sedate her, so she was given a heavy anesthetic. When she came to, she was still very restless, so an hour ago Dr. Delamare gave her an injection of Domopan."

"Domopan?"

"Yes, monsieur. You see, that was a very strenuous operation for madame, a complete face lift, throat, eyelids, and all at once."

"Yes. But Domopan . . ."

"As I just told you, madame was very restless." I watched the black cross rise and fall over her breast and looked away fast. "Please don't be worried. You are worried, aren't you?"

"No."

"Oh, but I can see that you are."

Such a sweet gentle voice. So I began to imagine things, as I did whenever I found myself face to face with a woman, any woman, anywhere in the world and whatever the situation. Such a habit can make you quite wretched, your honor, believe me.

"Dr. Delamare has left, but I can connect you with his apartment."

"Please do, sister."

She walked over to her desk with dignity and grace, and dialed. Then I was speaking to Dr. Delamare. "Good to hear your voice, monsieur."

Dr. Delamare owned the clinic and was one of the most renowned plastic surgeons in the world. Kings and queens, actresses and actors, singers, society ladies—the elite—let him restore whatever they wanted restored. And there wasn't an anatomical area that Delamare couldn't restore: breasts, legs, stomachs, buttocks, hips, throats, noses, ears, eyelids, whole faces! World-famous car racers who had been dragged alive out of their burning cars, multimillionaires whose knees had been mashed by some goon shooting to cripple them, carpenters who had fallen off a scaffolding into a trough of burning lime or secretaries with a harelip. For the last two categories, Delamare didn't charge anything. The man had a conscience. He made the rich shell out fortunes, but the unfortunate poor he treated for nothing. With a voice smooth as velvet, he calmed me.

"We operated for three hours and fourteen minutes, monsieur. What a good thing it was that we made such a thorough examination! Everything went very well, I assure you. The results are going to be fantastic."

"But we agreed that I might see her in the evening. You know how very much she wanted . . ."

"I know. But believe me, monsieur, we had to give her the Domopan. She had to be calmed down to keep still. So of course now she's sleeping very soundly."

"Should I wait?"

"She may not wake up for hours, monsieur. Of course, you may stay overnight if you like. Sister Hélène will give you one of the free rooms, but actually I'm against it."

"Why?"

"The first hours are always the worst. I would prefer it if you came back tomorrow evening." That made me feel good. I could go.

"I understand, doctor. I'll come back tomorrow evening."

"That will be fine, monsieur. Good night."

"Goodnight, doctor, and thank you, thank you so much."

"Please, monsieur. I consider it a great honor," he said, and I wondered what his bill would be.

"Feel better, monsieur?" asked angel-face Hélène with the hornrimmed glasses as I put down the receiver.

"Yes, thank you. And I'll go now. But would you do me a favor, please?"

"But of course, monsieur."

"Would you tell madame when she wakes up . . ."

"Yes, monsieur?"

Be serious now, Kaven. Get it out with feeling!

". . . that I was here, that I love her more than anything else in the world, and that I'll be back tomorrow evening."

"I shall tell her, monsieur, and I shall pray for you both."

"What did you say?"

"That I shall pray for you both," she said gently. "You read about it in the papers, but you don't believe it. But now I can see for myself . . ."

"See what?"

"Such a great love," said Sister Hélène. "God wants us to love each other. I shall pray that He protect you, and that He grant you many, many beautiful years and keep you from harm."

When I recall everything that has happened since then, your honor, I always think of what Sister Hélène said that night.

6

I shook hands with Sister Hélène and walked down the passage to the elevator, only one thing on my mind—to get out of there fast. Then I could still get to Suzy's on time and grant myself a few peaceful hours. Sylvia was terribly jealous, your honor, but I was equally clever; I had to be, or I would have lost my mind. In the cities we visited I had always managed to find a young woman with whom I could find solace when the stress of my position became too much for me, when Sylvia's unreasonable behavior became unbearable. Even someone like me isn't anxious to get a heart attack in the course of his profession, right? So, in order to remain fit and able to put up with her capriciousness—actually I did it *for* Sylvia, because only then could I stand by her in difficult, dangerous moments, well balanced and with a clear head—I always managed somehow to find a pretty little sweetheart wherever we happened to be.

I don't want to give you any advice, your honor. You may be happily married, I wouldn't know, but I feel the need to explain. In a position like mine it is naturally of the greatest importance that such a little girl doesn't get the smart idea to blackmail you, or to sell her experiences to some magazine or other, or even to boast about it to her friends. How does one avoid that? Very simply. One selects one's pretty little creature from among those who are well off and married, preferably to a rich man. That's all there is to it. If you follow this rule you can sleep in peace. Alone or with the young lady.

Here, in Paris, I had started a little something with a beautician. Wild girl! Suzy. Officially she was engaged to the son of a count, the former still a minor whose father had been the owner of several large textile factories in Roubaix. Papa's will directed that on coming of age, he was to come into possession of the factories, two or three castles, some vineyards, and acres of forestland. Then he could do as he pleased. Until then there were trustees, attorneys, guardians. Suzy had manicured the young man's nails one day when I was having mine done by someone else. I could hear every word being said in the booth next to me, whether I liked it or not, and I liked what I heard. As soon as my hands were done, I knew everything. And Suzy knew who I was. Certainly! My manicure took place in the afternoon, the rest followed that evening.

Whenever I was in Paris, I somehow managed to see Suzy. In her apartment. We always had ourselves a time that left both of us shaking at the knees. Oh yes, one more thing—I told Suzy right away and frequently after that that I had no intention of ever leaving Sylvia and marrying her. And that such a marriage would be crazy anyway, because I didn't have a penny to my name, not even enough to buy her flowers or a box of candy. Strangely enough, all my girlfriends always accepted this. They knew I was speaking the truth when I said, "You can't depend on me." Just the same—they were crazy about me. . . . Strange how the sun of Sylvia's fame cast its radiance also on me.

I had wired Suzy from Zürich that I was coming to Paris. She was beside herself with joy, especially when I told her later that this time I would be staying two or three months, and she had begun to cry. I had to stay in Paris that long because Sylvia couldn't leave Dr. Delamare's clinic until all the stitches were out and the swelling was down and not a trace of the face lift remained visible. So Suzy wept for joy. . . .

I walked quickly down the passage, pressed the button for the elevator—I was looking forward to Suzy. I could see her in front of me, naked. She had the most exciting . . .

25

"Monsieur! Monsieur!"

I turned around. Sister Hélène was running toward me.

"What is it, sister?"

"Madame just rang! She asked if you were there, monsieur!"

"And?"

"Of course I said yes."

(Dumb cluck, Angel-face!)

"Of course, sister."

"I said you'd just left this minute"—the elevator arrived—
"but I'd see if I could still catch you."

"That was good of you, Sister Hélène," I said, hoping that
what I was producing was a smile. The elevator disappeared
down the opaque glass door, and with it my élan. . . .

"And I did manage to catch you!" Sister Hélène was radiant.

"Yes," I said. "Fortunately."

"Madame wants to see you." She hurried on ahead.

So you see how things can interfere with one's plans.

7

"Pepito . . ."

"Yes, my darling."

"Give me . . . give me your hand."

Sylvia's hand was above the covers, feeling for mine. A
floor lamp was on in her room now, but she couldn't see
anything. With her bandages, she was blind.

The light made everything even more horrible. Her bandaged head seemed swollen like a balloon too full of air. I
shuddered.

"You're . . . you're to give me your hand."

She was speaking in French now. Our first words had been
in German, and so it went, in three languages—English too.
Domopan. Sylvia had regained consciousness, but only temporarily. She was miles away from being really awake.

"Here it is." (In French.) I had laid my hand on hers. It was
hot and damp. A few threads of the bandage fluttered over
her blue lips whenever she spoke, with a voice that was quite
changed. I would never have recognized it if I hadn't been
told my patient was in Room 11, still full of dope.

"It was dreadful, Pepito."

"My poor Silky!" I was breathing as shallowly as possible, because now that she was speaking, the hospital smell was stronger than ever. I gagged.

"Pepito"—that's what she called me, because, as a child, she'd had a little toy donkey, woolly, her "feelie" that she hadn't been able to live without; I called her Silky because I'd told her once that her skin was like silk. She had given us both the names. According to her, lovers had to have nicknames.

"Dreadful ... dreadful ..." In German this time. "They ... they didn't give me an anesthetic. They ... they couldn't ..."

Yes, I thought, when someone consumes so much alcohol, the doctors have a hard time.

"I still ... I still feel it. I'm ... afraid. Don't go away ... away ... more ... more." Then in French, and more vehemently, "Take the champagne away! What nerve! ... Because it has a cork ... a cork," and in German again, "Not enough anesthesia ... wasn't possible ... my circulation ..."

Have you ever tried to speak to a big white ball with two holes in it for nose and mouth? "My poor Silky!"

In German, "Poor Silky? Am I your poor Silky?"

"Of course."

"And what else?"

"My poor beloved Silky."

"Only beloved?"

"My poor beloved Silky whom I love above everything else."

No man could have been more obedient—or more dependent.

Sylvia gave me my cue in German. "Whom I love more than ..."

"Whom I love more than I have ever loved before, more than anything else in the world," I said, with feeling.

I was sitting uncomfortably on a hard chair, my wet hat on my head, and I was sweating, although I had hung up my coat in the small anteroom.

"Whom *I* love more than anything else in the world," she said in that sluggish, hoarse, slightly slurred and totally strange voice, issuing from the white ball which by now had assumed grotesque proportions in my mind. She went on in English, a *non sequitur*. "Sell them, Mr. Joyce! Sell them! Three points higher than ... you're my broker! What do you mean? Zanuck? On the phone? Transatlantic call? Idiot!"

27

And suddenly, in German again, "That's not true, Mama. In the well? Nobody's weeweeing in it. . . . Who . . . who took all the furniture away?"

The words were coming more slowly now, more softly. At last—silence.

"Silky?" No answer. "Silky?" Louder. Nothing. Well, in that case . . .

I tried to free my hand. At once, fast and in German, "If you ever leave me, if you ever deceive me, I'll kill you!" My hand was crushed in hers.

"What nonsense, Silky! I could never leave you. I could never deceive you!" I could go to Suzy in the middle of the night. She wouldn't mind.

Softly, in French, "A yacht . . . Elizabeth . . . Richard . . . I'll buy you one."

"I don't want a yacht."

"So what do you want?"

"You. Nothing but you!"

"Oh . . . sweet." And in German, "You are the sweetest of all Pepitos." And in English, "Sell IBM, Mr. Joyce. Remember . . . remember Unilever. I know . . . I know . . . only three points, but they're lost . . . lost . . ." A long silence. Deep breathing. The OR stench. I thought I could make it . . . "It's hurting again." And then, very clearly, in German, "It hurts terribly, Pepito, behind the ears . . ."

"My poor Silky, my poor, poor Silky." I hoped Suzy wouldn't be asleep when I got there.

"Didn't I tell you, Jack?" In English. "It's not clear. My rear end's blurred. We'll have to do it all over again. . . . We're landing? But this flight's nonstop! To refuel? That does it! Next time we take SAS over the North Pole. Tokyo . . . you can't steal my ti—" And she was gone, in a split second, in the middle of a word. Lying there, flat on her back, she began to snore. I got up soundlessly and inched my way to the door. One more step . . .

In a plaintive voice, "Pepito!"

She was gesticulating wildly with her hands. Nothing to do but go back to her, and fast.

I was lucky, as lucky as a cemetery during a plague.

8

For your information, your honor: It is very unusual for a woman as young as Sylvia Moran to have a total face lift. But you see, in her case it was a professional necessity. After years of putting on makeup, frequently with risky lotions and adhesives; through years of little sleep, plus quantities of alcohol and cigarettes in restaurants and nightclubs and at lavish parties; through pressures that didn't get less—through all this, Sylvia's skin did not improve. Added to that, her skin was exceptionally beautiful and therefore exceptionally susceptible. If Sylvia's had been a different profession there would have been no need for a face lift; under existing circumstances, however, it had become unavoidable. She knew it, the VIPs at Seven Stars knew it. In her last film, in which her partner had been the famous old Italian actor Alfredo Bianchi, her cosmeticians, Katie and Joe Patterson, a couple who had been working for her for years, had encountered a lot of difficulties. And Sylvia's career had to proceed flawlessly, without incident. It was a case of losing or making millions of dollars. So that was why Sylvia was lying there, clutching my hand.

Breathlessly now, in English, and filled with hatred, "Leave me alone, Romero! Go to hell, you filthy bastard!" And she was gone again, with my hand clutched in hers.

My thoughts began to wander. Yes, your honor, now when it is too late I can recall how she cursed Romero, "the bastard." And that evening I thought she must be referring to Romero Rettland, the ex-actor, but I didn't pay much attention, didn't ask questions.

No. I sat there, my hat on my head. My wrist watch read 7:47, my hand was just as hot and damp now as Sylvia's, and I thought of what had happened the day before, on November 23, 1971, and closed my eyes. . . .

9

"Phil!"

Babs jumped up and ran over to me as I entered the suite in which she was staying with her governess. She was wearing blue jeans, a yellow sweater and soft yellow moccasins. Her blue-black hair was flying wildly around her head. She was smiling at me.

She had the same hair, the same long lashes, the same big blue eyes and white skin as her mother. She was tall for her age, almost nine, and because she looked so adorable, the whole world loved her; only I felt something like acid indigestion when she threw her arms around me now. "Dear, dear Phil!"

"Dear, dear Babs!"

I picked her up, stroked her hair back. Dr. Wolken was sitting beside a small rococo table, looking at me affectionately, blissfully—the old idiot! The World's Greatest Little Sunshine Girl had a tutor, Dr. Alfons Wolken from Winterthur. He had been with us for three years and looked after Babs's education. He flew everywhere with us. Babs had to have regular, standard tuition, the California court insisted on that. Dr. Wolken rose now and greeted me with a deep bow.

Babs gave me two kisses, one on each cheek, and I did the same. Her skin felt hot. "What's the matter with you, young lady?"

"What do you mean, sir?"

"Have you got a temperature?"

"Clarissa just asked the same thing. We took it."

"And?"

"Nothing." She coughed several times, a hard, dry cough. "Ninety-eight point six—and that in my rear end!"

I took another look at her. Her eyes looked red. "Well . . . I don't know . . ."

"I assure you, sir, everything's A-okay." She sneezed, directly into my face. "Oh, *pardon, monsieur, excusez moi!*"

"Pas de quoi." I put her down again. "And how do you feel?"

Back to German again. Babs was taking German lessons, even though it was her mother's native tongue. Sylvia Moran hadn't always been American, and her name hadn't always been Sylvia Moran. But that's another story. "How are things?"

"Shitty," said Babs.

"You know you're not supposed to say words like that, young lady," I said, and Dr. Wolken smiled at us.

"I know," said Babs. "I'm sorry. But just look at this crap! What we kids are supposed to learn. As if we were idiots!"

She drew me over to the table where she had been working, coughing a few times—it sounded dry, more as if she were barking—and pointed to her schoolbooks.

That was yesterday afternoon, at about 4:00 P.M. Babs always took a nap until 3:00, then she studied again. This particular incident took place in Zürich, at the Grand Hotel Dolder, high up in the hills above the city.

Babs, at the table, picked up her arithmetic book. "Here. Wait. I'll have the page in a minute." And she began leafing through it.

Dr. Wolken said softly, in German, "She is a very perspicacious child. Above average in intelligence. I didn't write these books, Herr Kaven. They're the most recent ones I could get, but you'll find this type of standard textbook all over the world."

Dr. Wolken had a habit of bowing whenever he spoke to you. Then he jiggled up and down on his feet, his head bobbing the same rhythm. As far as I could see, there was no reason for such exaggerated servility. The man had been recommended to us by the Swiss boarding schools organization as the most suitable tutor for Babs, and that he certainly seemed to be.

Babs had begun to read aloud from the book, her face supported on her little fists: " 'Dame Curiosity asked Grandfather how old his grandchildren were. Grandfather answered, "George and Erica, both together, are twelve years old. Erica is two years older than . . ." ' " She sneezed and wiped her nose with the back of her hand.

"Gesundheit!" said Dr. Wolken with a bow.

"Thank you, Herr Doktor! 'Erica is two years older than George. Hubert and Martin both together are twenty-three years old. Hubert is . . .' " Babs had to draw breath. It wheezed a little in her chest. She had been reading so fast, she had become breathless. " '. . . three years younger than Martin. And Thomas is the same age as George and Hubert

31

together.' " She looked up at me, frowning. "Did you ever hear anything like it? Do you think there's any grandfather on earth who would tell how old his grandchildren are like *that?*"

"But it's written that way on purpose!" I said. "So that children trying to learn how to do sums have a little riddle to solve at the same time. That's why the grandfather talks like that."

"Yes, but to Dame Curiosity! If a child had asked the question, and he'd cooked up that answer so that the child should have some fun doing the sum—would have been stupid too, but okay. But a grown woman asks the question, and Dame Curiosity yet! I guess it's supposed to be funny, so that we kids can learn what's funny." She coughed again. "What do they think they're doing? If they'd taken a, b, c and d and given us a few equations . . . but no, the old guy has to present us with a whole exposé!" "Exposé" . . . she knew the word and its meaning. Babs knew a lot of adult words. Now she shook her head angrily. "When children get older are they still going to have to put up with such stupefying stuff?"

Dr. Wolken laughed.

"You see . . . Dr. Wolken thinks it's idiotic too."

"It seems idiotic to you, Babs," I said, "but I'm sure there are a lot of children who like it."

"Oh, come on, Phil," said Babs. "I don't know many children, but I do know a few. Aunt Elizabeth's kids, and Aunt Romy's and Aunt Claudia's children. They're being raised the same way I am. The next time I see them, I'll ask them. But I can tell you right now—I'm sure they find it just as silly as I do. Fun doing arithmetic! With this sort of nonsense they spoil any fun you can have. Really, Phil! And why? Do they want to make jackasses of us?"

"Of course not."

"But that's what they're doing. They behave as if they were dealing with a bunch of idiots!"

"Since you're so smart, young lady, I suppose you know how old all these children are."

"Sure I know," said Babs. "I only had to read it through once and I knew. It's a first-grade primer, that's what it is!" She sneezed.

"Look here, did Clarissa take your temperature properly?"

"Of course she did. I lay quietly on my side and held tight. It's only because I've been talking so fast. No, really, Phil— it's enough to make every child in kindergarten laugh.

32

You're wearing my favorite blue suit with the thin white stripes. *Très chic.*"

"And you've got to change, Babs. I'm sorry, doctor, but that's it for today."

He looked at the watch he carried in his vest pocket. It opened on a spring. "Oh my, yes," he said. "You must forgive me, Herr Kaven."

"Not at all," I said. The man got on my nerves with his obsequiousness. "*You* must excuse *us*. Babs, go over to your mother's suite. Clarissa's there. They'll tell you what to wear."

"Oh God, yes! I have to get ready." She jumped up. "I forgot all about it, and there's something I really do enjoy. The press conference is at six, isn't it?"

10

"Well, yes—first Uncle Rod wanted to tell you, and then Phil did, and then Mama said she'd tell you, and when I heard all this back and forth, I said, 'If you can't make up your minds, *I'll* tell them,' and everybody thought it was a great idea," said Babs. "I've been to such a lot of press conferences, but this is the first one *I'm* holding, and I'm not the least nervous."

That was at 6:15 P.M., and Babs was seated at a table with a red brocade cover. Sylvia was on her right, I was on her left, and Rod Bracken was sitting on Sylvia's other side. Three large vases filled with red roses were standing on the table, and there were ninety-one people present.

Of course, it had been Rod's idea to hand the conference over to Babs. A great idea? Well, that was his job, wasn't it, to have great ideas? You find my answer given in a tone of irritation? You sense aversion and rivalry between Bracken and me? You sense correctly, your honor. Mutual aversion and rivalry. I couldn't stand the guy, he couldn't stand me, but we had to get along. Sometimes I imagined we were like two oarsmen on an ancient galley who sat side by side and couldn't abide each other, who hated each other like the plague, but who had to row, neither could escape. After all, they were chained, and chained together.

"Well, it's really quite simple," Babs was saying, then she sneezed. "Excuse me."

It was terribly hot, because so many strong lights were focused on us. Babs was speaking English. "During the last three years, Mama has made four films, hasn't she? Things have never been so hectic since we started filming. I ought to know. I'm her child. I've known it was getting to be too much for Mother, known it for quite a while. Ever since that time when we were Aunt Romy's guests in Paris, Mama, Phil and I. I played a lot with little David—I say little because I'm almost nine and David isn't quite six yet. Why are you laughing?"

The reporters, the photographers, the cameramen and their assistants, *were* laughing; Sylvia, Rod and I were laughing. I was laughing enviously because I saw Bracken watching me as if to say, "Well, how are we doing? I knew what I was talking about when I said the kid should give the opener today, not one of us. And you, you asshole, said Babs wouldn't know what to say. I said Babs'll know damn well what to say. She's as sophisticated as hell and knows what the score is better than her mother and you and I put together. So there you have it, lover boy!"

Babs was looking at us, sincerely astonished. "Why are they laughing, Mama? And you, and Phil, and Uncle Rod? I *am* older than David." And then of course Sylvia threw her arms around Babs and held her close and kissed her, and all this started a veritable uproar. Every camera was rolling, all you could see were lights flashing, reporters taking notes, taping—everybody there: German television I and II, Swiss television, the French ORTF, the Italian RAI, the English BBC, the American CBS and NBC, and at least a dozen other foreign stations with their Swiss camera crews.

The TV remote vans, huge vehicles, were standing in the courtyard of the Dolder Hotel, blocking the entrance completely. Those who hadn't found a place to park, especially the radio recording vans, were drawn up along the driveway and the narrow serpentine road that led from the Dolder down to Zürich or up into the woods, where the heavy batteries for the floodlights were ticking away. And the Hotel Dolder guests were seated in the round lobby or in their rooms, watching the goings-on on television, and all of them were probably laughing too. Swiss television was broadcasting the show live, ditto ARD and ZDF. You could get reception from far-off West German stations here.

"So what I said was apparently funny," Babs went on, "and I'm glad you're laughing."

It was quiet again in the Dolder salon. The men working on the large cameras stood on raised platforms, earphones on, getting their directions from the broadcast directors who sat in front of monitors in the various control rooms. The photographers crouched, stood or lay on the floor, shooting with Hasselblads, Leicas and Rolleis from the craziest angles. The sound men knelt in front of their controls. They had on earphones too. Every now and then one of them hurried up front to fiddle with some of the microphones—at least a dozen—clamped to the table in front of Babs, Sylvia, Rod and me. The various television and newsreel cameramen had hung microphone booms that dangled over our heads. And the men behind the lights saw to it that we were properly lighted.

"... So I played with David, and Mama and Aunt Romy talked, and of course they thought we weren't listening—please forgive me, Mama—I won't do it again, but ..."

"What won't you do again?" Sylvia asked, smiling and looking puzzled.

"Eavesdrop."

"You eavesdropped?"

Babs coughed, that dry hard cough. "Yes, Mama. I know it's something I'm not supposed to do, but you were talking quite loudly and I became interested because you said how dreadfully tiring it was to make one film right after the other. And Aunt Romy said she knew what you meant, and that one simply had to take time off sometimes, and you said you couldn't, you *had* to finish this picture. You'd only just started it. And then you said, 'And so much depends on it. We've got so much riding on it, and I'm practically in every scene. When I get back to the hotel in the evening all I want to do is sleep, sleep, sleep ... but then there's the child ...'"

Shouts, or let's say cries of compassion, but loud!

"My poor, poor darling," said Sylvia, holding Babs close again. "I'm terribly sorry. Yes, I said it. I can remember. But you heard it—that's dreadful!"

Babs freed herself energetically. "I have to sneeze," she said, and did so.

This everybody also found funny. You know, your honor, once somebody starts laughing in the movies or in the theater, the audience will laugh at every possible opportunity;

then you might as well stop the projector and ring down the curtain. In this case Babs's sneeze was a bull's-eye hit. Rod, tbe fink, was beaming. I'm sure if there were a Nobel Prize for this sort of thing he would have expected to receive it.

"Well," said Babs, to the pack facing her, "then I knew how hard my mother was working when she said something like that. Because it meant, of course, 'and then there's my child that I can't do anything for any more in the evenings because I fall asleep at once,' and often she did fall asleep, right when she was eating. And then Phil would read to me—*Winnie the Pooh* or *Oliver Twist* or *Tom Sawyer* and *Huckleberry Finn*. Don't be mad, Phil," turning to me, "I don't mean it that way. I was grateful to have you read to me." She laid her little—hot—hand in mine. "But it was something Mama used to do for me, and then we'd say our prayers together."

"I never prayed with you!" I said, doing my surprised routine. By now I had a routine for every situation connected with Babs. Prayer, too. I could see Rod grinning. The bastard! "I mean . . . I didn't know that you prayed," I stammered. Routine embarrassment. I could have puked.

"But Phil . . ." said Babs. All cameras on the two of us. "I knew you didn't know that Mama and I said our prayers together. So, when she wasn't with me, I prayed by myself, for all of us. But all I could think of since our visit to Aunt Romy was that Mama simply had to do what Aunt Romy had advised." Babs turned to face the cameras and microphones again. "And now I'm coming to the point, and you'll understand why this has to be. The film with Uncle Bianchi is finished, but before Mama does another picture she is going to take a vacation. For the first time in four years!" Babs coughed again.

"We're terribly excited about it, especially me. Because it's the first time that Mama and Phil and I aren't going on vacation together. Because Mama is going off all by herself so that she can have a proper rest." Babs laughed. "Uncle Phil and I, and Uncle Rod, and Clarissa, and Herr Doktor Wolken are going to let her go alone. I guess I'm going to miss Mama a lot, but then . . . it's not for long. And I'll have a lot of fun with Uncle Rod and Clarissa and Uncle Phil and Herr Doktor Wolken in Paris and Madrid, and we're going to some other places too. And oh yes, something else. Mama is going to fly far, far away. It's going to be a secret where she takes her vacation. I know all of you love Mama, so I hope you'll do me a big favor. Please don't try to follow Mama and photograph her and all that. Please. I don't want this to sound mean, but please, please, leave my Mama alone, just for a while. Will you do that?"

A few seconds' silence, then shouts of "Yes!" "Sure!" This time I didn't look at Rod. Babs got up and curtsied to all sides, then she lifted her hand and it was quiet. "Thank you," she said. "I knew you were all A-okay. Thank you."

Rod Bracken rose. He is a big, strong man, was forty-one years old at the time. He has the pale complexion of someone who spends little time in the fresh air, and he wears a crew cut, which happens to suit his long face very well. His hair is graying a little. He has very light, cold eyes, but they can look friendly and warm on notice. Bracken can do whatever he likes with his eyes. He has a prominent nose and narrow lips, and his eyebrows have grown together over the bridge of his nose. He raised both arms. "Thanks, buddies!"

All journalists were his "buddies." He also addressed them as "boys, chums, friends, *amici, copains,*" depending on where he happened to be. He spoke three languages fluently, and could get by in two more.

"You have promised to grant Sylvia Moran her vacation and not to try to follow her. Anyway, she's flying so far away, you'd never find her!" (Forced laughter.) "And now I have a few words to say. Next year Sylvia Moran is going to realize at last the most important project of her career. She will play the role of her dreams in the biggest and most ambitious production Seven Stars has ever undertaken. I am in a position to reveal to you today that for this film, and on my advice, Sylvia Moran has formed her own company—Syran Productions. The name is, of course, a composite of her first and last names. Syran Productions will produce the picture for Seven Stars in an entirely new color process and"—effective pause—"will let it cost them *twenty-five million dollars!*"

I could see Rod speaking, but suddenly I stopped hearing him. Only for about three seconds. But it is surprising what you can remember in three seconds. . . .

11

On September 25, 1960, there was a movie premiere which has gone down in motion picture history as "Bracken's Chutzpah." It took place in Munich. Title of the film: *Black Heaven*. Cost: 6.5 million German marks, or DM. Earned to date: 157.7 million DM.

Bracken's chutzpah picture was based on a novel by a writer named Erich Walden, who died in poverty in 1931. *Black Heaven* is as famous today as the novels by the elusive writer B. Traven. German film companies had tried again and again to get the Walden novel on the screen, but it had never been possible to raise the money. Author Walden, who died almost immediately after the death of his wife, left only one heir—his son, Otto. In 1958, Otto Walden was working in Munich for a real estate company. Financially he wasn't doing well. He had divorced two women and was paying them alimony, and was living with a third woman.

On April 12, 1958, he had a visitor. A certain Rod Bracken had asked to see him. This fellow had said that he was employed by a firm of accountants in New York. Walden had tried to find out more about this firm, but to no avail. The only thing he did find out was that Bracken was staying at one of the tackiest boardinghouses in Munich.

Bracken arrived punctually at Walden's apartment—shabbily dressed, gaunt, a poor specimen. Before he had even taken off his raincoat, he told Walden, "We're going to produce your father's novel, my friend."

Walden immediately decided that Bracken was crazy. Ten minutes later Walden, desperate and up to his ears in debt, was convinced that Bracken was a genius. He listened to him, mouth agape. Bracken spoke German quite well, but with a strong accent. He spoke fast, firmly, seemed absolutely sure of himself and blessed with the sensibilities of a banker. He didn't waste any time on preliminaries but declared at once that he was in a position to do what the biggest German film companies hadn't been able to do, namely raise 6.5 million DM, *and* in record time.

"I have made a study of German tax laws," said stranger Bracken with the lopsided shoulders, creased suit and hollow cheeks, "and I know somebody here in Munich who is willing to let me have seventy thousand marks as a loan to the end of the year. And we don't need more."

Didn't need more? A 70,000-mark loan when the picture had been estimated by innumerable producers and distributors at 6.5 million?

"We don't need a distributor. We produce it on our own and sell to the distributors who make us the best offer, worldwide. Can you figure out how much more there'll be in it for us?"

So the man *was* crazy! What could you do with 70,000 marks? Rod Bracken told Otto Walden what one could do, after which Walden again decided that Rod Bracken wasn't crazy. Next morning both gentlemen appeared at the Munich Hall of Records, and registered a company under the name Schwarzer Himmel (Black Heaven) Film Produktion G.m.b.H. KG (limited partnership, the only partners at this point being the gentlemen Walden and Bracken). Starting capital: 70,000 DM. Bracken's friend actually came through with the money.

Now Bracken had fliers printed on bond paper, very elegant, which he sent out to 8,500 men in the Bundesrepublik. He had hired a professional survey company to furnish him with the names of the 8,500 men to be approached. All these men were rich or earned high salaries, all of them were highly respectable men with the same problem—they were in the top tax bracket.

In this flier, the Schwarzer Himmel Film Produktion G.m.b.H. KG stated its intention to start filming this legendary novel before the end of the year. A little-known aspect of the Bundesrepublik tax laws was pointed out. It was the fact that no tax had to be paid on money contributed toward the financing of a major project, for instance the making of a film; the sum could be deducted in full. The men receiving this elegant flier were therefore given the opportunity to participate financially in the production of a motion picture. The fame of the novel, the actors, the director, and so on, all seemed to assure a sensational success. And an old Bremen trust company was willing to guarantee that everything would be aboveboard. This form of film financing was unknown in Germany and now took place for the first time. Rod Bracken had really done his homework. He was soon wearing tailor-made suits and living in the Hotel Vier Jahreszeiten.

On that evening, April 12, 1958, Bracken, the man who had come in out of the dark, told the son of writer Walden, who had died a poor man, what the flier told so elaborately, but in more folksy terms, somewhat like this: "These fat cats have to pay taxes through the nose! If they give us money, a lot of money, then the first thing they have is a psychological triumph—the goddam internal revenue service isn't going to get the money! Then there's the second effect, also psychological: 'If the film makes money, I get my share and get richer. If the film doesn't succeed, I haven't lost a thing because taxes would have taken it all anyway!' And there's always the chance of winning, with which you have the third psychological effect: the gambler's itch!"

Otto Walden was fascinated. He was even more fascinated when the first monies came in after the Bremen Trust Company had sent out the fliers. First 100,000 DM, then 300,000, 500,000 . . .

That summer Rod Bracken traveled a lot. He signed up his director, producer and technicians, always the best he could find. In August, three Italian scriptwriters handed in a surefire scenario, and Rod Bracken had assembled his dream cast. However, also in August, Otto Walden and the Bremen Trust Company became hysterical. So far they had accepted partners who had paid, all in all, 1.7 million DM. And 6.5 million was the sum needed. The Bremen Trust Company used harsh words. The 6.5 million had to be on the books by the end of the year. Production had to begin before the end of the year. Otherwise the worthy Bremen Trust Company would be forced to bring suit against Bracken and Walden on behalf of the investors.

"You bastard!" Walden to Bracken.

"Take it easy." Bracken to Walden. "The money couldn't possibly have been here by August."

"I don't get it."

"I didn't expect you to," said Bracken. "But I have something to suggest. We have our own private contract, on a fifty-fifty basis, right? We each get half of what's left of the net balance."

"And nothing will be left!" cried Walden.

"That's your opinion and you're entitled to it. I suggest that I take over thirty of your fifty percent, and we go to a shyster lawyer and wangle a contract so that nobody can do a thing to you if things go wrong. I'll be the one who gets the shit, all of it. Does that appeal to you?"

Walden nodded. By now he was weeping.

"That's what I thought," said Bracken.

It took three lawyers and one notary to ensure Walden legal protection so that he could sleep peacefully again. Bracken always slept well. And what he had been expecting soon happened. In September there were seventeen partners with contributions amounting to 2.8 million. October brought in only one man, with 320,000. The film industry gloated. Until November. Then, suddenly, there were fifty-four contributors, with 3.8 million; December first, a hundred and eleven with 6.49 million; on the tenth, 22.7 million, and the trustees found themselves having to turn down everything above 6.5 million.

Work on the film began before Christmas, as planned, and ran on to September 25, 1960. Then the film was finished, dubbed in twenty-eight languages, subtitled in nineteen, and distributed around the world to the highest bidders. And after the premiere the results for the investors came in—an avalanche of profits!

Now Walden tried to increase his percentage, but Bracken shrugged. "Not a penny more, idiot!" he said. "In August you wept because all we had was a million seven and were shitting in your pants at the thought of jail. Because you couldn't *think!*"

"Think?"

"That the fat cats don't look for ways to unload their honestly or dishonestly earned money until toward the end of the year! Anyway, even with your twenty percent, you have more than enough, you dumb asshole!" And with that Rod Bracken left Munich and was gone from the Bundesrepublik. Practically the next day he surfaced in California, soon had a home in Beverly Hills, a fleet of cars consisting of a Mercedes, a Rolls, and a Bentley, two Chinese servants, the prettiest and at the time most expensive starlet in Hollywood, antiques, and an aquarium, in which, with the help of an expert, he bred the most remarkable and terrifying fish in the world.

By the time I met Rod Bracken he was already Sylvia Moran's agent. She had made him an absolutely absurd financial offer. He got a higher percentage than any other agent in the world. Sylvia said at the time, "He earns every cent I give him. He's the smartest man I've ever come across in my life, so of course I've got to have him!"

41

12

"... and Sylvia Moran will tell you herself what this latest and most important film of her career is all about." Suddenly I could hear Rod Bracken again.

There we were, at the press conference in the Dolder salon, there were the cameras, the spotlights, the microphones, there was Sylvia, beautiful, ethereal Sylvia—"The Beauty." Bracken's name, of course.

"Yes," said Sylvia, smiling seriously, since it happened to be the right thing to do. "We are getting ready for our greatest picture, ladies and gentlemen, and that is why it really is necessary for me to have a good rest first. Because this picture, this new role which—it is true—I have been longing to play all my life, is going to demand everything I've got. I know that the most satisfactory but also the most difficult period of my life lies ahead of me."

"And what's it going to be about, Madame Moran?"

A reporter from AFP, Agence France Presse, stood at the front and asked the questions.

"We are going to film *The Caucasian Chalk Circle*," said Sylvia Moran slowly.

Commotion in the room. Repressed cries. This *was* a sensation! (Don't look at Bracken, I kept telling myself.)

"By ... Bertolt Brecht?"

"Yes. I shall play Grusha, the kitchen maid. As you can see, a very different role from any I have played before."

"And not at all your type!" said AFP.

"Not at all my type? Oh, you mean physically. That's true. But otherwise ... You know, I am sure, that this play, *The Caucasian Chalk Circle,* concerns a kitchen maid who takes the child of the governor's wife, which she has abandoned while fleeing a civil war. Grusha brings it up and protects it as if it were her own child. When the governor's wife is returned to power she claims the child, and the famous test of the Chalk Circle takes place. According to Brecht, the judge awards the child to the maid, who let go of it and didn't drag it out of the circle because she didn't want to hurt it. Because the woman who is a mother is not the most precious being on earth—the most precious being on earth is the woman filled with motherly love." Her arms around Babs, who had to sneeze again. "This little girl sitting beside me, my beloved child, is one of the reasons I have always dreamed of playing this part."

"So it's to be Brecht, Madame Moran. We French are great admirers of Brecht. But an American film company and a playwright from Eastern Europe . . . ?"

"The greatest German playwright of this century," said Sylvia Moran.

"I agree. Absolutely. But how are you going to go about it? Aren't you going to encounter a lot of opposition?"

Sylvia looked at me, smiling. It was my turn. With my head turned slightly to the right—it's the better side—I said quietly, nonchalantly yet impressively, "We haven't run into any opposition so far."

"But the East, Monsieur Kaven . . . the heirs . . . the rights . . ."

"Exactly," I said. "With everything you mention, no difficulties. Absolute harmony. You see"—I leaned forward a little—"we have been given governmental encouragement to do this film. We are living in a period of reconciliation between East and West, not because we're angels but for reasons of self-preservation, if for nothing else." Every word—and how I hate to admit it—composed by Rod Bracken. "And in times such as these, this picture is to be symbolic of the intentions of both sides to live in peace with each other, in an atmosphere of goodwill, ready to understand each other and make coexistence possible."

"Both sides? Do you mean to say that you enjoy the support of East *and* West?"

"That's just what I intend to convey." More commotion. "Governmental agencies in East Berlin and Washington are working together to give us every assistance possible. So are the representatives, the trustees, heirs, and owners of the rights to the works—and now I must quote Madame Moran, because she is absolutely right—of the greatest playwright of this century."

"And you're going to shoot the picture in Spain, Madame Moran?"

"Yes. In the Estudios Sevilla Films in Madrid, and in the Pyrenees near Saragossa and Barcelona. We find Spain ideal for the Caucasian background."

"That's where they filmed *Dr. Zhivago,* isn't it?"

"That's right." Sylvia nodded. "We have been preparing fo this production for years," she went on. "We were determine to cast even the minor roles with the best actors available We have hired the best technicians, cinematographers, soun men, architects, and so on. We have the best scriptwriters . . ."

So her listeners got a lot to digest that day, all of it—n denying it—the work of Rod Bracken. Sylvia knew why she paid him such an insane salary. And Rod was working up t the next item on our agenda—the denouement: the announcement that Sylvia was about to disappear for a while. O course, Babs also believed that her mother was going on a vacation. Nobody would be so idiotic as to try to explain a face lift to a nine-year-old child!

The AFP now said, "And for this film . . ."

"The title will be *The Chalk Circle,*" said Sylvia.

". . . and for this film, *The Chalk Circle,* you have formed your own company—Syran Productions?"

"Yes. With such an important project, it seemed advisable."

"Because of the taxes!" somebody shouted, and Sylvia smiled amiably. "Naturally. For that reason too. I don't intend to work myself to death to pay seventy, eighty, ninety percent in taxes. With my own company, I should make out a little better. Any objections?"

"Of course not, Madame Moran," said the AFP man, sounding a little embarrassed. "And who is going to manage Syran Productions?"

Sylvia looked at me, her eyes shining. Deeply moved and proudly, she said, "Philip Kaven!"

"Philip Kaven?" The AFP man was obviously flabbergasted, which he tried to hide behind a display of enthusiastic astonishment. "But that . . . that's . . . now that you are going to work so closely together professionally . . . that's splendid!"

"You know," said Sylvia, "Phil and I have been together now for almost three years and we are as happy today as on the day we met. And why?"

"Because you have remained true to your belief that marriage spells the death of love and have therefore never married," said the AFP man on cue.

"That's right. It's what we happen to believe. Not that we want to recommend it to anyone. It just happens to suit us. Because ours is a love in which everything is right—everything physical, and everything that concerns heart and soul. And

44

eart and soul are what will endure. Phil and I are absolutely
ompatible, yet we are two completely independent crea-
ures. I know that Phil is clever and fair, kind and unselfish
.." (I am telling the truth, your honor. That's what she
aid.)

After a touching pause, the AFP reporter said, "Madame
Moran, on behalf of my colleagues and all your friends in the
audience, I thank you. Together with the millions of your
admirers all over the world, we are happy for you and wish
that you and Monsieur Kaven, and of course our Babs,
remain as happy always as you are today. And we hope that
The Chalk Circle will be enormously successful. Thank you
very much, Madame Moran."

"And we thank all of you gentlemen," said Sylvia. The AFP
reporter stepped forward and kissed Sylvia's hand.

13

And then we were off!

My Maserati Ghibli could easily do 290 kilometers. It holds
the road like a rock; you can do hairpin curves without taking
your foot off the gas pedal. There are a few curves like that,
narrow too, from the Dolder down the mountainside. I took
them at high speed. The tires whined when I swerved sharply, left, right, left. The only thing that bothered me was the
shoulder of Sylvia's sable coat and her crazy, floppy sable hat
. . . she was famous for her crazy hats . . . that tickled my
face in the curves. Heusteig. Watch it—main highway
Bergstrasse. And in the rearview mirror I could see the pack
behind me, at least twenty cars. Great!

Watch it again! Rämistrasse. We reached the city and
crossed the Limmat; I couldn't drive fast here, but cleverly.
And I can drive. There is always *something* a man can do
well. The drivers of the cars behind us were probably
sweating—Rod's friends, chums, *amici*, buddies. Whoops! Drove
through a red light. Drive slower, chum, otherwise they'll
lose us! But there they were again. I stepped on the gas. A car
like that, your honor, is a lot of fun. Left, right, right, left,
sable coat and hat bothering me.

She turned around. "Don't worry," I said. "They're there. Every last one of them!" And we had arrived at the autobahn, direction Bern. Now I could drive faster, and the ones following us could too. Derlikon exit. Two or three more exits and we'd made it to where I wanted to go—the Autobahn Brückenrestaurant Würenlos.

This Brückenrestaurant complex, eighteen kilometers from Zürich, lies high above the autobahn. There are six restaurants, eighteen shops, a bank, telephones, showers, restrooms with diapering tables for mothers with babies, and fourteen gas pumps next to parking lots that can accommodate approximately seven hundred cars. And all this is open daily and—almost—around the clock.

I drove to the parking lot and stopped the car. We got out and walked arm in arm across the dark lot. From the six restaurants, we chose the sixth—Landbeiz. That's Schwyzer-Deutsch, or Swiss German, and has a meaning somewhat equivalent to "Little Country Inn," where one usually drank more than one ate. We sat down. It was warm and cozy, and I ordered a bottle of St. Saphorin '69. Our posse should show up any minute now.

A waiter brought the St. Saphorin in a silver bucket. As he was opening the bottle, the first of Bracken's buddies, chums, boys, appeared, their cameras at the ready. I stared at them, my face expressionless. I helped place Sylvia's sable across her shoulders, helped her remove the hat. She put it down on an empty chair beside her.

"Merde!" cried one of the reporters. The other just stared at us. Because the woman sitting beside me was not Sylvia Moran. The woman sitting beside me had worn Sylvia Moran's sable coat and hat. (This had been my idea, just for once, not Bracken's!) The woman sitting beside me was Babs's governess, Clarissa.

14

The waiter had poured a little wine into my glass. I tasted
t. The St. Saphorin was tart and good. I nodded, and he filled
ur glasses and mumbled something I took to be a toast. We
hanked him and drank. The reporters stood in the doorway,
ndecided, speaking softly to one another, then a tall blond
German fellow came over to our table and said, "That wasn't
air, Herr Kaven."

"Fair!" I cried, outraged. "Bracken begged you to leave
Sylvia Moran in peace. *I* never considered you people fair—
that's why I'm sitting here with Miss Clarissa."

"And where is Sylvia Moran?"

I didn't bother to answer. He went back to the others, and
after a few minutes all of them left except the tall blond
German. He ordered beer, evidently determined to sit it out. I
told Clarissa, "Now we've got to wait for the call."

"Yes, Mr. Kaven."

She came from Los Angeles, but her origins were German.
Her name was Clarissa Geiringer. She had known Babs since
she was a baby—a good loyal soul, twenty-seven years old,
very pretty, very blond. But Clarissa met none of the standards
I demanded of my girls. Throughout the years we had become
good friends. Unlike Rod Bracken, Clarissa respected me,
and there was one thing about her that was, in the end, to
prove disastrous. She really loved Babs.

The big blond German glowered at us as he drank his beer.
I knew the call couldn't come through for quite some time, so
we sat there happily, watching the cars rushing by below us.
It was there that Clarissa told me how Rod had boasted to her
about the way he had organized the press conference. He had
said to Clarissa, "If they didn't have me, they'd be sunk.
When things stink, I'm the one who comes up with the right
spray!"

"He'd better learn to keep his mouth shut," I said, immediately furious. Clarissa couldn't stand Bracken any more than
I could. I could speak openly to her, and I did. "If he thinks

he's such a bigshot and doesn't think he's appreciated, why doesn't he get the hell out of our lives?"

"He can't, and you know he can't, Mr. Kaven," said Clarissa "You know what he's scared of."

I knew. Sylvia had told me. Once, when he had been drunk Rod had told her. He came from the South Bronx. His father had been an alcoholic, his mother a prostitute. Both had died before he was ten. He was put in a home where there was little to eat and a lot of cruelty. He grew up in the slums. Rod begged and stole, shined shoes, washed dishes, cars, corpses was apprentice to a sadistic mechanic, then worked for a crippled pickpocket who trained bands of young boys and sent them out to do business for him. At thirteen Rod had his first sexual experience and his first case of VD. He was a roofer, a gas station attendant, a messenger boy for Western Union. He was a maintenance man in a skyscraper and slept beside the boilers in the basement, punched tickets on the Staten Island ferry, worked on a garbage truck, pimped for a brothel—there was practically nothing Rod Bracken hadn't done until he found a job hustling clients for a financial consultant.

In Germany they had lifted the man's license, for good reason. He moved his business to New York, where he worked on one crooked deal after the other for his clients. Once he had been a truly great man, an expert on tax questions covering many countries, and, like dragging a brick around to show what a house he'd once built had looked like, this crooked tax consultant had brought a vast library to America with him. The books were stacked on shelves in a windowless back room, and in every free minute he had, Rod Bracken read them, night after night, especially those concerned with German tax laws. On top of all that he was dogged enough to learn languages.

By the time he went off to Munich to make a career for himself with his chutzpah film, he was a tax expert. But ever since then he had been pursued by a sense of panic that followed him into his dreams. He had only one, single, miserable and overwhelming thought—never, never to be poor again!

"You know all about it, Mr. Kaven," said Clarissa. "And you know that's why he'll never leave Miss Moran. And if she threw him out, he'd go down on his knees and lick her shoes and beg her to keep him on at any price and under any conditions!"

48

"I know why I can't stand Rod," I said. "It's because he treats me like a pimp—yes, yes, he does! Don't contradict me! But why does he do it, Clarissa? Why?" And the big German sat there glowering at us and drinking his second beer.

"Because he admires you, Mr. Kaven!" cried Clarissa, who was usually so calm; suddenly she was terribly excited.

"Admires me? What is there to admire!"

"Because of your charm, your wit, your spirit! Because you are educated, and his university was the brothels and dives on the waterfront. Because you are a gentleman, Mr. Kaven, something he'll never be, not with all his money. And because everybody likes you and you like everybody." And I thought that actually nobody had ever really *liked* me, not even Sylvia, but then our relationship was something quite different. And I didn't really like anybody either.

The waiter who had brought our wine came to our table. "Excuse me—Herr Kaven?"

"Yes."

"You're wanted on the phone. Follow me, please."

I went with him, and the tall German followed us. The telephone was in a niche in the hall; the receiver lay on a small ledge underneath it. The German took up a stand at my side. "Get out of here," I said, "or you'll regret it."

This seemed to impress him. He withdrew. I picked up the receiver. "Yes?"

"Herr Kaven? This is Buerli."

"Hello, Buerli." The director of the Seven Stars Swiss distribution office. "Frau Moran's private jet left Kloten ten minutes ago."

"Thank you, Herr Buerli."

"Auf Wiedersehen, Herr Kaven."

I went back to the table. The German was sitting there, and he looked at me bitterly. I told him, "Miss Clarissa and I are driving to Kloten Airport now. At ten-thirty we're flying to Paris on an Air France plane. If you want to come along— you can't be my guest, of course—you're welcome to join us."

15

He didn't fly with us. No reporters did. And I hadn't seen any at the airport. They hadn't given up, of course, only realized that they were on the wrong track.

Our plane left on time. It had been agreed that chauffeurs from the Dolder would drive my Maserati and Sylvia's Rolls to Paris and leave them in the underground garage near Orly. They had duplicate keys. The papers for the Rolls in which Bracken, Babs and Sylvia had driven to Kloten, unnoticed, were locked in the glove compartment. Before my flight I had locked my papers in the Maserati.

I didn't see Sylvia's Rolls in the Kloten airport's parking area. Her private jet, a Super-One-Eleven with a crew of four, had arrived in Zürich that afternoon from Frankfurt. The reporters hadn't noticed it; the plane had been directed to a distant runway. Herr Buerli had driven Babs, Sylvia and Bracken right up to the boarding ramp in his car, as arranged. Our luggage was on a cargo plane on its way to Paris to be delivered to Philip Kaven, Hotel Le Monde.

Clarissa and I had a pleasant fifty-minute flight. She slept a little and we were there. No reporters at Orly either. We passed through customs, as quickly as possible. At the Iberia desk, which was closed, stood a powerful-looking man in a blue flannel coat. No words were exchanged. We followed him.

It was cold in Paris. When we walked out of the airport building, a black Chevrolet drew up. Clarissa and I got into the back; the man in the flannel coat sat beside the chauffeur. We drove off and almost at once were on one of the major highways that led to Paris. Fifteen minutes later the chauffeur drove into a parking lot where a second black Chevrolet was waiting for us. "Goodbye, Clarissa," I said. "See you later."

I walked over to the second Chevvy and opened the door. "Thank God you're here!" said Sylvia, holding me close. She was trembling and crying. "I'm afraid, Phil. I'm so terribly afraid!"

16

Two big men accompanied us in the second Chevrolet. They didn't say a word. The one who wasn't driving kept looking back to see if we were being followed. We drove very fast, but still it took us a good half hour to reach Neuilly.

"Afraid? Why? Has anything happened?"

"No, no. Nothing. Everything went smoothly. Rod and Babs and I have been at Le Monde for ages. And you?"

"Went absolutely smoothly. So why are you afraid? Of what?"

"Of the operation, Pepito," she sobbed. "I . . . I'm terrified. And then there's Babs."

"What's wrong with Babs?"

"She . . . she was simply impossible. Throughout the entire flight. Cross, aggressive, restless, just . . . just quite changed. I've never known her to be like that. It scared me. What *could* be wrong?"

"No idea. Nothing, I'm sure, Silky."

"But there *is* something wrong with her, Pepito. It's all so strange. Do you suppose Babs resents the fact that I'm going to leave her alone?"

"Nonsense! I think she has a cold. Maybe the flu. She felt awfully hot this afternoon."

"Children get a fever so easily."

"Clarissa took her temperature. It was normal."

"Then there you are. No cold, no flu. No. She was furious because she can't go with me. She believes I'm going on a vacation, doesn't she? Oh, darling, I love Babs so much, and then she goes and has to be nasty to me just before this . . . this terrible operation. I'm so afraid, Pepito . . ."

During that whole ride, your honor, during the whole miserable way to the city of Paris and halfway through and around it to Dr. Delamare's clinic in Rue Cavé, I had to comfort Sylvia, dry her tears, try to quiet her. When we finally got there, I had succeeded in calming her down. She wasn't crying any more, she felt confident about the future, and even managed a smile as the doctor on duty received us.

I said goodbye to her in the doctor's office and told her I'd come back that evening (by now it was past midnight) and that I loved my Silky into all eternity, and her response was a farewell scene that somebody should have been filming.

One of the giants then drove me to Le Monde. When I got out I gave him a lavish tip, for the other one too. He thanked me and drove off, and I walked into good old Le Monde, where I had stayed so often.

17

"Monsieur Kaven!"

Lucien Bayard, who worked on the night shift, came toward me, his arms outstretched, genuinely happy to see me. For years he had been betting the horses for me. And Jean Perrotin, his colleague, also on night duty—I'd known him for ages too—was behind the desk, smiling and bowing. I'd known all of them for years—the reception crew, the bellboys and their captain, the head manager; I knew all the bartenders, waiters, maître d's, all the floor waiters, maids, and the managers, high and low, and Monsieur le Président Directeur Général of the Le Monde, big, sturdy Pierre Maréchal. But right now the lobby was empty. Lucien Bayard was facing me and I said, "I'm so glad to be with you again, Monsieur Lucien."

"And that's how we feel, all of us, Monsieur Kaven. Truly delighted to see you. Everybody's upstairs already. Your luggage has arrived too."

For years we had been renting the same suites, 419 for Sylvia and me, 420 for Babs and Clarissa, 421 for Rod, and 422 for Dr. Wolken, whom we weren't expecting until tomorrow. "I'll bring it upstairs at once." He was walking beside me toward the elevators. "Une de Mai is running next Sunday. At Longchamps, monsieur."

"Somebody told me Une de Mai wasn't running any more."

"Only does occasionally, Monsieur Kaven. And won't be much longer. I just thought you'd like to know. Not much use betting on Une de Mai, though, that horse always wins. But things are going to be very interesting next Sunday in

Auteuil." He let me get into the elevator ahead of him, and we started up to the fourth floor. "You know I never pay much attention to what they say in the papers, but this time—well, there are three fillies I've been keeping an eye on—Poet's Bay, La Gauloise and Valdemosa. They're very special, monsieur, very special. I'd advise monsieur to bet on Poet's Bay, La Gauloise and Valdemosa, in that order, a three-way bet. I don't think the word's out yet"—he lowered his voice to a whisper—"about what winners they are. Only among those in the know. I'm betting on them."

I am repeating this conversation about horses in the middle of the night, your honor, because it is important if you are to understand what made me what I am today.

The elevator stopped; Lucien got out first—"*Pardon* ..."—and walked along the passage ahead of me to Suite 419. "So place the bets for me," I told him.

"Be glad to. How much, monsieur?"

"I leave that to you, Lucien, as usual."

"Thank you for your trust in me, monsieur," he said, bowing. "I'll give it careful thought and go ahead as I think best."

"Do that, Monsieur Lucien," and we had arrived at Suite 419. "Thank you, Monsieur Lucien," and we shook hands.

"Thank you, Monsieur Kaven." The old night clerk pocketed his tip. "Goodnight, Monsieur Kaven."

"Goodnight, Monsieur Lucien." I knocked on the door, didn't wait for an answer, and walked into the suite I knew so well. To my surprise all the lights were on, even in the foyer, and three people were staring at me as I walked in—Bracken, Clarissa and little Dr. Lévy, the doctor who always looked after us in Paris. "What's the matter?" I asked. There was an antique clock on the mantle. One thirty-five A.M.

"Goddam fucked-up situation!" said Bracken. He was slightly drunk.

"I want to know what's wrong!"

"Ask the doctor." Bracken gave me a mean look. He emptied his glass, then he burped. Clarissa began to cry.

"Dr. Lévy, what are you doing here?" I asked.

"I was called in."

He was a short, completely bald man, he wore thick glasses, and the expression on his face was always infinitely sad and kind.

"By whom?"

"By Mr. Bracken."

53

"Why?"

"Babs is ill."

"Ill?"

"Yes, Mr. Kaven."

"Where is she?"

"We put her to bed in madame's room, since it's not going to be used. When I arrived she was in bad shape. Temperature 103.1. Chills. Very restless. Couldn't seem to stand any light. Her eyes were inflamed, her throat too, with white spots. This must have been going on for two weeks."

"What's been going on for two weeks? Stop crying, Clarissa!" She didn't.

"In the case of this illness there is a characteristic early stage," said Dr. Lévy, "that usually lasts about nine to eleven days. Then it really breaks out."

"Dear Dr. Lévy, would you please tell me what's wrong with Babs?"

"She has measles," said Dr. Lévy. "Only measles. I hope."

"What do you mean—'only'? And 'I hope'?"

"I'm not sure. There are . . . there are other symptoms that I can't diagnose. I'm not sure that it's only measles. Monsieur Bracken has been to a pharmacy and brought us everything for our immediate needs. But if it's something else . . . right now it's impossible to tell."

"When will you know?"

"Tomorrow, I hope. If . . . if these symptoms continue . . . it's all very complicated. Forgive me . . . but you wouldn't understand if I explained it in more detail. If things go on like this, though, I'd like to have another opinion." He sounded lost. "Yes . . . yes, another opinion."

Bracken drank again, burped again, and said, "A goddam fucking mess. If it's measles, she'll have to go to a hospital. They won't let her stay here. No hotel will keep a measles case."

"Le Monde will. I'll talk to Maréchal tomorrow. He'll arrange it. For instance, we can say it's just an allergy, can't we? You'd back us up on that, Dr. Lévy, wouldn't you?"

"Yes, yes," said Dr. Lévy. "Certainly. If it's only measles. But certainly not if it's more than that."

Suddenly I had to close my eyes.

18

I opened them again.

"Pepito . . ."

"Silky . . ."

Her hand had slipped out of mine and was hanging down, very white. "The . . . the key . . ."

I got up, turned her covers back a little and saw that she was wearing a gold chain with a key hanging from it. I unfastened the necklace and took the key. "What's the key for?"

"There." She pointed.

I looked around me. Ah, there, in the wall that led to the bathroom. I walked over to it and opened the door of the little metal safe built into the wall. There was jewelry in it, in a plastic bag. A small part of Sylvia's famous jewelry. So she had taken it with her. In spite of all her nervousness and fear, Sylvia had taken her jewelry with her, here, where she couldn't possibly wear it.

"Let me . . ."

I brought the jewelry over to her.

"Let me feel . . ."

I sat down again, opened the plastic bag, and we were off!

The first piece. Her hands felt it gently, tenderly. "My ruby ring."

Next: "My ruby earrings."

Next: "Turquoise necklace . . ." Persian turquoises and diamonds, $100,000 worth. "How . . . how is Babs?"

"Fine. Here's your turquoise bracelet." I handed it to her. She felt the pieces, then let them drop on the covers. "Babs is just fine."

Babs wasn't just fine, but her condition had improved. Dr. Lévy had brought a colleague with him, a Dr. Dumoulin. They had examined Babs for almost an hour, after which they had finally come to a decision. Babs really had measles, nothing more, even though her case could not be diagnosed as typical because of the nonconforming symptoms that had troubled Dr. Lévy the night before. The fever had gone down somewhat. Babs was thirsty. She ate a little. Now her whole body was covered with red spots. Still . . . only measles. Incomprehensible that she had never been inoculated against them.

Dr. Lévy had been overly apprehensive; nothing new about that. He'd overevaluated secondary symptoms before. Now that he and Dr. Dumoulin had examined Babs thoroughly, I could stop worrying about her. Sylvia had been inoculated for measles, so had I, and Clarissa and Rod. It occurred to me that when I finally got to her—and by God I was going to get to her before the day was over—I'd have to ask Suzy if she'd been inoculated or had measles as a child. If she got them now, I wouldn't be able to have any fun with her for weeks.

"My beautiful turquoise ring." It was lying on Sylvia's palm. She felt it for a long time, a Persian stone worth $20,000. "I was angry with Babs," she said.

"Angry?"

"In the plane. Yesterday. My solitaire." And when I didn't put it in her hand right away, "My solitaire!"

"Here, Silky." Forty-five carats. Marquise; value $1,400,000.

"Poor Babs . . . I . . . so nervous. Give me the emerald ring . . . *my emerald ring!*"

She pressed the ring over the opening in the bandage for her mouth, as if she wanted to kiss it. I knew that she often kissed her jewelry. "Now I'll be beautiful."

"You were the most beautiful of them all before this."

"For you! But the bastards wanted to have it done. They think they can . . ."

I gave her the earrings that went with the emerald ring. They were heavy. Sylvia had said often that they hurt, a pain that was evidently bearable.

"Had to be . . . this . . . this face lift."

"Of course, Silky."

"Close-ups, Pepito. Katie . . . Katie's an idiot! Says . . . says she can't do it any more, especially the left . . . the left . . . *help me!*" The last words a scream.

"The left eyelid."

"Yes. Katie said she couldn't . . . how does my jewelry look?"

"Fabulous!"

She was wallowing in it with her hands. "That lousy television!"

"Yes, Silky."

"Marlene won't appear on television. A million assholes

56

out there counting every wrinkle," and she went on cursing television and fingering her jewelry. Funny, I thought, because she'd been so successful on television two years ago. They'd be talking about it for years to come. . . .

19

Twenty seconds to 9:00 P.M., MEZ—meaning Middle European Time—on July 25, 1969, a Friday. The second hand on the big electric clock in the control room of TMC—Tele-Monte Carlo—jerked forward every second. It was like a countdown at Cape Kennedy. The control room was very small, and it was filled with equipment. Five men and one young woman sat on director's chairs in front of a long console with signal lights and controls, and a row of six video monitors. Nine . . . eight . . . seven . . . Above the monitors a glass panel ran from wall to wall. Through it you could see what was going on in the studio, the only studio of Tele-Monte Carlo. Three men in linen pants and colored shirts, wearing earphones, were poised behind three cameras.

A light-blue wall. A long narrow table, the kind daily talk show panels have in front of them. A tall vase with Baccara roses. No room for lights on the floor; at least twenty-four hung down from the studio ceiling. This studio, belonging to the smallest television station in the world, was not only tiny, the ceiling was low, and the lights hung down deep. The room was fully lit. It had to be hot down there, I thought, hotter than here.

I was standing beside Rod Bracken in the rear of the control room. Both of us had taken off our white dinner jackets. Hot. Hellishly hot! I looked down into the studio.

Behind the narrow table sat Sylvia and Babs, side by side. She was seven years old at the time. Because of this broadcast we had flown nonstop from Los Angeles to Paris, and from there south to Nice. Sylvia had brought the Pattersons with her to Monte Carlo, and Katie and Joe had just finished making them up. Mother and daughter had the same blue-black hair and very light, smooth skin. Sylvia's black eyes

57

were huge, and they glittered; Babs's eyes were open very wide too. Six . . . Five . . . Four . . .

The extraordinary telecast that was about to take place was a Eurovision program to be seen simultaneously in twenty-four countries. What could be seen and heard in all Europe would be rebroadcast later from hundreds of other video studios. Presumably 700 million people would see this program now or hours later.

Such an important telecast from such a small station had been made possible by the cooperation of practically every government, of UNICEF and UNESCO, and of numerous other organizations. The star of the evening was one of the most famous and beloved figures of our time—Sylvia Moran. Actually there were two stars—Sylvia Moran and Babs.

Three . . . two . . . one . . .

Nine P.M., Central European Time, in Monte Carlo. The director of this spectacular telecast raised one finger. Sylvia and Babs, who could see him, nodded. Sylvia licked her lips; Babs waved to us in the control room. Mother and child knew that they wouldn't be on the air until the director raised two fingers.

The opening sequence of the broadcast had been taped earlier, and from the monitors we could hear the well-known theme of Eurovision and see the wreath-of-rays logo. Then, at the same table at which Sylvia and Babs were waiting now, we could see Frédéric Gérard, sitting in front of a different background, no flowers beside him. He was wearing a tuxedo and a ruffled shirt.

Frédéric Gérard himself was standing behind me, watching his picture on the monitors. Like us he had removed his jacket and opened his shirt. He was a few years short of forty, and the most popular anchorman and commentator on Radio and Tele-Monte Carlo. Frédéric Gérard was a man of infinite charm. He looked marvelous, and I knew from experience that he could be helpful, was always amiable and extraordinarily astute. He was a legend in Monte Carlo and all surrounding areas served by TMC. The day before, after our arrival at the Hotel de Paris, I had noticed that practically everybody in the street smiled at Gérard, or waved, and he answered with a smile, a joke or a compliment of sorts.

Babs was crazy about Frédéric, right from the start. He let her ride piggy-back in the suite, even appeared in the lobby with her triumphantly astride his shoulders, and played with her for hours on the Casino square.

Yes, everybody loved Frédéric. He told me immediately to call him by his first name. Nobody called him Gérard. Our chambermaid asked me to get her his autograph, and blushed furiously when I gave it to her. She told me that the weather was going to be fine on the night of our broadcast.

"Are you sure?"

"Absolutely sure, monsieur. Frédéric said so last night, and he is in touch with Paris." She might just as well have said "with God."

Frédéric—a legend in his own time. Usually he wore pants and a sports shirt for his broadcasts. Now he was on the monitors in a tuxedo. We could see him and hear him speak on all six monitors, in French, seriously yet with great charm.

"Good evening ladies and gentlemen all over the world. You know that Her Royal Highness Princess Gracia Patricia of Monaco, on the occasion of her yearly ball for the Red Cross, is presenting a gala on this July 25, 1969, the total proceeds of which are to go to a project especially dear to her heart. One thousand two hundred guests from the four corners of the earth have been invited. One thousand two hundred have come, filled with goodwill and prepared to give Her Royal Highness support in her efforts to raise at least a small part of the money so bitterly needed for the research and care, the housing and rearing of mentally retarded children. Ladies and gentlemen, our guest of honor—Sylvia Moran." The director raised two fingers; Sylvia and Babs saw him. As Frédéric's figure slowly faded out, the telecast began—live. The director in the absurdly small control room said to his assistant, and at the same time into the microphone in front of him, "Camera One."

The red light began to flash on Camera One, directly in front of Babs and Sylvia. Cameras Two and Three were on their right and left. Now there were three pictures on the monitors in the control room—a close-up of Sylvia on Camera One, Sylvia and Babs from the left, in profile, on Camera Two, Sylvia and Babs from the right, on Camera Three. Nine-three and fifteen seconds P.M. on Friday, July 25, 1969. Now the whole picture was filled with Sylvia's beautiful face. She began to speak in French:

"Your Royal Highness, Princess Gracia Patricia, Your Royal Highness Prince Rainier of Monaco, my dear friends in Monte Carlo and all over the world—I am overjoyed and more honored than I have ever been in my life that Her Royal

Highness invited me to address you today on a most sad and serious problem which concerns all of us, yes, all of us, whoever and wherever we may be. It is the problem of those children who are not like healthy children, and who therefore need our help as if they were our children, because *no man is an island*. Every one of us is part of a whole, joined with humanity and interwoven with the fates of all human beings, like the threads of a gigantic carpet, the carpet of our fate, our lives, our times, our world . . ."

"Godammit!" said Bracken, wiping the sweat from his forehead. I looked at him, then at Frédéric, who was smiling. I was smiling too.

20

There are a few famous thoroughfares in Europe. Whenever I think of them my hands begin to sweat. For the driver of a car the worst one is the Promenade des Anglais in Nice, *the* main artery, *the* connecting link between the airport and Monte Carlo, between the airport and Cannes, between the airport and everywhere else in the world. It's the only route you can take.

During the summer months, the Promenade des Anglais in the direction of Monte Carlo is choked with traffic, bumper to bumper, in spite of the fact that there are three lanes in each direction. The cars—if they're not standing—are crawling a few meters forward, stopping, starting to crawl again, stopping, and all this in subtropical temperatures and high humidity. So we were driving along the Promenade des Anglais, Sylvia, Babs, Bracken, and Katie and Joe Patterson, Sylvia's cosmeticians. We formed a small convoy: a Rolls, a Lincoln Continental, a Mercedes 600, all air-conditioned. In front of us three Monegasque motorized policemen in white, with gold epaulettes. They looked like admirals. Blue lights revolving. Didn't do us a bit of good. We crawled right along with the rest.

I was in the second car, the Lincoln Continental, sitting beside the wife of the American consul, who, with her husband, had come to the Aéroport Nice-Côte d'Azur to meet us, together with two Monegasque ministers and a certain Alexandre Drouant, head of the Monte Carlo security police. He and I took to each other right away. A black chauffeur was driving.

Sylvia, Babs, the American consul, and a third Monegasque minister were in the first car, the Rolls. One of the prince's chauffeurs was driving. Bracken, the Pattersons, Clarissa and two directors of the Sporting Club were in the Mercedes. The chauffeur was an Arab. It was 2:45 P.M. The French employees were going back to work from lunch. To put it in a nutshell—it was hell!

I knew the consul and his wife. I had met them in London. Nice people. She was a beautiful woman. She told me how happy she was that Sylvia had agreed to participate in this worldwide appeal from Monte Carlo. The minister of finance told me how happy the prince and princess were, and I said how happy we were. Commissioner Alexandre Drouant was also smiling. He was a man in his forties who spoke five languages and whose job it was, as *gala flic*, to see to it that the event ran smoothly. Drouant was perfectly calm even though the duties he had to perform were taxing. His hair wasn't gray and already sparse without reason.

After what seemed like an eternity our convoy finally reached the Old Harbor and the end of the Promenade. Our cars wound their way through the narrow streets of Nice until they came to a traffic circle where the Moyenne Corniche, the middle one of the three coastal highways, branches away and at once starts climbing steeply. Here, at last, our cars were able to pick up speed, and we began to converse—the pleasant chatter that actually tells nothing and which one indulges in on such occasions, you know what I mean, I'm sure, your honor. But I've forgotten something. The last car in our convoy was a small bus. It contained Sylvia's wardrobe trunks and our luggage.

One hundred four degrees Fahrenheit today," Commissioner Drouant told me, calm, thoughtful and sympathetic as usual. And I could see the effects of the heat. In many places the asphalt had softened and turned into glistening puddles. Signs at the side of the road warned about it. A cement wall on our left. It served to hold back any rock slide from the stony hills that rose up beside us. The wall was covered with vines of blooming bougainvillea. On the rocks red, yellow and gold patches of flowers gleamed between the deep green of cypress groves. Now we were quite high. On our right the rocks fell off sharply. A precipice. Below me I could see more flowers, blooming shrubs, a beach and the deep blue sea stretching out endlessly, heaven and sea merging, a miraculous sight. Every time I came here I thought that the earth had been transformed once more into paradise.

"Their Royal Highnesses have asked me to beg you to be their guests tonight, at the palace," said the minister. "Madame Moran, you, Babs, if that's possible, and Monsieur Bracken. I'm sure the long flight has tired you, but perhaps a little later? Let's say at seven?"

"Very good," I said. "That will be fine."

"Then we'll pick you up at six forty-five at the Hotel de Paris, if that will be all right."

"Indeed yes. Thank you, your excellency."

"My pleasure, Monsieur Kaven."

"You can't imagine how proud we Americans over here are, Phil, because Sylvia is going to be our speaker tomorrow," said the wife of the American consul.

"Madame is just as popular and beloved here in Monaco as everywhere else in the world," said Commissioner Drouant, smiling. "Her latest film has been playing in Monaco for eleven weeks now."

And so on and so forth. You can converse like this without any strain, if it's routine for you, as it is for me. I was so used to this sort of thing, I could carry on the conversation and think of something else at the same time.

Suddenly I was a thousand miles away, in Sylvia's house in Beverly Hills, 705 Mandeville Canyon. The princess's personal secretary had just called up. He had flown from Monaco to California especially to see Sylvia and was staying at the Beverly Hills Hotel. He told us over the phone why he had come, and Sylvia invited him to tea.

Sylvia, Bracken and I were sitting in the living room, which had glass walls on three sides. Bracken said, "Of course you've got to accept this invitation, Sylvia."

"I don't know." She sounded hesitant. "There's just so much going on . . ."

"There can never be too much going on! Sylvia, darling, think of the publicity! God knows when anything like this will come up again. Six, seven, eight hundred million people will see you! And just when your new picture's coming out. Maybe you could open up your big mouth and say something, Phil."

"I think you should do it, Sylvia." At the time I had only known her a little over a year and was very cautious about everything I said, did or recommended.

"There you are!" said Bracken. "Lover boy agrees with me."

I could have bashed his teeth in for the "lover boy," but, as just mentioned, I had only been with Sylvia a year. I had to watch my step. I knew that Bracken despised me, just as I despised him, but Sylvia needed us both.

I thought of what had taken place in Beverly Hills on that day as I made small talk with our hosts in Monte Carlo. We came to a fork in the Moyenne Corniche. To the left the road led to Mentone, on the right down to the sea and Monaco. A curve, another curve, and suddenly this independent little principality, one and a half square kilometers in size, half the size of New York's Central Park and only a tenth of the size of the small state of Liechtenstein, this Lilliput state, age-old and immensely rich, lies below you. You can see the peninsula rimmed by precipitous rock. It looks like a slightly crooked thumb and juts out into the sea, protecting the harbor with its many yachts. I could see the palace, a golden yellow, perched on the rocks, the government buildings, and the business district, brick red, yellow and white. There were the towers of the gaming casino, dwarfed by the highrise buildings perched on the precipitous hillside. I knew that this little country had only approximately 25,000 citizens, but more than two million foreigners came every year from all over the world. Many reside here; more foreigners than Monegasques live permanently in Monaco. Today this little principality is totally built up, has been since 1969. Nothing edible grows here, nothing but flowers and age-old palm trees and spurge laurel from Abyssinia. Since there was no room for any more people, the Monegasques began to build vertically, one apartment house beside the other, reaching up into the sky. I had been to Monte Carlo often, before I knew Sylvia, and I had always wished I could live here among these friendly, helpful, gentle people, in this beautiful, peaceful bay. . . .

"Are you out of your fucking mind?" Bracken was excited. "You adore di Sica's films. You consider him the greatest European producer, Fellini excepted. So? Have you ever seen a di Sica film without children?"

"No."

"Children, animals and priests—if they're in a picture,

you've got it made. This time around the animals and priests are out. Leaves the children. Everybody loves them. A picture with a child, and you can't miss. Millions in your bank account, guaranteed. Especially if something goes wrong with the child. The children, Sylvia! And they're asking you to talk about children to whom something terrible has happened and what that terrible thing is! Total misery! Do you get what I'm saying? The response will be tears, tears, tears!"

"But what should I say?"

"I'll write it for you," said Bracken. "And Babs must go along. That's a must!"

"Babs?"

"Sure."

"But won't it upset her when I . . . when I talk about these unfortunate children?"

"Upset her? Babs? She's much too young for anything like that. She'll never get it."

"She gets everything, Rod."

"So she'll be upset. For how long? Half an hour, then she'll have forgotten all about it. Dammit, Phil, would it hurt you to put in a word from time to time?"

"Rod's right, Silky. It's a chance in a million. And of course Babs must go along, if only for the contrast. Babs beside you on the screen, healthy, smiling, and you appealing to the world for understanding and help for children who are not healthy and smiling."

Sylvia looked at me for quite a while without saying a word, then she said, "Well, if you really think so . . ."

"At last!" Bracken sighed. "I'll attend to everything," and with a look at me, "as usual. Children! Children! A great man—di Sica."

"Violà," said Commissioner Drouant as our car coasted slowly downhill, past the red-and-white border posts of the principality. "We made it!" And I was back in the present.

"I don't recognize anything," I said, looking out the window. "So many skyscrapers, so many new buildings!"

"When were you here last, Monsieur Kaven?" asked the minister.

"Four years ago, your excellency."

"Ah well . . ."

"But you know where the Hotel de Paris is, and the casino, don't you?" asked the wife of the American consul.

"Oh, yes."

Our convoy came to the Boulegrins, an immaculately tended lawn area with flower beds, the rarest and most costly blossoms glowing in them. And tropical trees—banyans, cacti high as pines, and there was the casino! I knew it had been built by the same architect as the Paris Opera sometime during the nineteenth century, its ornamentation opulent, with little towers at the corners and big bronze angels perched on the roof. On one side stood the Hotel de Paris, built in a similar style. On recently erected grandstands I could see photographers and cameramen, and many curious people being held back by the police. Our cars stopped. Employees of the hotel, in white uniforms with gold braid, rushed forward, opened the doors of our cars and helped us out. Photographers yelled their wishes to us; Sylvia, Babs and I did our best to gratify them. Babs smiled and waved, and the curious onlookers clapped and cried "Bravo!" The manager of the hotel, Monsieur Jean Boeri, an elegant, handsome fellow whom I also knew, came down the steps to greet us. He kissed Sylvia's hand; Babs curtsied. Then Monsieur Boeri led us into the huge hotel lobby. Yes, that had been our reception on arrival the day before, in the early afternoon.

21

The program that was going to be seen worldwide had started. Sylvia spoke without pathos, calmly but impressively.

"I have been very fortunate, not that I can say I deserved it, and that often troubles me . . ."

The director gave an order over his microphone; Camera One backed slowly and Babs was included in the picture. Every now and then she smiled at her mother, and now Sylvia laid an arm across her shoulder. "And I am not talking about my profession; I am talking about my daughter. Babs is a loving and clever child, she makes me very happy, and, my dear friends, Babs is *healthy*."

"Two!" said the director. His assistant switched Camera Two on "take" and there was a close-up of Babs, looking up at her mother, the happy face of a little girl, then the camera backed away again. Babs of course knew, with the routine of the World's Greatest Little Sunshine Girl, that she was on camera. Out of the corner of her eye she could see the light on Camera Two blinking red. The expression on her face switched to serious.

"With every passing day," Sylvia was saying, "we realize more and more that we are living in times of great change, but one thing we can be sure of—in the year two thousand, if it still exists, our world will be a very different place to live in. Since the beginning of this century an ever increasing number of people recognize that the laws of our coexistence will have to be changed, but to determine these changes seems to pose an insoluble problem. Yet we try. But can we honestly say that any one of us feels we will succeed? Conscious of his limitations, man tries again and again to bring law and order to our civilization—by force, by sacrificing his life or the lives of others. He lifts his voice or his gun, or he demonstrates loudly, very loudly, what he thinks or wants. But what I am about to say today, my friends, is not for or against this or that social system. I hope that what I have to say will impress all of you, free of politics, as humane thinking directed at humanity."

"A fantastic actress," said the director, and unbuttoned his shirt down to his navel. It was getting hotter all the time in the little room.

Frédéric, usually so blithe, looked serious. "She isn't acting," he said. "This is sincere, Michel, every word she's saying. What a wonderful woman!" And he couldn't seem to take his eyes off her. I looked at Bracken, the old son of a bitch. He nodded, closed his eyes and crossed his fingers.

"Three!" said the director, whose name apparently was Michel. Camera Three showed Sylvia and Babs from the right.

"But," said Sylvia, and now I could see her and Babs in three different close-ups, "beside the articulate and active people who make up this humanity there are those who are quiescent, totally quiescent, sometimes mute . . ."

The man behind Camera Three moved forward and gave us Sylvia's beautiful face, filled with emotion, and this was what 700 million people on five continents were seeing now, or would see within hours.

"And with these quiescent, sometimes mute suppliants I am referring to those who are most helpless, the poorest of the poor, those to whom our world pays the least attention— our brain-damaged mentally retarded children."

66

Sporting Club, Monte Carlo.

The gala took place in the open air on a summer night. Twelve hundred of the most powerful, smartest, most creative and richest men and women in the world were present, men and women who felt concern for the welfare of mankind and for the future of creativity. Famous people from all over the world were present, the women in the most expensive and fashionable dress available, wearing priceless jewelry, the men in tuxedos, in uniform, in religious habits; heads of state from East and West, church dignitaries, representatives of various religions, kings, aristocrats, Greek shipping magnates, American financiers, heirs to immense fortunes, top-ranking officers, presidents of airlines and hotel chains, automobile manufacturers; ambassadors, Nobel Prize winners, directors, doctors, writers, publishers, newspaper moguls, architects, actors, musicians. The admiral of the American Sixth Fleet (Mediterranean) was present, and of the Soviet Third Eskadra (Mediterranean); one empress, innumerable princesses, stars of stage and screen, singers, painters, sculptors ... twelve hundred human beings. (Everything I am telling now and what is yet to come concerning the events at the Sporting Club that night, your honor, I learned later from Commissioner Drouant.)

There they sat under a starry sky, surrounded by palm trees, exotic plants and shrubs, the blossoms of which carried a scent that was almost stupefying. There they sat at long tables with damask cloths set with the finest china, glass and silver (dinner was to be served later). A whole army of waiters stood ready to serve, their white jackets bright.

Three Tele-Monte Carlo vans were parked at strategic positions, men with cameras stationed on their roofs. The gala was to be telecast worldwide too. The Prince and Princess of Monaco, with their daughter, Caroline, and their son, Albert, heir to the throne, sat at a table among all the others. Grace Patricia's classically beautiful, clear-cut, eternally youthful face was serious.

The jewelry worn here was worth countless millions. Not only because of the jewelry but also for the protection of the numerous famous and powerful people present, utmost security precautions had been taken. Many had brought their private bodyguards, but beside the official or private detectives, there was Monegasque Police surveillance. You could see the men if you looked closely, in tuxedos, quiet, observant, smoking thoughtfully, scattered strategically throughout the area. And some of the waiters weren't waiters. Nobody was aware of the guns that these detectives, police officers and phony waiters were carrying. And the armed men in tuxedos, hidden among the bushes outside, were just as unobtrusive. They formed an impenetrable cordon around the entire area, their walkie-talkies in their hands. And nobody saw the men in evening dress, equipped similarly, watching the events with their binoculars from the windows of the Sporting Club or from its roof, and from the roof of the Hotel de Paris. Men were positioned on the rooftops of many nearby houses and in top-floor apartments rented for the occasion. Even the maritime police were participating. Their speedboats were docked in the harbor among the yachts, all the way to Cap Martin, their lights out, their motors running. All of these men in close communication with their colleagues, and all of them in constant contact with the person who was responsible for the security and undisturbed procedure of this gala—Alexandre Drouant. He was on the roof of the Sporting Club.

Commissioner Drouant, married, five children, looked down at those assembled and saw the huge screen where every guest could see the picture. And millions could see it simultaneously on their own sets. Sylvia's voice came out of loudspeakers behind the screen. And Commissioner Drouant, on the roof of the Sporting Club, his walkie-talkie in his hand, saw and heard Sylvia and Babs, and thought of his five children. . . .

"And in their still and sometimes mute way, these children are asking you: how do you feel about us out there in that world of yours?"

Television sets had been installed in the corridors of 16 Boulevard Princesse Charlotte and in the entrance to the tiny broadcasting station. Cleaning women, secretaries and other employees were collected in front of them, watching and listening. "In your efficient world," Sylvia Moran was saying, "and in the many societies you have created or want to destroy in the name of freedom and brotherly love in order to establish freedom, prosperity and security, in order to achieve equality and happiness for all . . ."

"Well, how are we doing, lover boy?" Rod Bracken speaking softly in the hot control room. An asshole with a halo!

"Just fine, you son of a bitch," I said.

68

"Don't say that again!"

"And don't call me lover boy again, not once. Or you'll regret it!"

This uplifting dialogue was whispered in English. Filled with envy and hate I concluded with, "We're doing all right, jerk!"

And Sylvia was saying, "We have so many goals, so many causes, we long for so many things on which I can't and don't want to pass judgment, but one thing I know—the great majority of people seem to be agreed that whoever is useless, whoever cannot be counted as a full member of our society, cannot be counted as a member of that society at all . . ."

At one of the tables in the Sporting Club the wife of one of the diplomats began to sob. Her husband tried to calm her. Not many of those present knew that she had two children—a healthy daughter and a mentally retarded son.

"Cut! Camera One!" The director took off his shirt. I would have liked to do the same thing. The red light on Camera One blinked.

"We are living in an era of lonely people leading communal lives," said Sylvia, and Babs looked up at her, astonishment written all over her little face. "Unfortunately this is how things are in our frighteningly soulless world. In the world of these lonely communes the retarded child doesn't count as a human being."

"From here on I can get twice the percentage for Sylvia's pictures," said Bracken, grinning with satisfaction.

Sylvia was saying, "A retarded child is not recognized as a full member of the human race. I am not blaming anyone. It is only natural for the so-called healthy person to reject the sick and the handicapped."

The wife of the diplomat was still weeping. Her husband rose and led her away. Commissioner Alexandre Drouant, up on the roof, could see it through his binoculars. He laid them aside and watched Sylvia on the huge screen.

"The only thing that can correct this antipathy toward retarded children," she was saying, "is a proper attitude toward them and above all, the establishing of regular contact with them. Only thus can we hope to change our aversion into sympathy. Let me put it this way—the first step toward love is to know one another. Lack of recognition can lead only to antipathy and injustice . . ."

* * *

69

In the tiny TMC control room, the director, whom Frédéric had called Michel, was saying, "Cut! Camera Two." Sylvia spoke directly into the camera. "It seems to me that in our human community we still have a lot to learn before we can call it humane." Babs was looking up at her mother thoughtfully. "The healthy among us—the so-called healthy—and those who are retarded have much more in common than we realize. Those who are retarded yearn for happiness just as we do, who are healthy. Those who are retarded want to give love as well as receive it, even if many of them can only express themselves with great difficulty and in a way we find hard to understand . . ."

There was a television set in the hotel room of Sylvia's cosmeticians, Katie and Joe Patterson. They were seated in front of it with Babs's governess, Clarissa, hearing Sylvia say, "The retarded child wants to give something too but is not in a position to do so. They too want to contribute positively. And who among us has the right to decide what is contribution or what is achievement?"

The Pattersons and Clarissa sat silently in front of the screen. Joe was holding Katie's hand.

"Cut! Camera One. Close-up!" said the director. He was holding the script of Sylvia's speech in his hand. "That is why," Sylvia was saying, "we have to grant these retarded children every possible opportunity if we are to call ourselves humane. And with that, my friends, we have arrived at the core of the matter." Babs laid one hand on her mother's; Sylvia looked at her and smiled. Babs's face broke into a smile too. Sylvia looked ahead at the camera. "Thanks to medical progress, thousands of these children survive today who not so long ago would have died. And I am talking about children who are *retarded but alive!*"

"Shit!" Bracken whispering in my ear. "Why should Seven Stars get all the gravy while taxes bleed Sylvia white? This broadcast puts her right on top. Want to know what Sylvia's going to be next?"

"What?"

"Her own producer. She's got to have her own company. Seven Stars can contribute. After this broadcast Sylvia will be able to write her own ticket in Hollywood!"

"Very soon, before we know it," Sylvia was saying, "the

70

problem of our retarded children will force us to reconsider if only because of its size . . ."

My shirt was wet through. I could see Babs lick her lips. The child was thirsty. Down there, under those lamps, it had to be hotter than up here. "Cut! Camera Three!"

"We shall have to realize that not only the capable person, the achiever, the prodigy and the one most likely to succeed are members of our community, but that the handicapped and the weak, the mute and the brain-damaged have just as much right to 'belong.' "

Sylvia's delivery had grown increasingly passionate, her voice more importunate and pleading. "Yes, yes! They *are* a part of our world in which no one should be permitted to think that the neediest souls are of no concern to him. They too are his brothers and sisters!"

"In any event," Bracken was saying, "she's got to do *The Chalk Circle* with her own company, and she will. Want to bet on it? And we'll make you producer!"

"You can kiss my . . ."

"That would suit you, wouldn't it? But don't worry. I know you're not up to it. Never did a stroke of work in your life. I'll attend to everything for you and you'll have your own credit line at last."

"Yes, my friends," Sylvia was saying, and now Babs moved a little closer to her, "today we know how to improve the condition of these children in some of the most serious cases. We don't know what medical research holds in store for us tomorrow. Progress, I am sure, but probably not a solution that can totally heal these unfortunate children."

"Cut! Camera Two!"

"The time has come when the culture of any given society must be measured by the extent to which the retarded child is accepted as an equal, even if the retarded child can never accomplish what the healthy child can, in spite of all medical and educational efforts. It may sound banal, my friends, but it is true—what is lacking above everything else today in man is humaneness!"

The heat in the control room was unbearable. The same seemed to apply to the studio. Babs was getting restless, Sylvia's voice increasingly labored. "I don't want to frighten anyone, but consider for a moment the fact that what has already happened to so many parents can happen to you. Husband and wife may suddenly have to adapt their way of life to a brain-damaged child. One harmful medication during pregnancy, one slip of the obstetrician's hand during the birth, a devastating lack of oxygen in the brain, or, perhaps, years later, a fall, an inflammatory disease, an infection . . . no one is immune from such disasters."

"Cut! Camera One! Close-up of the child and hold it!" said the director.

"You know, I am sure," Sylvia was saying to the twelve hundred guests in the Sporting Club, "that I am not only addressing you on behalf of myself but above all on behalf of Her Royal Highness the Princess, to beg you to give, and to give generously. I am asking all of you here in Monte Carlo and my friends the world over who are listening to me—please help us by donating money! There are organizations in every country whose concern it is to care for retarded children. Send your donations to such organizations, send as much as you can, however little—the smallest amount helps, the smallest amount is a good deed in a good cause. I am begging from the bottom of my heart! These retarded children are not a negative aspect of our society as so many people seem to think. There *is* a positive aspect to their presence among us, because, in our response to them, we can prove what is paramount above everything else: that we want to live with and for one another, that the same stream of life carries all of us . . ."

In the control room, the sound engineer spoke into his microphone: "Central! Central! Calling all three mobile units in Sporting!" One after the other, three male voices answered. "Okay," the technician responded. "Get ready. We're switching over to you in a minute." And Sylvia was saying, "The major role, the most important role of the helpless in our midst, is that by their very existence they can force every one of us to rise up out of the personal tragedies and catastrophes of our private lives, from which there sometimes seems no escape, and meet on a common ground as brothers and sisters. My friends, I thank you."

She lowered her head. Twelve hundred people in the Sporting Club, and seven, perhaps eight million people around the world, saw it. The tears were coursing down her cheeks. The picture switched quickly to Babs, whose happy, smiling face grew larger and larger, came closer and closer until it filled the entire screen.

A few seconds passed in silence, then, thunderous applause. The lights went on and lit up the scene bright as day. The director had switched from the TMC control room at 16 Boulevard Princesse Charlotte to the three camera crews in the Sporting Club, who now began to show us the beautiful and dazzling members of the audience, the worldy and religious potentates, sitting at their white tables in front of palm trees and luxuriously blooming flowers and shrubs. A stage rose up from the depths, an orchestra began to play. I could see three different views on the monitors in the control room. The director was communicating with the men at the club. Frédéric had dashed down into the studio; Bracken and I hurried after him. The spotlights were out; only the regular bulbs in the ceiling were on now. The three cameramen were still standing beside their cameras. Sylvia and Babs had risen.

"I want to thank you, madame," said Frédéric. "You were wonderful!" He kissed her hand and bowed low. Sylvia kissed him spontaneously on both cheeks. Frédéric bowed low in front of Babs, then threw his arms around her and kissed her. Babs laughed and threw her arms around him just as Rod and I walked up to them. Sylvia looked around at all of us. There were still tears in her eyes. "I thank *you*, Frédéric," she said, "and both of you—Pepito"—she called me that in public, your honor, without a thought that it might turn anyone off—"and you, dear Rod, for your advice and help. It was the most beautiful effort of my entire life!" She looked up at the window of the control room behind which the technicians and the director's assistant were still seated, and said (the studio microphone was still on), "And I thank *you*, all of you," and wiped her tears away. She embraced Rod. He kissed her. "Great, kid! Just great!" She embraced me. I kissed her. I said, "I love you." That's what I said, your honor, "I love you."

"And I love you, Pepito, so much!" Then she turned to Bracken. "Rod, would you please take Babs back to the hotel."

"Oh Mommy, Mommy, I don't have to go back *yet?*"

"It's bedtime for good little girls, and you're a good little girl, aren't you?" Sylvia was kneeling now, and she kissed Babs. "Mommy and Uncle Rod and Phil still have a lot to do. If you're very good you can watch us on television for half an hour, from your bed, with Clarissa."

"Goody!" cried Babs. Rod took her hand. "I'll come straight back to the club," he said.

"I'll take off my makeup, then I'll be right along with Phil," said Sylvia.

"And I'll get my car and be waiting downstairs," said Frédéric. "I'll drive you to the club. I'm needed there too."

"I'll be a while," said Sylvia. "You know how it is, Frédéric."

"I certainly do, Madame Moran."

"Not Madame Moran, please. Sylvia!"

"Sylvia." He blushed like a boy. "I'll be waiting for you at the entrance." He turned to Rod Bracken and Babs, and took her other hand. "Come on, let's go together. I'll drive you and Monsieur Bracken to your hotel."

"Oh yes!" Babs was delighted. "What kind of car do you have, Uncle Frédéric?" He told her. "That's one I don't know," she said. "Bye, Phil, bye, Mommy!" and the three left together. Sylvia and I smiled at each other as we heard Babs ask, "Does it have automatic transmission?" Sylvia called out once more in the direction of the control room, "Thanks again! So much! And goodnight." And five male and one female voice answered in the studio loudspeaker, "Goodnight!" And the six people in the control room waved. We waved back. They couldn't leave yet. They had to monitor the broadcast from the club.

Sylvia and I walked down the narrow corridor that led from the studio to a steel door. Nobody in sight. I opened the door for her. I had been here before. It was a small dressing room, close to the studio, soundproof I imagined; anyway, the steel door was padded. I let Sylvia enter ahead of me, followed her, closed the door and turned around. And was shocked. Because never in my life, your honor, had I seen such an expression of savage hatred on any face as I saw now on Sylvia's.

22

"What on earth's the matter?" I asked, and Sylvia began to rave, shrilly, coarsely.

"Never! Never! Never! Do you hear me? Never again, as long as I live, if they pay me a million, will I do anything like this again!"

"Never? Anything like what? What are you talking about?"

74

I stammered, but to be on the safe side I turned the key in the lock, shutting us in.

"I'm telling you that nobody, nobody on this godforsaken earth, not Grace, not the President of the United States or anyone else, will ever get me to go on a show like this again!"

I thought, What if the room isn't soundproof? And I said, "Shut up, Sylvia!"

She went for me, her fists pounding my face, my chest. I couldn't stop her—she screamed. "You bastard! How dare you speak to me like that, you filthy, fucking bastard. It's your fault just as much as Rod's who wrote all that shit I had to read!"

"Sylvia . . . please!"

"You heard me!" Like a fishwife, screaming hoarsely, Sylvia Moran, beloved by the whole world and worshiped like a goddess. "Yes—shit! I could puke!"

I drew the key out of the lock. Two steps took me to the makeup table. A bottle of cognac stood on it. I took out the cork, filled a glass and walked toward Sylvia with it. She stepped back, an expression of panic on her face, as if she were afraid I was going to strike her. That was something new in my book; I must have had a terrifying expression on my face too. She finally backed into the couch and fell onto it. I knelt beside her, held out the glass and said, "Drink!"

"No!"

"You're to drink!"

"I . . . I don't want to!"

I took hold of her by her hair, forced her head back; she opened her mouth to scream and I poured the brandy down her throat. She choked, coughed. I let her go and filled the glass again. "You dare to strike me, you fucking bastard!"

"I did not hit you!"

"You hit me, you motherfucking bastard! I took you out of the gutter, I—"

"Shut up!" I shouted again.

She did. And stared at me wide-eyed. You have no idea, your honor, how effective out-of-character behavior can be. Then she said, "More!"

"More what?"

"More cognac. I want to get drunk fast. Hurry! Or I'll throw up all over the place."

I gave her the bottle, she drank from it, said again, "Throw up all over the place." Drank again, said, "I don't know why I didn't throw up on the air."

There was a television monitor in the corner of the room. Suddenly I could see Princess Grace, then the prince, young Albert's face, the faces of men known the world over, eerie, all of it, because a monitor like that brings only the picture, no sound. The faces and jewelry and gowns of beautiful women. TMC broadcasting from the Sporting Club.

Good, I thought, any minute now she'll be stoned. Then I can get her out of here and back to the hotel. I'll think up an excuse for why she didn't put in an appearance at the club. But she started all over again. "Rod! That motherfucking imbecile! That he could do something like this to me. But he'll get what he deserves—I'll fire him!"

"Quiet!"

"You be quiet! Give me the bottle!"

Glad to—only trouble was she didn't get stoned.

"If I'd had a bottle on the air—"

"Have you gone crazy? A few minutes ago you were on the air with the tears rolling down your cheeks. Everybody—"

"Tears? Tears of revulsion, that's what they were! And rage!"

"Rage over what?"

"That I had to read all that crap Rod had written! That you two had got me into this mess! Humanity! Charity! Understanding! Compassion! Give me the bottle!"

I gave it to her. On the monitor: President Podgorny. Nelson Rockefeller. The begum. Sammy Davis, Jr. Jean-Paul Sartre. A representative from the Vatican. Rose Kennedy. Pompidou. Princess Anne. Queen Juliana. The three Apollo 10 astronauts. A dark beauty. A chinese in a white uniform. And on the couch—Sylvia. "Help me up!"

I helped her up. She stood in front of me, the bottle in her hand. "The poor sick children? Drooling idiots, that's what they are! Worse than animals! And I gave my good name for them!"

She was off again. If the place wasn't soundproof we were finished. "The stream of life? That means being successful and rich and *stronger* than all the rest. To enjoy life? A kick in the ass to whoever's weaker. *That's* the stream of life! And when you grow weak and old, you die, without batting an eyelash! But to be on top to the end and then have the courage to say it's all over! Not to cling to a miserable existence! *That's* humane! *That's* normal! And I'm going to stay on top. But not with the bullshit I had to dish out today! I'm taking money out of the pockets of those damn fools out there! For what? For nothing! A fraud. A fraud all around!" Her voice broke. Fearfully she asked, "What results do you suppose it'll have, Phil?" Phil now, not Pepito.

"Only the best, Sylvia. Absolutely. Nothing but the best . . . for you, for everybody."

Without another word she began to undress. She sat down in front of the mirror, took off her jewelry and began to restore her makeup. "Nothing but the best," she said. "That's what you think. Catastrophic—that's what the results will be. Where does most of my money come from? From the U.S.A. And where are they clamoring most about euthanasia? In the U.S.A. What am I talking about? They're clamoring for it everywhere, all over the world. And why not? It's normal. Thousands of dollars are thrown out every year for those idiot kids. Joe will love it when he hears about it!"

Joe Gintzburger was the president of Seven Stars, one of the biggest motion picture companies in the world. Sylvia worked for him. "He'll love it! What sort of a cream is this anyway?" Looking down at the jar. "He'll love you. Rod."

"Why me?"

"Because you talked me into doing it." Face cream. Sponge. Her true face reappeared, and now *I* needed the bottle. Was it possible for such obscenities to come from such a beautiful mouth? For such a demon to rage behind such an angel's countenance? You are nodding, your honor. You know your people. "How many people do you suppose tuned it out?" she cried. "That shit speech of mine? *You're* crazy, Rod and you, not I! You're a menace, both of you! You've ruined me!"

"Sylvia, please!"

"Shut up! Give me the bottle." She took it from me and drank like a sailor, then she smashed it down on the plate-glass cover of the vanity table. The top broke in two. "Fraud! That's what it was—fraud!" Busy with her face again, talk-ig all the time, loudly, much too loudly. "They stammer, they shake—ugh! Mongoloids, spastics, cripples." A long drink. "They sent me an album to the hotel, with pictures. So that I'd say my speech with feeling! I nearly threw up. I'd never seen anything like it in my entire life! Hideous! Hideous! I'm going to have nightmares about it. I'll never be able to forget those pictures!"

Yehudi Menahin on the monitor. Alberto Moravia. Ali Khan. Abba Eban. Andrei Gromyko. Sophia Loren. George McNamara. Norman Mailer. Marc Chagall. And Sylvia screaming into the mirror, "You and I know that creatures like that have got to go!"

Now I'd had it. Everybody outside could hear. "For God's sake shut up!" I shouted. "Can't you get it into your head that there are many cases—many, do you hear?—that can be helped today?"

The cognac was dribbling down her chin, her neck, between her breasts. Suddenly she laughed, a crazy laugh. "Helped? Sure! So that ten years from now they can count to three, if they can talk at all! So that in fifteen years they can shit on the john and don't just let go wherever they are. And that's what you call help?"

"Shut up, godammit, woman! Shut up!"

But she didn't shut up.

"I've seen the pictures. I wonder what damn fool had them sent up to me. Those pictures . . . those pictures . . ."

"I saw them too." On the screen I could see dozens of waiters serving dinner.

"So?" She was glaring at me. She had removed all her makeup from her beautiful face, the face of a saint, your honor.

When Sylvia looked up at me I knew suddenly what I had to do. In my own interest. In hers, incidentally, too. Because after all, her success guaranteed mine. So I didn't find it difficult to say, "What do you mean—so? You and Rod knew from the start that you should do this for the *publicity!* It took me quite a while to decide you were right, but that was what the three of us finally agreed on, wasn't it? And you had nothing to say against it, not in the end. Correct me if I'm wrong." I laid my hands gently on her bare shoulders. "And believe me, Silky, it was marvelous publicity. An around-the-world coup. You've never had anything like it. The director's assistant in the control room cried. I'll bet anything you want that millions cried. You were fantastic!"

"Fantastic?"

"Ask anyone here."

"I'm a guest here. Don't be an ass! Nobody would dare to say no." She was smearing cream on her face again. "But ask anyone in Hollywood, New York, Paris, London, what they thought of my performance today." She turned around. Her hair was piled high, the cream made her face glisten. "Ask whoever you like! They'll all say the same thing—that they don't give a damn for those idiot children! Let them rot! And *fast!*"

I slapped her, hard as I could. The effect was instantaneous. Her voice dropped to a whisper. "Let them die! *That* would be humane! God knows, I hated the Nazis, but in that respect they were on the right track. These cretins deserve euthanasia! They have it coming to them." After that she was silent, covering her mouth with one hand. The alcohol had evidently taken effect, or the fact that I had slapped her, or perhaps just time. Time can work wonders.

I bent over her and began to massage her neck and shoulders. She liked that. It excited her. "I can only say again, and I wish you'd grasp it, Silky—Rod and I had nothing on our minds but the prestige this would mean for you. So that the whole world could see what a remarkable woman you are, not only as an actress. For God's sake, Silky, how many times have you said in a picture, and said with absolute sincerity, things you didn't believe in? That you thought were idiotic or worse? Spoken up for things you hated, just as you did for these children? Come on—try to count. How many times?" And in the mirror I could see her begin to squirm as I massaged her, saw the expression on her face—a mixture of growing excitement and triumph. "So," I said, into the mirror, "you understand finally, don't you?"

"Yes," she murmured.

"Good."

She was writhing like a snake under my fingers, her eyes glittered, she was breathing hard. "Hypocrisy," she said, "That's what it was. Right?"

I said nothing but went on massaging her, down her bare back now. "Hypocrisy," she said again, her breasts rising and falling faster. "My hypocrisy, Rod's . . . and whatever they're donating out there at the gala and all over the world—that's hypocrisy too."

I went on kneading her flesh between my fingers. "Rotten reformers! Pompous asses! Good Christians! Good Jews! Courageous idiots! And all of them—futile people loaded with millions, trying to attract attention. Look how charitable we are! Look what we're donating for these cretins!" Now she was breathing very fast.

"Millions!" I said. "And you'll be able to read in every newspaper in the world that you were colossal. You always were great, now you're on top! On the very top!"

Suddenly she trembled hard and her body curled up under my hands. She was experiencing just what I had expected. When it was over she said, "Was I really that good?"

"Really."

"And you think it will be useful?"

"My word of honor."

She stared at herself in the mirror for a while, then, sounding perfectly satisfied, she said, "Well, then everything's okay."

"Everything's okay," I said, and thought: I know my business. Hats off to me! "And now will you please tell me how an intelligent woman like you could fly off the handle like that?"

She shrugged and said as she began to put on her makeup, "I guess I just lost my cool, Pepito." Pepito again, your honor, not Phil. "Because I kept having to think of those repulsive pictures. Of course they meant well, but it *was* stupid of them to send them to me, wasn't it?"

"Of course it was, Silky. And now put on your face and get dressed, because we've got to go over to the Sporting Club. You're sitting beside the prince, and all the cameras will be turned on you, the most beautiful, most wonderful woman in the world!"

"You're sweet, Pepito. Kiss me!"

It was quite a kiss. She groaned, sighed; finally I let her go. "Everything all right again, Silky?"

"Everything all right, Pepito." Sylvia was looking at the monitor. "Look at that Dumb Dora . . . that's the wife of the president . . . the way she lets her breasts hang out. Silicone, right?"

"Right."

"But her diamond necklace, Pepito." Sylvia's voice was dreamy. "I don't have anything like it."

"So you'll buy one like it."

"So I'll buy one like it. You're right, Pepito—that's what we'll do." Suddenly she laughed. "Want to know something?"

"What?"

"Funny, but all that screaming's given me a terrific appetite. I could eat a whole lobster!"

23

She managed to down one and a half, two bottles of Comtes de Champagne, and quite a bit of whiskey. And every camera was turned on her, just as I had prophesied. Then the Monte Carlo Dancers pirouetted around the stage. After that there was an auction—paintings by Picasso, Chagall, Modigliani, Léger and Buffet. Frédéric was the auctioneer. They sold for 11.5 million francs. Sylvia joined in the bidding—*noblesse oblige*—and acquired a Léger. I would have preferred the Modigliani—a reclining nude in violet—but after all, it was her money and not a bad Léger. Slightly overpriced at 800,000 francs.

Rod Bracken turned up and told me that he'd handed Babs over to Clarissa and come back with Frédéric, and what a howling success it had been, hadn't it? So I told him just how howlingly successful it had been and he swore one obscenity after the other, and then he thanked the good Lord for how lucky we'd been in spite of everything, and we killed a bottle between us. And it was the closest we ever came to liking each other.

Two days later we flew back to Hollywood. As we were crossing the Atlantic I thought the whole incident through again. Had I slipped up on anything? Was there anything that could catch up with us? Had nobody really heard Sylvia's hysterical ravings? No. The whole thing was foolproof, I was sure. When it turned out that I had been mistaken and I had to fly to Monte Carlo again with Rod, it was not to prevent a catastrophe—for that it was too late—but to learn how to live with the menace of a catastrophe which could destroy Sylvia's career. On that second visit, when we went to see Frédéric Gérard because there were things we had to discuss with him, I walked once more into the small dressing room and saw the little black box on the dressing table for the first time. On that terrible evening of Sylvia's outburst I hadn't noticed it.

As you probably know, your honor, dressing rooms in theaters and studios frequently have a speaker to inform the actors when they are due on stage, how much time they still have, things like that. What you perhaps don't know is that these speakers frequently don't only carry the message from outside; there is a switch that enables them to pick up voices in the dressing room, like a microphone.

24

Suzy Sylvestre, my Paris beauty salon girl, had had the measles as a child and was therefore immune. Both of us were lying stark naked on her crazy bed (very large and circular) in her bedroom with its way-out modular plastic furniture, light effects and posters, everything from Che Guevera, Andy Warhol's tin cans and the fist in barbed wire of Amnesty International. I felt at home here. Sylvia had fallen asleep quite suddenly around 8:00 and hadn't wakened again. I was able to leave. I finally got to Suzy's around 9:30, and we had fallen on each other without exchanging a word. Suzy Sylvestre, age twenty-four, blond, long legs, large firm breasts, blue eyes, and the most beautiful rear end I'd ever seen in my life.

"And you have three months this time, *chéri?*" asked Suzy.

"Three months. I'll have to leave you every now and then, but not for long."

"We'll end up in the hospital ourselves, the two of us," said Suzy. She had dark-red, almost black, finger- and toenails. I found them hideous; she adored them, it was all the rage. "Two cases of absolute exhaustion. You're some man! I've never known anyone like you!"

Other ladies had told me the same thing. When they get hold of someone like me who can get them to function, they go crazy. Sylvia, for instance . . .

"*Chéri,* do you think we could live happily together?"

"On what?"

"Don't ask me on what. I have my salon. I make plenty. Enough for the two of us. I'll give up François and . . ."

Things were getting dangerous. "Give up François? Over my dead body! You know I'm worthless, have nothing, couldn't even bring you a flower today. I'll scrape up enough to bring you one tomorrow. But no castles, no factories, no millions. And you'll be a countess! I'm only a playboy who needs to be supported."

"Don't say things like that! I hate the word. And I hate Sylvia Moran."

"I don't like things the way they are either," I said. "But what do you want me to do? If Sylvia throws me out I'm finished."

"Never! I'll always have enough for us both!"

"But I won't accept anything from you, Suzy. We're too much alike. We understand each other too well. I could never take money from you."

This impressed her. And she was such an intelligent girl!

"But Sylvia—you can take from her?"

"Yes."

"Why?"

"Because it's all quite different with Sylvia." (How many times had I said this?) "Intellectually, sexually—all quite different."

"Is that true? Word of honor?"

"Word of honor!"

"But . . . but you hump her too, don't you?"

"Well, of course! Do you think I'd be as well off as I am if I didn't? Sylvia doesn't give something for nothing."

"I hate her!"

"You already said that."

"But . . . but the sweet things, the really sweet things that . . . oh, you know what I mean. You don't do those with her, do you?"

"Never!" I lied. "Only with you."

"And not with any other woman?"

"Never!"

"Swear!"

"I swear." Funny that every one of my little darlings asked me that. Sylvia of course too. Seemed to fascinate them. Poor things . . .

Suzy laughed.

"What's so funny?"

"I was just thinking . . . I'll be a countess with millions, and we'll go right on deceiving François whenever we see each other."

"Yes," I said. "That *is* funny," and I laughed too. Why spoil her fun?

"Will you do it once more?"

"With pleasure, countess."

"You're so sweet, *chéri.* Now I can smell you again . . . you smell," and she kissed me on the chest, many little kisses. "Your typical Philip smell. No other man smells like you . . . like an animal. When I smell you I nearly come . . . and the smell stays. You can take as many baths as you like . . . you just took a bath, didn't you?"

When I had arrived, she had wrinkled her nose. "Yuck! What's the matter? You smell like a hospital."

"That's where I come from. Visiting a friend. And just imagine—he's got the measles! That's why I called you before I came up, to find out if you'd had measles.

"Yes. And thank God I have," said Suzy. "But now take a bath, *chéri,* please."

She had scrubbed my back, and it happened for the first time in the tub. Nice girl, Suzy . . .

25

"I love you so much, *mon petit chou,* so much," said Suzy Sylvestre, now that we had the first round behind us. "You'll never know how much." She had put on a record—John William. The man can sing. *"Ô Dieu, merci, pour ce paradis, qui s'ouvre aujourd'hui à l'un de tes fils* . . . O thank you, God, for this paradise which opens up today for one of your children . . ."

"I love you just as much, Sil—" Dammit, that was close! *"Mon petit chou."*

"I'd do anything for you, Philip, anything! Believe me. You think I'm just one of the girls, and I am. But it's girls like me who will do anything for a man."

". . . pour le plus petit, le plus pauvre fils, c'est pourquoi je cris: Merci, Dieu, merci, pour ce paradis . . ."

"That always makes me want to cry," said Suzy, a cigarette in her mouth, the glass of whiskey in her hand, sitting beside me, naked. I was naked too. And she really did cry, your honor, "for the smallest, the poorest of your children . . ." Lovely text.

Suzy said, "You know all about me, about the count, about all my men. I've told you everything."

"I didn't ask you to."

"But I wanted to tell you everything, *mon petit chou*." I like the French pet name "my little cabbage," don't you, your honor? "And it was very sweet of you, Suzy, to tell me everything."

"That's because I am very sweet. But you . . . you haven't told me anything. I don't know anything about you."

"You know everything that counts," I said, stroking her gently. "Give me the glass. Thanks. You know that I'm worthless and don't have a cent and that I'm Sylvia Moran's gigolo."

"Don't say gigolo!" she cried.

"But that's what I am."

"But you're not to say so!" Now she was in tears again, my little beauty-parlor girl. Of course she was one of the girls, a prostitute, but at the time, your honor, I believed they were loyal, courageous and honest *and* the most humane creatures on this earth. Where little prostitutes like Suzy were concerned, I was sentimental. "All right. I won't say it any more."

"Tell me how you met the old bag."

"Well, now . . ."

"Yes, yes, tell me!"

"There isn't much to tell. I met her in Baden-Baden, in Iffezheim."

"Iffezheim?"

"A famous racetrack. Like Auteuil or Longchamps."

"Go on. Talk."

"Well . . . I have a brother. Karl-Ludwig. My father had a cable factory in Duisburg."

"Was he rich?"

"Very rich. But then he died in a plane accident, with my mother. That was in 1960. I was nineteen. My brother is ten years older. We inherited the factory, Karl-Ludwig and I. Then, to make a long story short, we didn't get along. He kept expanding the factory, everybody respected him, nobody believed in me."

"Don't you believe in yourself?"

"I've never believed in myself."

"What about work? Have you never worked? It's only a question, *mon petit chou,* not a reproach. Haven't you ever tried to work?"

"Yes, I have. And worked hard."

"When was that?"

"When I was twenty-two. I made a marvelous deal in ball bearings. Carloads of ball bearings. Hard work. Had a terrific partner."

"So what happened?"

"He turned out to be not so terrific. The ball bearings were defective. My partner left, took all my money with him."

"What money?"

"What I'd inherited. Plenty. I've really tried, Suzy, but everything always went wrong. I tried to help my brother too. That was even worse. Everything I proposed failed. So I decided he was better off on his own."

"Did you really think that?"

"What?"

"That he'd be better off on his own?"

"Of course not."

"Tell me, *mon petit chou*, do you believe anything you say?"

"Never. Why?"

"You're sweet," said Suzy. "You simply wanted to make things easy for yourself and have your share of the money and never have to work again, right?"

"Right."

"Oh God, how I love you! How much did you get?"

"Half."

"Was that a lot?" Suzy asked reverently. She was always reverent when there was talk of money. The atmosphere in the crazy room with its disheveled circular bed and posters on the wall—above us "Make Love Not War"—was suddenly churchlike.

"Thirteen million marks," I said.

"Jee-sus! And what happened to them?"

"Where have all the flowers gone?" I said. "It's not nice of you to ask me that, *mon petit chou*."

"Are you trying to tell me that from 1960 to 1967—that's only seven years, *chéri*—you managed to run through thirteen million marks?"

"In *eight* years, *chérie*. Not seven. I didn't meet Sylvia until 1968."

"So in eight years."

"Actually a few months more than eight years."

"My God—how did you do it?"

"Well," I said, working myself up to the theme, "there are really quite a lot of ways to do it."

"For instance?"

"For instance, sweeties like you are a help. What a crying shame that I didn't meet you before. But the way it was . . . there were quite a few friendly ladies, and these friendly ladies had to have presents . . . oh my, yes! In those days things were different. I was the one who gave presents."

"Jewelry?"

"Jewelry too."

"That's why you know so much about jewelry."

"Cost me a lot, that knowledge did. One might say a fortune."

"I can see that. Apartments, furs, clothes, and not so petty cash for innumerable friendly ladies . . ."

"That's it. One likes to be gallant and give presents. And then there's always the stock market and brokerage houses that go broke. And then there are farms. Did you know that a farm makes a very nice present?"

"Nobody's ever given me a farm."

"They will. Wait till you're a countess. And then there are penthouses, and town houses. Town houses are very expensive. Co-op apartments are cheaper, but not much. And expensive cars. Your *petit chou* has always had a weakness for very expensive cars. And for the track. Las Vegas. Freudenau. Grafenberg. Epsom. Santa Anita in California. That's the most beautiful racetrack in the world."

"And you've seen them *all?*"

"And more. You can gamble anywhere, *chérie.*"

"You're a *gambler?*" Suzy sounded horrified.

"No. I'm not a gambler. I'm a madman when I'm sitting at the baccarat table and see a *cheval* that's almost as beautiful as . . ."

"Now don't get vulgar!"

"As Christmas," I said.

"So you managed to run through thirteen million marks in eight years."

"If you want to be that exact about it—yes."

"Chapeau!" said Suzy. "And then? I've got to know all about you!"

"Well, now you know all about me. In 1968, in Baden-Baden, I was broke, and when I say broke, *ma petite,* I mean broke. I'd borrowed from everybody who'd give me a cent and I owed money all over the world, even in Baden-Baden. The Brenner Park Hotel."

"The best?"

"Always the best. Hadn't paid my bill for three weeks but was still eating caviar and drinking champagne in the restaurant. Put it on my bill. Nobody seemed to care. If worst came to worst, my brother would pay. Would have to pay. Had done so many times. They didn't know that my brother had just told me the well was dry. Not a penny more. Even if it meant jail for me and a scandal for him. But nobody knew that but me. I was sorry for the night clerk, though."

"Why?"

"Because I'd borrowed from him too. Borrowed from all the clerks, my dearest friends, day and night clerks in every hotel. They always helped. So I thought: Try Iffezheim once more. When your last mark is gone, you shoot yourself. And that afternoon, I met Sylvia."

"What was she doing there?"

"She had a premiere in Frankfurt. She came with a lot of people—her agent, her public relations manager, the directors of Seven Stars, the president too—Joe Gintzburger. They all stayed at the Brenner. And all of them were in Iffezheim. The only thing I still had was something decent to wear. I'm a snob about clothes, as you know."

"My sweet snob! Do you still clean your own shoes?"

"Yes. And I always will. I won't let a maid or a butler or any hotel person near my shoes. I'll let you in on something, sweetie. None of them know how to clean shoes."

"But you know how."

"Yes, by God! So there you are—there *is* something I can do well."

Other records had been playing while we chatted; now there was John William again, thanking God for the paradise opened up to his children, the smallest, the poorest . . .

"Does it bother you? I didn't realize I'd put it on twice."

"Doesn't bother me in the slightest," I said. "And I can remember exactly—all I had was two thousand marks, borrowed from the night clerk. And it was during the third race—there were six in all—that she came up to me and said, 'Let's play together. Half and half if we win.' "

"The old bag came up to you?"

"Yes. *She* came up to *me*. She took a fancy to me on sight—at least that's what she told me later. So she walked up to me and spoke to me. She is like that."

"A whore, that's what she is," said Suzy.

"No. She's not a whore. In her circles you do as you please. She's a famous actress, a big star. Nobody would dare to stop her. And she has no intention of ever marrying me."

"A super whore, that's what she is!"

"Well, have it your way. And of course I said, 'My pleasure, madame.' Remember, all I had was two thousand marks, and they weren't mine. And I owed the hotel, my tailor, my shirt maker, the tax people. And—"

"And you lost."

"We won! Won like crazy. Then of course we had to celebrate. I lost it all again that evening in the Casino."

"Did you fuck her right away? First night?"

"Yes."

"And I pay ten francs to see a bitch like that in a movie," said Suzy. "You can spare me the rest. And from then on you were on a leash."

"And what a leash!"

"And you still are."

"And I still am."

"And always will be?"

"And always will be."

Suzy was quiet for a while, and John William sang his song of paradise for his children to the end.

26

When I finally got back to Le Monde it was almost 1:00 A.M. Again the lobby was empty and again Lucien Bayard came up to me, smiling, and escorted me to the elevator, whispering, "I've worked out a system for you, Monsieur Kaven." He gave me an envelope. "I've written it all down. Have a good look at it. I don't have to know until tomorrow evening. I placed your bets on Poet's Bay, La Gauloise and Valdemosa. I hope this is all right with monsieur."

"Absolutely, Monsieur Lucien."

"I took the liberty of suggesting the amount to be placed . . . it comes to quite a lot of money. Of course I need monsieur's approval."

"I'll take a good look at it," I said, and shook his hand. "Then tomorrow night we'll have our conference."

"I'm looking forward to it, Monsieur Kaven. I'll . . ." I could see him through the glass door of the elevator as it began to ascend, still talking.

In the corridor it was very quiet. I walked down the passage to 419. Lucien had told me that Clarissa was with Babs and had the key. The door wasn't locked. I walked into the suite. All the lights were on, and Clarissa wasn't the only one waiting for me. There were Rod Bracken, sad little Dr. Lévy, Dr. Dumoulin, whom Dr. Lévy had called in for consultation; and there was a tall slender man whom I had never seen before.

They stood there like figures in a wax museum, staring at me, their faces expressionless. Not a word was spoken. Sudden fear coursed through my body. "Good evening," I said. No reply.

"What's the matter?" I was taking off my coat, my hat still on my head. "Dr. Lévy—is something wrong? With Babs?"

"Yes, Monsieur Kaven," said the little doctor with the bald head, fiddling with his strong glasses.

"What is it? What's wrong with her? She has measles, hasn't she? You diagnosed measles, you and Dr. Dumoulin."

"She doesn't only have measles," said Dr. Lévy.

"So what else is wrong with her?"

Why was Bracken looking at me like that, the fink? Why was Clarissa looking at me like that, the dumb cluck?

"This is Dr. Sigrand, Dr. Robert Sigrand." Dr. Lévy gestured in the direction of the tall slim man with the gray hair. Dr. Sigrand bowed slightly. "Dr. Sigrand is chief of staff of the ear, nose and throat clinic at the Hôpital Sainte-Bernadette. My colleague, Dr. Dumoulin, and I asked him to come here because we didn't want to bear the responsibility alone."

"What *is* wrong with her?"

"Her condition is critical, Monsieur Kaven." Dr. Sigrand spoke very slowly and clearly. "We've been waiting for you for three hours. We couldn't reach you, and Monsieur Bracken said we could do nothing without your permission."

"I tried to reach you," said Bracken. He looked pale. There were dark circles under his eyes. "Where have you been all this time?"

"I had dinner . . . I didn't know . . . I had no idea . . . what do you mean, doctor—her condition is critical?"

"It means," said Dr. Sigrand, "that we've got to get the child out of here. Every hour counts."

"Out of here? Where to?"

"If you are agreed, to my clinic. I consider that the best solution."

"But what's wrong with Babs? What does she have beside measles?"

"As I feared at first . . ." Dr. Lévy was stammering. "But my colleague, Dr. Dumoulin, also didn't want to . . ."

"What has she got?"

"Sh!" said Dr. Sigrand. "Please don't shout, Monsieur Kaven."

"What do you think it is, gentlemen?" I asked quietly, and had to lean against the wall for support.

"We are afraid . . . no, we know, that there is an infection of the inner ear . . . *otitis media*. You can go in and look at her and see her condition for your self. She won't recognize you. She has a fever . . . over 104. That much we know," said Dr. Sigrand. "Inflammation of the inner ear and measles. What we fear is meningitis."

"And what exactly is meningitis?" My voice was a whisper now.

"Meningitis is inflammation of the meninges or membranes covering the brain, Monsieur Kaven," said Dr. Sigrand, and then they all stared at me again. Meningitis . . . *Dieu, merci, pour ce paradis . . .*

27

I walked over to the bar and poured myself a glass of whiskey and drank it down—no ice, no water, neat and warm. Then I walked into the bedroom. The three doctors came with me. Only the bedside lamp was on, its shade on the floor. Babs was lying in a large double bed. It made her look tiny. The wind was raging outside; you could hear it rattling and howling in the room.

Nothing but Babs's head was visible above the bedclothes. Her hair was wet with perspiration, so was her face, and there were the red spots of the measles. I could see that the pillow under Babs's head was wet too. Her eyes were open, but veiled. She looked dreadful.

"Babs!"

". . . and ships," said Babs. Her voice was hoarse.

"What ships?"

". . . fire . . ."

I could barely hear her. This was what I had just gone through with her mother. I went down on my knees beside Babs's bed and tried to understand what she was saying. "Babs!"

She was looking up at the ornate ceiling. "Babs! It's me! Phil!"

". . . flies . . ." said Babs.

I felt her forehead. It was hot. I tried to move her head a little, to face me, and she screamed like an animal. I let her go, startled.

"Don't do that, Monsieur Kaven!" said Dr. Sigrand.

He examined her eyes with what looked like a small pocket flashlight. She didn't wink. She stared straight into the light. "Her vision is affected, her hearing too," said Dr. Sigrand.

"And an hour ago her temperature was 104.9," said little Dr. Lévy, and lowered his bald head. He had to speak loudly, because Babs hadn't stopped screaming. It sounded like an animal being tortured, like someone mute who has found her voice through torture.

"Stop!" I shouted. "Why doesn't she stop?"

"Don't shout, Monsieur Kaven!" said Dr. Sigrand.

"Gentlemen, please!" Dr. Lévy was wringing his hands. Babs babbled something, then she suddenly lay still and silent.

"What's the matter with her now?" I asked, just as horrified by her silence as by her screams. The three doctors said nothing.

Babs remained motionless. I touched her head very slightly and she started to scream again. *"You're not to do that!"* This time Dr. Sigrand's tone was sharp. He hates me, I thought.

"Why does she scream like that when you barely touch her?"

"Pain," said Dr. Lévy uneasily.

"In her head?"

"And at the nape of her neck," said Dr. Sigrand while Babs went on screaming. "Her neck has stiffened. And her right ear hurts. She also has pain throughout her entire body. That's why she lies so still. The child is completely disoriented and confused."

". . . fused," said Babs. Her mouth was open, she was gasping for breath, apparently exhausted from screaming. The perspiration was trickling down her face onto the pillow. Hypodermics, an instrument for recording blood pressure, a thermometer, and medication stood on the table beside the bed. "What have you been giving her?"

"What she needs right now," said Dr. Sigrand. "No use explaining to you, you wouldn't understand. Actually, we've only prepared her for her removal to the clinic."

"Tried to prepare her," said Dr. Lévy.

"Yes. And I hope we've been successful."

Babs whimpered, gasped, screamed, cried. Dr. Sigrand asked, "Are you going to decide or wait until it is too late?"

I could see Bracken, standing in the doorway. He looked green. "We've got to get the child out of here fast," Sigrand was saying, "or I refuse to take any further responsibility."

Bracken gave me a sign. I told Sigrand, "Wait a minute. I've got to discuss it with Monsieur Bracken."

Babs groaned. The sound was sepulchral. "There you are," said Sigrand. "Can't you grasp how serious the situation is? We've been waiting for you for three hours. You knew the child was ill. Why didn't you come back earlier?"

"You want to know something . . ." I started to say, but little Dr. Lévy didn't let me finish.

"Gentlemen, gentlemen, please!"

I walked over to Bracken, who drew me into the salon and closed the door. Clarissa and Dr. Wolken were waiting for us. I had forgotten all about him. There he stood, embarrassed and servile as usual, ready to hide his face. "Good evening, Herr Kaven. I arrived three hours ago. This is terrible . . . simply terrible. Poor, poor Babs . . . oh, my God!"

"That's enough!" I shouted, and he shrank visibly.

"I'm sorry, Herr Kaven. Please forgive me."

"No, no." I passed a hand across my forehead. This wouldn't do. I had to pull myself together. "I beg you to forgive me, Dr. Wolken. I've got to . . . right now I've got to speak to Mr. Bracken. Would you mind going to your suite with Clarissa for a while?"

"Of course, Herr Kaven, of course." He bowed three times, then he withdrew with Clarissa, who was still weeping.

"Where have you been fucking?" asked Bracken.

"Shut your filthy mouth!"

"I'll find out where you were," he said, "and now you're shitting in your pants, right?"

I said nothing.

"I've been expecting something like this to happen," said Bracken. "If a word, a single word, leaks out about what's happened to Babs, Sylvia's finished, and you can go fuck old women. I could see it coming; I felt it in my balls. Now, if anything leaks out, the guy'll want a hundred thousand, maybe more, and more, and in the end let it all hang out anyway. Do you realize what a mess we're in?"

Still I said nothing.

"If only the kid would die, if only she was dead! But we can't depend on that. You heard what he said—hospitalization. No, it's curtains for you, lover boy, and for Sylvia." And then I did say something.

"Hasn't it penetrated your skull yet, that you're going to have to kiss my ass until kingdom come once Babs is in the hospital? That you're going to have to kiss my feet, fall down and worship me and shout for help?"

"You? Help me?"

"Because when this thing leaks out, if she really has meningitis—and you know what can happen if you survive meningitis—if just one person finds out about it, then *you're* back where you started, *and* where you belong—on the manure pile, motherfucker!"

"So are you!"

"Oh no! I knew nothing. I'm Sylvia's great love and she's mine. *You're* her agent. I didn't know anything about your little caper with the tapes."

"You're voice is on them too! And you don't know anything about it?" His voice was trembling.

"Of course not!"

"You agreed with her when she went beserk about the idiot children!"

"I did not!" And I knew I was right. At the time, in the TMC dressing room, I had known I must not agree with her. How had I known that, your honor? With a sixth sense. "I only tried to calm her down."

"By slapping her and pouring cognac down her!"

"Right! To try to snap her out of it. I behaved like a doctor. Like a psychiatrist. Got her off the topic of the children onto

94

the publicity tack. All to calm her down. And because I love her!"

"You love her, you miserable fink?"

"Try to prove me wrong!"

"I can prove that you were with me in Monte Carlo the second time. Frédéric is my witness."

"When?"

"In December 1969."

"The gala was in July, six months before. When I called Frédéric, it was the end of October. And I called him because you came to see me, Sylvia and you, desperate, and begged me to help you. Because you'd received three of the packages by then."

"You were there when the first one came. And all the others."

"Prove it! You can't. Neither can Sylvia. After all, the packages were addressed to her. Nothing you can do about it. You came to me in October and told me what had happened, and what was going to happen, and that you didn't know what the hell to do about it, and because you hoped Frédéric could help. That's why you asked me to call him, because he's my friend. And that's why I flew to Monte Carlo with you in December. Only because I love Sylvia. To help her. I was horrified, absolutely horrified, when I heard how long Sylvia had been paying the guy, or I should say how long you'd been paying him with her money. *You* were always the one who sent the money; I never did, and I can prove it. But then, when you came to me with the whole dismal story, it was too late. You had to go on paying—you, not I! I would have forced you right at the beginning to go to the police! I suppose that's why it took you such a long time to come clean. You came to me, when you didn't know what to do next! And I called Frédéric as a last resort. Until then I'd had nothing to do with the whole shitty mess, didn't even know about it!"

He said, "You fucking bastard!" But he had to take a drink.

"You know, Rod," I said, "you're a tragic figure. And why are you a tragic figure? Because you have no choice. From now on you're going to have to honor and obey me, just as the Bible tells children to honor their fathers and mothers, you asshole! One more filthy word out of you, one more dirty look, and you're finished. A tragic figure, that's what you are. Like Othello."

"You goddam egghead!"

"Don't know who Othello is?"

"Sure I do."

"Then tell me!"

He was silent and drank.

'You don't know that Othello lost everything in the end. And because he couldn't face life any longer, he stabbed himself to death. Give it a thought! Doesn't have to be a dagger; poison works just as well. An overdose of sleeping pills, or jump out of the window, you motherfucking bastard who has just one last chance."

"And what's that?" He sounded weak.

I could hear Dr. Sigrand calling me. "I'm coming, Doctor!" Now I said, "If I help you by making it possible that not a soul finds out that Babs has meningitis."

"Maybe she doesn't."

"Okay. If that's what you want, we can wait and see."

"No," he said. "No. Please. I've . . . I've always hated you, Phil."

"The feeling was mutual."

"But that's . . . that's all over."

"Balls!"

"No. I mean it. I swear it's all over. I don't hold anything against you any more. You're . . . you're the way you are, and I . . . I'm a lot worse."

"You can say that again."

"And you're right. I'm finished if you don't help me now, if we don't stick together. Because then . . . then it really would be the end for me."

Now he was eating the crow he'd fed me for years. And couldn't defend himself, couldn't take revenge, nothing left for him to do but kiss my ass. He'd got the message.

28

I am going to report later on what happened not long after Sylvia's television appearance in Monte Carlo, but first, your honor, let me relate what we did with Babs that night, or I'll lose my perspective of the events.

Babs had to be moved to a hospital, that was clear. The problem was how to get there without a reporter, if possible without anyone, learning anything about her condition. Not an easy thing to do in a big hospital. Dr. Sigrand, who couldn't stand me, now burst into the salon and said he would wait five minutes more, then it was his intention to call the authorities if I hadn't come to some sort of agreement with Bracken about moving the child. His patience was exhausted; so was mine, but I kept that to myself. Instead I said, "Please try to understand, Dr. Sigrand. Of course we must get Babs to your clinic, but you are dealing here with Babs Moran. Nobody can find out what's wrong with her."

"Why not?" he asked angrily. Through the open door I could hear Babs crying. "Would it hurt her mother's business?"

"Yes, it would," I said. I'd had just about enough of Sigrand. "You'd better resign yourself to it or you'll be in trouble too. I'll explain later why it would be damaging to Miss Moran. Right now there's no time. Right now I've got to see how we're going to get Babs out of the hotel. I'm sure your conscience as a doctor will permit me to grant me a few more minutes."

I must have spoken with an expression and in a tone of voice that baffled him. He didn't say another word as I walked to the door. "I'll come with you," said Bracken.

"You stay here," I told him.

"Yes, Phil. Whatever you say." And that's how you cut a big mouth down to size, your honor.

I took the elevator to the lobby. Five women with vacuums and mops were cleaning the place. I walked over to reception. Not a soul in sight. "Monsieur Lucien!" No answer. Louder: "Monsieur Lucien!"

There was a door beside the mahogany wall with the keyboard and the pigeonholes for the mail. I knew that it led to the night clerk's private quarters. Sometimes he slept for a few hours while his colleague relieved him. The door was ajar. Lucien looked out. He had heard me. In the room behind him I could hear voices.

"Monsieur Kaven!" Lucien had undone his tie, opened the top button of his shirt. His usually pale face was flushed. "Has anything happened?"

"That's what I'd like to ask you." I could still hear the excited voices coming from his room. "What's going on in there?"

"Well ... we've just heard ... what can I do for you, Monsieur Kaven?"

"May I come in for a moment?"

"Certainly, monsieur."

I walked into his room—couch, television set, radio, a few pieces of furniture, a rug. The radio was turned on. Lucien's colleague, Jean Perrotin, was sitting in front of it, biting his fingernails. The voices I had heard were coming from the radio.

". . . snipers posted in the house opposite . . ."

"Three Japanese terrorists, armed with hand grenades and pistols, have stormed the French embassy and taken hostages. They are holed up on the fourth floor of the building . . ."

"Beside the three terrorists, the nine men being held hostage in the embassy are: the French ambassador to the Hague, Count Jacques de Senard; four directors of the French Petroleum Consortium Compagnie Française des Pétroles-Total; a twenty-one-year-old telephone operator, Bernardine Geerling; the ambassador's secretary, Joyce Fleur; and two security guards . . ."

"Merde!" said Jean Perrotin.

It is not my intention to go into the events that took place in the early morning hours of November 25, 1971, at the French embassy in The Hague, and what happened on the following day. I am sure you recall the incident, your honor. A Japanese, Yukata Furuya, had been arrested at the Orly Airport on July 21. He had on him three passports, ten thousand dollars in counterfeit hundred-dollar bills and a letter in code. He was locked up in the Paris Santé jail. To free him three Japanese had stormed the French embassy in The Hague. They had declared themselves to be members of Rengo Sekigun, or the United Red Army, the same organization that perpetrated the bloodbath at the Lod Airport in Tel Aviv in 1972. Rengo Sekigun works with the Palestine Liberation Organization.

One of the cleaning women stuck in her head. "Anything new?" Her voice was hoarse. A cigarette dangled from a corner of her mouth.

"They want Furuya, the bastard who's in the Santé."

"The yellow pigs!" said the cleaning woman. I put my hand on Lucien's arm. "Where can I talk to you?"

"Wherever you like, monsieur. Here? Somewhere else? What can I do for you?"

"Not here," I said. "Where nobody can hear us."

29

Fifteen minutes later an ambulance drove soundlessly into the courtyard of Le Monde and stopped in front of a ramp that was ordinarily used by delivery trucks. Lucien called our suite, where I was waiting. "Two men are coming up with a stretcher. I'll come up with them."

"Good," I said. The three doctors, Bracken, Clarissa and Dr. Wolken were staring at me as I put down the receiver. "They're on their way up," I said. Nobody spoke. Dr. Sigrand walked into the bedroom. I saw him give Babs another injection. She had fallen asleep, whimpering. Now she was crying again, loudly, the last thing we wanted on our way out. Bracken had turned on the television set.

There was a soft knock at the door. I opened it. Two orderlies, overcoats over their white coats. Lucien came in with them. The orderlies were carrying a stretcher with blankets. "In there," I said, pointing to the bedroom; to Lucien I said, "Thank you, Monsieur Lucien." He had seen to it that nobody knew what we were doing with Babs, not even his colleague, Perrotin. I told Lucien I'd explain everything to the manager in the morning. He was a very old, very wise night clerk in a very old, very fine grand hotel.

"A lot of the guests are awake, monsieur," said Lucien. "They're watching the events in The Hague on television. I imagine most people in Paris are."

"Lucky for us," I said.

"What do you mean, monsieur?"

"Never mind."

I walked into the bedroom. The orderlies had moved Babs onto the stretcher, covered her and strapped her down. She was still crying loudly, then she began to whimper, taking deep rattling breaths, then she said something. "What did she say?" I asked Dr. Lévy.

"I didn't understand."

Babs said something again. "Bears," said Dr. Sigrand, who was directing the transport.

"What bears?"

"She said something about bears. Let's go." The orderlies nodded, lifted the stretcher. "Careful!" said Dr. Sigrand. "Be very careful."

They carried Babs into the salon. Clarissa started to cry again. On the screen you could see a wide street and a high building. Underneath the picture the words: "Live from the Hague."

"The nine hostages and the three terrorists are on the fourth floor . . ." The camera zoomed to a row of windows. The doctors had on their coats; I slipped into mine. "I'm going with them," I said. "You stay here. Clarissa and Dr. Wolken, please go to bed."

"No!" sobbed Clarissa.

"I can't sleep now," said Dr. Wolken, and bowed.

"Then don't," I said. "Rod, you stay by the phone."

"Will do," he said. Suddenly he was cold sober. He looked as if he had aged ten years during the last hour. I probably didn't look any better.

The door of the suite closed behind us, and we were in the empty corridor. The orderlies moved fast, lithe as cats. I had a hard time keeping up with them. I could hear men's voices. It took a while before I realized they were always the same voices. They came from the rooms where the guests had turned on their sets too loud. We reached the service elevator. There was enough room in it for all of us. It descended slowly. "Bears," said Babs. "Of course there are all kinds of bears . . ."

30

It was a big ambulance. The orderlies had secured the stretcher; the three doctors and I sat in front of it. The ambulance drove fast, Babs whimpered, Sigrand felt her pulse, listened to her heart with his stethoscope, took her blood pressure, all with the utmost gentleness. I didn't have the courage to ask him how she was doing. Sigrand looked at the other two doctors and shrugged. That was all.

I wiped the sweat off my forehead with my handkerchief. One of the orderlies had turned on the radio softly. They didn't want to miss the news. The ride was a routine thing for them. I looked out of a small side window. I couldn't see a living soul. It was barely 2:00 A.M. and not a single person on the streets. In the heart of Paris! I'd never seen anything like it, and I knew Paris like my own pocket. Now the blue light on the ambulance was blinking and the siren was wailing. "Can't they turn that off?" I asked.

"No!" said Dr. Sigrand, and looked at me as if I'd murdered my mother. What in God's name did the man have against me?

"But there isn't a soul on the street."

"A car could come out of a side street. We have to have the siren. It won't kill you."

I looked out of the window at the street again. We had left the Place de l'Étoile and the Arc de Triomphe behind us. Now we were driving along the Avenue de le Grande Armée, the siren wailing, the blue light blinking. Babs was mumbling something. Place de Verdun. Porte Maillot. Avenue de Neuilly. In many of the houses we passed the lights were on. The whole city seemed to have come to life with the taking of the hostages in The Hague.

Avenue de Madrid. Just a minute . . . that wasn't far from the Bois de Boulogne. Oh God! Across the avenue, the second crossing left and up the Rue de Longchamps for about a kilometer, and we were there. The orderly at the wheel blew his horn as he drove into the courtyard of the Hôpital Sainte-Bernadette.

They were expecting us. Several men and women came hurrying out. Everything happened fast—the stretcher out of the ambulance and onto a gurney. I could see, shadowy and unclear, that the hospital covered a vast area and consisted of various clinics and courtyards. We had stopped in the courtyard of the ear, nose and throat clinic. Now we were inside. White-tiled passages, white fluorescent lighting, everything white. And I'd been through it all once before today. A service elevator. I said, "Dr. Sigrand, there is something I must ask you to do for me."

No reply.

"I know you don't like me—I don't know why, but I must ask you to do something for me just the same. Do you hear me?" I spoke the last words very loud.

"I hear you," said Dr. Sigrand.

"I'll explain everything later."

101

"What will you explain later?"

The elevator was still ascending. "Why I have to ask you to do this for me. Right now there's no time. Please, I assure you, it is of the greatest importance. The child must *not* be registered under her right name."

"I can't think of any reason why the child shouldn't—"

"There's a damn good reason!" I said. "I beg you to do this for me."

Sigrand stared at me, baffled again. "Well, then?" I asked.

He shrugged. "What name do you want?"

"An American name. As neutral as possible. And I get the same name. I'm her father. That's what you tell everybody."

"You can't give orders here!"

"But that's just what I'm doing, and you'll do as I say!" I took a pair of dark glasses out of my pocket—I always carried them with me—and put them on. "I'm asking you again—do you realize who your patient is, and the consequences if . . ." I was speaking into his ear.

"All right. Another name, if you insist. What name do you want?"

"I'd like you to suggest one."

"Paul Norton?"

"Fine. And Babs Norton. We must keep the Babs. She answers to that."

"Very well," said Sigrand.

The elevator stopped. Another corridor, many doors, most of them open. Offices, labs, consultation rooms. A smell of disinfectant. Men and women in white came up to us, at least a dozen. Sigrand had called from Le Monde to say we were coming. Now he said hastily, "This is Monsieur Paul Norton and his daughter, Babs." I said, "Good evening." A young doctor said, "But we thought . . ."

"You thought nothing. The name is Norton. Understand?" said Sigrand.

"No," said the young doctor.

"You will. Let's go."

We walked down the long corridor, and passed an office; the door was open. A television set, men and women standing in front of it. One of the orderlies asked, "How are we doing, Jacques?"

The man called Jacques, whom I couldn't see, replied, "This can go on for weeks. The government's just announced that they have no intention of letting the Jap out of the Santé."

102

"And the Japs say in that case they'll kill all the hostages," said another voice.

We passed by, and the sound of voices grew fainter. Dr. Lévy was saying, "Dr. Sigrand is the best doctor in Paris for this sort of thing. He and his colleagues will do everything they possibly can."

The Rue Cavé, where Sylvia was lying in Professor Delamare's clinic, started at the Boulevard Richard Wallace. I asked, "How far is the Boulevard Wallace from here?"

"On foot, twenty minutes. Why?" asked Dr. Lévy.

"I was just wondering," I said. Only twenty minutes away. That mother and daughter were quartered so close to each other was to turn out to have a certain advantage, a highly bizarre advantage.

We arrived at an opaque glass door with "No Admittance" painted on the glass. Dr. Sigrand unlocked it, and the stretcher was rolled into another passage. Dr. Sigrand said, "This is as far as you can go. We have to examine the child at once. The gentlemen you see here are all specialists, Monsieur Norton. Have a seat on the bench there."

"How long is this going to take?"

"A long time," he said, and walked away, behind the others. Dr. Lévy and I were left alone. "I'd better go with them," he said. I nodded. "Dear Monsieur Ka . . . Norton," said Dr. Lévy. "Try not to worry." Then he walked through the door and closed it behind him. I sat down on the white bench.

Suddenly I was exhausted. I couldn't keep my eyes open. I sat there alone, the collar of my coat turned up, still wearing my dark glasses. I remember thinking of what Babs had said a while before. "Of course there are all kinds of bears." Then I fell asleep.

31

"They're redfire fish," said Bracken. He was breathing fast with excitement. "Look at that! Have you ever seen anything so beautiful?"

"No."

"But I have! Never get tired of watching them." He moved closer to the glass wall of the aquarium. "Look at those fins! Like a veiled dancer. Gorgeous!"

The light-striped purple fish, with their exotic shapes and winglike fins, *were* fascinating to watch. "And they're poisonous too!" he gloated. This aspect seemed to please him especially, which didn't surprise me. He loved the piranhas who tore the flesh of their victims before eating them, until nothing was left but the skeleton. I looked at my watch. Four thirty-five P.M., Saturday, December 13, 1969, and Frédéric was an hour late.

Bracken and I were in the aquarium of the Monte Carlo Marine Life Museum. An hour and a half before we had landed in Nice and had rented a car. At the end of the year, the Promenade des Anglais was deserted. Black clouds hung low, the wind was lashing the sea against the quay walls of the old harbor. The Moyenne Corniche looked desolate—no flowers, no trees, everything bare and gray. Winter. It was cold and we were wearing overcoats.

"And there—look! Scorpion fish from California," said Bracken, the fish expert. "Just as deadly. Related, too." The thought passed through my mind that he would have happily decamped with one or two specimens, if that had been possible. But it wasn't. The illuminated tanks had been built into the walls at regular intervals.

The famous Musée Océanographique, now under the management of Commander Cousteau, is a big building. It stands on a rock behind the palace. The back wall is a part of the rock itself, high above the sea. The aquarium is down one floor. It starts with a huge enclosure for two sea lions. One of them is usually swimming, while the other slides back and forth tirelessly on a white fiberglass track. Down here there is a smell of water, seaweed and animals. Two long passages run from both sides of the sea lions' cage; in the center there are columns. The passages are lighted, but the light is unreal and one gets the feeling of being underwater. That afternoon we were the only visitors.

"One should have at least one stonefish," said Bracken. "*Synanceia verrucosa*. Belongs in this category too. Have large poison glands and can inflict severe wounds."

He had forgotten completely why he was here. The fish fascinated him. As far as he was concerned, next to money there was nothing like them.

Bracken waxed enthusiastic over the next tank too. "*Holocanthus!* Marvelous! Unfortunately they don't tell you what kind. I've never seen any like these. Look at that gorgeous yellow on the head and tail. A miracle, Phil! Do you believe in God?"

"I don't know."

"Well, you've got to when you see things like this. Look over there, the little ones. Funny, and as colorful as clowns, and they're sometimes called that—clown fish. Their scientific name is *Barbus everetti*." And Rod Bracken, most powerful agent in the world, agent of the greatest actress in the world, once beggar, dishwasher, procurer in the Bronx, went on and on like this.

I heard steps. Frédéric Gérard from Tele-Monte Carlo was running down the stairs. He was out of breath. He hurried up to us, shook hands, and the old friendliness of summer was there again, but not the blitheness. He was late because there had been a collision of two trucks on the Boulevard Princesse Charlotte.

We had chosen the Musée Océanographique as a meeting place because Frédéric had said that at this time of the year we would attract the least attention there. He looked troubled and guilty, although he certainly wasn't to blame for what had happened.

"Let's walk," he said, "and talk. Where are you staying?"

"In Nice. At the Negresco."

"Not in Monte Carlo. That's good."

"We're no fools."

"It's dreadful," said Frédéric. "You can't imagine how awful I feel about it, messieurs."

"But it isn't *your* fault."

"It happened on my station."

We walked up and down in the fantastic underwater atmosphere for a long time, side by side. "Have you found out anything?" I asked.

"Nothing." He sounded depressed. "Nothing at all."

I have already written, your honor, that about half a year after Sylvia's appearance on television in Monte Carlo, we had to come back to that city, Bracken and I, but not to prevent a catastrophe—for that it was too late. For half a year now we had been living with the catastrophe. No. We didn't return to Monte Carlo to prevent a catastrophe, only to try to control one. And this, too, didn't seem possible any more.

You see, your honor, to make a long story short, that summer, soon after our return home from Monte Carlo, on August 4, 1969, a Monday, a small package arrived at Sylvia's house in Beverly Hills. It came in the morning mail. There was a casette inside it. The package had been mailed in Vienna, air mail special delivery, from the main post office. Sylvia received mountains of fan mail from all over the world, daily, the craziest and most touching things. She had a secretary who took care of things like that, but it was Bracken who took over the tape. "There's something fishy about this one," he said. "I can feel it in my balls. Somebody's playing dirty tricks." And how right he was!

We played the tape. After the first few sentences Sylvia staggered and almost fell. I just managed to catch her and help her to the couch. As I listened to the tape I mixed some strong martinis for us, early in the morning—didn't matter. I knew we'd need them.

Sylvia's voice, coarse, raging, "The poor sick children? Drooling idiots, that's what they are! Worse than animals! And I gave my good name for them!" Pause, then, "The stream of life? That means being successful and rich and *stronger* than all the rest! To enjoy life? A kick in the ass to whoever's weaker. *That's* the stream of life! And when you grow weak and old, you die, without batting an eyelash! But to be on top to the end and then have the courage to say it's all over! Not to cling to a miserable existence. *That's* humane! *That's* normal! And I'm going to stay on top. But not with the bullshit I had to dish out today. I'm taking money out of the pockets of those damn fools out there! For what? For nothing! A fraud. A fraud all around!" A pause, then my voice: "Can't you get it into your head that there are many cases—many, do you hear me?—that can be helped today."

By that time we had drunk our martinis and I was mixing the next batch. Sylvia's voice again: "Helped? Sure! So that ten years from now they can count to three, if they can talk at all! So that in fifteen years they can shit on the john and don't just let go wherever they are. And that's what you call help?" A pause, then: "Let them die. *That* would be humane! God knows, I hated the Nazis, but in that respect they were on the right track. These cretins deserve euthanasia!"

Another pause. I had to sit down. My knees were shaking. I spilled some of my drink.

A distorted male voice came next: "Hello, dear Miss Moran. You know when you said all this and much more in Monte Carlo. I have sent you only a small sample. I have the entire text. I think it would be the end of you, dear Miss Moran, if any third person were to hear what you said to Mr. Kaven in the dressing room of TMC right after your touching speech, which was broadcast worldwide."

"The bastard!" said Bracken.

"Shut up!" said Sylvia. Her face was ashen, her hands were trembling.

"Yes," the distorted voice went on, "it would write finis to your career. I don't want to ruin you, Miss Moran, but only because I am not capable of cruelty. I have been unfortunate. I am poor. I am in debt. I need money. I have the following suggestion: You buy the original tapes from me, right away. I'm in a hurry. You pay me fifty thousand dollars. I think that's fair. As soon as I receive the money, I send you the tapes. Now let me explain how I would like to receive the money."

His explanation was lengthy, complicated and brilliant. The money was to pass through the hands of lawyers who knew nothing about what lay behind it, from the United States to Switzerland and from there, via more lawyers who knew nothing about what lay behind it, to a trust fund in Liechtenstein. The whole thing was foolproof for the man holding the tapes.

Bracken stopped the tape and let it roll back, and we listened to it a second time. We also drank our second martinis. Sylvia was in tears. I said that the only thing to do was call the police right away. Bracken said, "Idiot! If we do that, we're finished." That afternoon he sent off the $50,000, according to the man's instructions. *Fifty thousand dollars!*

The tapes arrived a week later. Two casettes. The entire text. Six weeks later another package arrived with a small tape, the whole thing a repeat of the first, only this time the distorted voice said, "I am a most unfortunate man, Miss Moran. Fifty thousand dollars did not suffice. I need more. I have nothing in the world but the few tapes on which I have transcribed the original tape. May I therefore please ask for another fifty thousand dollars? Forwarded to me the same way? And thank you, dear Miss Moran. Good luck. And be sure to send the money right away, otherwise ... you understand, I know. A poor man has little choice."

Rod sent off another $50,000, after which there was silence at the other end. For three months. Then a small tape arrived, again the same thing.

This is the situation we were in, your honor. One: We had hired the best detectives. They had flown to Vienna. Not a trace to be found of the blackmailer. Two: After the third package we realized that this was going to go on forever. The man probably had a hundred tapes, maybe only fifty, but he was certainly going to hang on to the original. He could therefore rerecord the dialogue as often as he liked. Three: Sylvia had to pay. If she didn't, if the thing got out, she was finished. No two ways about it. Four: If we informed the police—and here I had to agree with Bracken—it could only end in disaster. Then an uncontrollable number of people would know about it. Then the police in Vienna and Monte Carlo and God only knew where else would have to be informed, perhaps even Interpol. Because we would have to tell the police the truth. We would have to hand over the tapes. And that was impossible!

I could think of only one thing to do. I called Frédéric Gérard in Monte Carlo and told him everything. He *had* to know the truth. And I begged him to try to find out what he could, but on no account with the help of his friend Commissioner Alexandre Drouant or the Monegasque police.

Frédéric hesitated. I realized that he didn't like my suggestion, and the transatlantic call lasted an hour and a half. At last Frédéric gave in, still hesitant and very doubtful that he was doing the right thing. He said he was agreeing only because he wanted to help me. He didn't say: help Sylvia. In the end he said he would do what he could.

So that was why Bracken and I flew to Nice a second time; that was why we were standing in front of yet another tank in the aquarium of the Musée Océanographique on the afternoon of December 13, 1969.

"So you paid," said Frédéric, as we walked on slowly.

"Of course we paid. Had to. And the bastard'll go on blackmailing us as long as he lives. As long as *we* live. How was he able to do it, Frédéric? How was it possible?"

"I'll show you when we go to the station, Monsieur Kaven."

"And you weren't able to find any clues whatsoever that could lead us to the man?"

"I'm sorry, no," said Frédéric. "The whole thing is terrible. But . . . forgive me . . . Madame Moran said some terrible things in that dressing room."

"Nerves. I assure you, Frédéric. A case of nerves. Sylvia is the kindest, most charitable woman in the world."

Frédéric looked at me silently for a moment, then looked away.

"If there was a microphone in the dressing room and the conversation was taped from there, then it must have been a man who knew how it could be done," said Bracken.

"Yes," said Frédéric. "Do you have anyone in mind?"

"Well," said Rod, "there were two sound men in the control room, weren't there?"

"I've investigated both men, Monsieur Bracken," said Frédéric. "Only one—Jean Duval—could have done the recording. The other man doesn't come into question."

"What did you find out about him?" asked Bracken.

"You just heard," I said. "Nothing."

"But I'd like to talk to this . . . what's his name . . . just the same," said Bracken.

Frédéric looked at him silently.

"So—how about it? May I talk to him?"

"No," said Frédéric.

"Why not? Has he flown the coop? Then maybe's he's our man."

"He isn't your man, Monsieur Bracken," said Frédéric. "He can't be."

"Why not?"

"Because after the broadcast Duval broke a leg and had to be hospitalized. An infection set in that didn't respond to antibiotics. On the third day he was delirious, and four days later he was dead. So you see, it couldn't have been Duval. He didn't have a chance to pass on a tape, if he had recorded one.

And his colleague swears that Duval didn't record anything after the broadcast. It was practically impossible anyway—there were other people in the control room."

"Too bad," said Bracken.

Frédéric told us what he had done to get to the bottom of the thing, and there really was not the slightest clue.

When we left the Musée Océanographique it was already dark. I drove into the city behind Frédéric and parked in the courtyard of the radio station. We went up to the dressing room where it had all taken place six months before, and that's when I saw the little black box on the dressing table. As already mentioned, dressing rooms in theaters and studios have this type of speaker, so that actors can be notified when they're on, things like that. "It's a two-way speaker, Monsieur Kaven," said Frédéric.

"What do you mean?"

"Well, it works like an ordinary speaker. The stage manager calls through to the actor in here, but—you see the little white button?"

"Yes."

"If the actor, or whoever, presses it, then he or she can use the speaker as if it were a microphone, and the voice can be heard in the control room."

A little white button . . .

"Just a minute!" I said. "So it is possible that the speaker was functioning like a microphone, like a transmitter, the whole time, and somebody was able to record everything said in here."

"No, Monsieur Kaven, that wasn't possible."

"Why not?"

"Because then someone would have had to be pressing the button all the time. I'm sure Madame Moran did nothing like that."

"But the conversation *was* recorded."

"Right," said Frédéric. "But how, Monsieur Kaven? How?"

"I can't imagine."

"Neither can I," said Frédéric. "I must say, I'm baffled."

So we flew back to Hollywood none the wiser. Then, a week later, another tape. This time only with the distorted male voice. It told us: "You didn't get anywhere in Monte Carlo, gentlemen, did you? You never will get anywhere. But I am not a monster. I have the original tape, granted, but from now on I won't ask for such large sums. Starting with next month, all I shall want is ten thousand dollars, but I shall want it monthly, sent to me in the usual way. If the money has not arrived by the seventh of every month, I shall sell the original tapes to Seven Stars' biggest rival. I am sure I shall be offered plenty for them. Please be assured of my profound admiration, dear Miss Moran. I am a fan of yours and consider you the greatest actress of our time. . . ."

So, from the first of the next month, and for all the months and years to come, Rod Bracken was to transfer $10,000, and did, punctually, and for whoever was at the other end . . . tax-free.

32

"Monsieur Norton! Monsieur Norton!"

Somebody was shaking my arm none too gently. I opened my eyes. Behind my dark glasses they burned and my lids were heavy. It took me a while to realize where I was. It was the smell of disinfectant that brought me back to my surroundings. Hôpital Sainte-Bernadette! In the passage in front of the examination rooms. Sitting on a white bench. I had fallen asleep. Everything swam murkily before my eyes, my head throbbed, I had a terrible taste in my mouth.

"Please wake up, Monsieur Norton. We have to talk to you about the child."

An unpleasant, irritable voice. I blinked my eyes, then I recognized him. Dr. Sigrand. He had on a white coat and was leaning over me, one hand on my arm. Somebody was standing beside him. "Don't fall asleep again!"

I got up, swaying, took a step and stumbled. Sigrand grabbed me. The only thing he said, and it sounded like an order, was, "Let's go!"

And there was this second person—I could barely make him out in the veiled darkness. I must have slept very soundly; now I simply could not come to.

"Oh yes," Dr. Sigrand cleared his throat. "Allow me to introduce you. Paul Norton, Dr. Reinhardt. From Nürnberg. Worked there in a children's clinic. Has been with us six months."

"Good evening, Dr. Reinhardt," I said softly in German, still stupefied.

"Good evening, Herr Norton," said the calm, gentle voice of a woman, in German.

I took off my glasses. The sudden light blinded me. It came from a window opposite. An early-morning bright wintry sun was shining between black clouds. The light was so strong that both doctors appeared as silhouettes. I said, "I'm sorry . . . I . . . I thought you were a man."

"Ruth Reinhardt," she said. "I'm very pleased to meet you, Herr Norton." She held out a small firm hand. Why did this woman say she was pleased to meet me?

"Dr. Reinhardt is a specialist in what we are dealing with," Dr. Sigrand said in French. "She will come with us now to see Babs. Then she will explain everything and you can talk things over."

"Thank you," I said, also in French. "Thank you, Dr. Reinhardt." The light from the window was so bright that I could scarcely make out what she looked like. Medium weight, slender, her hair combed back close to her small head. Going by her voice I decided she had to be around thirty.

"We have a lot to discuss, Monsieur Norton," she said, in French now.

"Yes, Dr. Reinhardt. How late . . ." I had to clear my throat. "How late is it?"

"Ten past nine, Monsieur Norton."

So I had slept seven hours! Suddenly I was trembling because I realized what lay ahead. "Monsieur Norton!" said Dr. Sigrand. "You look . . . what's the matter with you?"

"He's afraid," said Dr. Reinhardt. "Of course." And in German, to me, "Isn't that so, Herr Norton?"

All I could do was nod. Yes, I was afraid. But only for myself, for my future. Babs meant nothing to me.

33

It was almost dark in the big room. A blue lamp was lit over the bed. At first I could see nothing, then I saw the shapes of old Dr. Lévy and Dr. Dumoulin. They were standing beside the bed, looking down at Babs, whom I now also recognized. She was lying on her stomach, her face turned sideways, and she was motionless. At first I thought she was dead. If she was, I thought, it was the best thing that could have happened while I was sleeping. Then I realized that Babs couldn't be dead or Dr. Reinhardt wouldn't have spoken to me as she had.

I walked up to the bed and looked down at her. All I could see was her little head with its disheveled, sweaty hair. I bent down. Not a sound. I straightened up again. The doctors were standing behind me. I almost backed into them. I said, "She's not breathing."

"She's breathing, Monsieur Norton," said Dr. Reinhardt, "but her breathing is shallow. She is fast asleep. We have given her some very strong medication. It was required after the lumbar puncture."

"Lumbar puncture?"

Dr. Dumoulin cleared his throat, then he came up to me with Dr. Lévy. "There is nothing more we can do here, Monsieur Kaven. The child is getting the best possible care."

We shook hands. "I'll be available, day or night, whenever you need me," said little Dr. Lévy, and we too shook hands. The two doctors nodded to their colleagues and left the room.

"The lumbar puncture," said Dr. Reinhardt, "is undertaken to obtain spinal fluid. Under the circumstances it was absolutely necessary and of course took place under anesthesia, Monsieur Norton."

"Why was it necessary?"

"To be absolutely certain," said Dr. Sigrand.

"About what?"

"About the illness." His voice was cold, angry and aggressive again. Why did this man hate me? "Unfortunately we

113

are now absolutely certain, and my fears were more than justified. Babs has meningoencephalitis—inflammation of the brain membranes and of the brain." I said nothing; my hands were fists. "I'm sorry," said Dr. Sigrand, "but that's the way it is," and I had the feeling he said it with satisfaction. You can see, your honor, what a state I was in that morning.

"Both are a result of the inflammation of the inner ear," Dr. Reinhardt explained, "and that followed the measles." She spoke very softly. "Unfortunately we are faced here with two very serious infections of the nervous system. Meningitis is the inflammation of the meninges, the membranes that surround the brain and spinal cord. In Babs's case it is unfortunately very much advanced."

"How so?"

"The infection has become blood-borne; the result is encephalitis or inflammation of the brain."

"Inflammation of the brain?"

"We rarely come across these two inflammatory diseases in a patient at the same time," said Dr. Reinhardt. "Diagnosis and treatment depend on the type of organism and the spinal-fluid findings. That's why the spinal tap was necessary and had to take place before we put the patient on antibiotics. Because after that the organism is hard to identify. Do you understand?"

"I understand, Frau Doktor," I said, in German this time. Babs lay there as if dead, dead, dead, and was alive, still. . . .

"The lab and the doctors haven't been able to decide yet whether bacteria or bacteria plus a virus triggered her condition. All indications point to the presence of a virus."

"Is it worse when a virus is involved?"

"Yes, monsieur. It complicates the treatment. Viruses are more difficult than bacteria. But we may be able to handle both. We've done it before."

"Dr. Reinhardt is a pediatrician and a specialist in neurology. That's why I called her in," said Dr. Sigrand.

I nodded, and passed a hand across my face. I hadn't shaved.

"Of course we have taken all sorts of other tests too," said Dr. Reinhardt. "There is a big increase in the white blood count, but the pressure of the spinal fluid isn't higher, thank God. We have made a urine analysis, and so on. And we have begun treatment."

"With what?"

"Immune globulin, antibiotics." All in the same gentle

voice. "Penicillin intravenously, cortisone derivatives, and so on."

"How long will it be . . ." I couldn't stand this much longer. I felt like vomiting.

"Nobody can answer that, Monsieur Norton," said my good friend Dr. Sigrand. With satisfaction. Now I hated him too. Yes, he said it with satisfaction, I told myself, irrational as I was with fear for my future, fury against Dr. Sigrand, and feeling sick as a dog.

"You must try to control yourself." Dr. Ruth Reinhardt's gentle voice. "Your hand is ice-cold." I hadn't noticed that she had taken my left hand in her right, as if she wanted to give me some support. Now she withdrew her hand.

"And what are her chances?" I asked.

"We'll pull her through, Monsieur Norton," said Dr. Ruth Reinhardt. "We don't know yet how the medication we are using is going to work. We may have to try something else. You're going to have to be patient."

"But it is possible, isn't it? That you pull her through this but that there's brain damage? Possibly severe brain damage?"

"It's too early to make any sort of prognosis, Monsieur Norton. Often the whole thing passes without any serious consequences."

"But more often than not it doesn't, am I right, Dr. Reinhardt?"

"Very often it doesn't, Monsieur Norton."

"Very well," I said. "Then all of us know where we are. And I'm going to have to tell you something. I told you last night, Dr. Sigrand, that I had a story to tell. Under the present circumstances it is of the utmost importance."

"So go ahead, monsieur," said Sigrand.

"Not here," I said. "And I have to make a phone call first." I had to call Bracken. He'd been waiting all night and morning.

"Then we'll go to my room," said Dr. Reinhardt.

I leaned over Babs once more. Not a sound. Gently I laid my hand on the nape of her neck. It was wet and hot. "Her fever is higher," said Dr. Reinhardt.

"Poor little Babs," I said, and as I said it I felt hatred, more hatred than I had ever felt in my life before or since. I hated Babs. I remember thinking, so now you had to go and do this to me, you brat!

"You love the child very much, don't you, Monsieur Norton?" said Dr. Reinhardt.

"Very much, Frau Doktor," I said. "As if she were my own."

She took me by the arm and led me to the door, which she opened. I looked back once more as I put on the dark glasses that were to disguise me, and I remember thinking, Perhaps she'll die after all.

34

Dear Frau Doktor Reinhardt,
   Here are the sounds Martin can make and the few words he can speak. I am letting you have them so that you and your colleagues can understand him better.

Mama
Papa
i—his brother Fred
o—himself
aaah—bad, horrible, unpleasant
mm—car, taxi
m—his father's business (insurance)
mmch—street car
mmtut—bus
mmtututu—train

That's what I read, written by hand, in German, on a cheap piece of writing paper. There was more to it. I read the first lines after I had told Dr. Reinhardt and Dr. Sigrand everything they had to know—that two years before, Sylvia Moran had made a speech, telecast worldwide, begging for help for brain-damaged children, and I also told them about the scene afterward in the little dressing room, and the hatred and revulsion she had expressed there, the vulgarities she had uttered, all directed against those very children, and that during the last two years she had been blackmailed by some unknown person who had taped that outburst, and that she had had to pay and pay and pay. That, under absolute secrecy, she was in Dr. Max Delamare's clinic nearby, in the Rue Cavé, after undergoing a total face lift, and so on—in short, everything, because these two doctors who were responsible for Babs now had to know all if I was to prevent a disaster, and this I had to do if for no other reason than to save my own skin.

Dr. Reinhardt and Dr. Sigrand listened silently. When I had finished, they looked at me without saying a word. I couldn't stand it, and looked down at the piece of paper which lay on Dr. Reinhardt's desk and began to read it. The desk was covered with papers, stopwatches, boxes of medication, books, a typewriter, two telephones. The room was big and flooded with the bright winter sunshine.

One wall was covered from floor to ceiling with shelves, medical books, and files. The room itself looked like a kindergarten. There were balls, hoops, simple dolls and games, large puzzles, and on the floor a lot of brown paper with crude pictures painted on it. Everything was in bright primary colors. A few pictures on the wall—red blotches, unidentifiable forms and symbols in water color, some painted straight onto the white wall. Under the window—two wheelchairs, small, Lilliputian, a dirty rag over one of them. A record player and records in a stand, a tambourine. An easel blackboard, a paper circle with a clock face in the center with only one cardboard hand. Inside the circle, the numbers for the twelve hours; outside it, naive pictures drawn by adults, showing children eating, sleeping, playing. Under the pictures the words *noon, afternoon, evening, night, sleep, morning,* and so on. Under these clearly written words—the board reached almost to the floor—several children had apparently tried to copy them in chalk. Their efforts looked trembling, scribbled, broken, all of it illegible. These pitiful efforts to write shocked me more than anything else as I walked into Dr. Reinhardt's office, even more than the sight of the small wheelchairs. And finally I saw six small helmets, not metal, but woven out of bandages. I could imagine who had to wear those helmets to protect their heads when they fell. A lot of the toys had been trampled on and broken. Dr. Reinhardt was holding a stuffed lamb in her hands.

She was sitting behind her littered desk, Dr. Sigrand beside her. I sat facing them. A framed picture stood on the desk, its back turned to me. The silence following my story wasn't broken. Finally, Dr. Sigrand, looking as if he found me absolutely repulsive, said, "Thank you for being so frank with us, Monsieur Norton. Now I understand your behavior."

"You understand?" Suddenly I felt happy. But my happiness was short-lived.

"I'm afraid I didn't use the right word," said Dr. Sigrand. "Let's say, 'respect,' rather than 'understand.' I am ready to respect your attitude, Monsieur Norton."

"You are?"

"I am willing to respect it," he said, "which in no way means that it doesn't disgust me."

I rose. "Now you listen to me," I began, but he rose too, poked a finger against my chest and shoved me back into my chair. "Now *you* listen to *me,*" he said. Dr. Reinhardt said nothing, but she never took her eyes off me. "Every one of us does what he has to do, what he feels is his duty," Sigrand went on. "We here believe it is our duty to help the sick to the best of our ability. You, Monsieur Norton, seem to feel it is your duty to protect Madame Moran's career, her business, because it is inextricably bound up with your well-being—"

"If you say one more word—"

"Please be quiet. I haven't finished. I haven't said yet that I am willing to help you in your miserable efforts. I don't have to and no one can force me to, least of all you. So keep your mouth shut!" He was terribly excited. He walked up to me and went on: "People like Madame Moran and ..." The pause that followed was an insult in itself. ". . . And people like you cause more misery on this earth than all the terrible sickness we have here put together."

"I don't have to put up with this!" I cried, jumping to my feet again.

"Then get out!" he said, his face close to mine. "Go on! Everything will be done for Babs that is humanly possible, but you get out, now!"

I stared at him. I was at his mercy—that was clear. "Forgive me, doctor," I said softly. "It's the excitement. I didn't mean it that way. You're quite right."

"Dr. Sigrand." They were the first words spoken by Dr. Reinhardt.

"All right, all right!" said Sigrand. "We'll keep the thing secret, just as you wish."

"Thank you," I said, and thought, Let the bastard take it out on me as long as he keeps the thing secret. "Thank you, Dr. Sigrand."

"Don't thank me," he said. "Thank Dr. Reinhardt."

"I don't understand. Why Dr. Reinhardt?"

"She wrote me a note while you were talking." I had seen her do it. "I'm only doing what she asked me to do."

"What did it say?"

"I asked Dr. Sigrand to keep the whole thing secret," said Dr. Reinhardt, and now she wasn't looking at me any more but at the piece of paper I'd been reading, with the sounds Martin could make.

"Why did you do that?" I asked.

She turned her face away, and it was silent in the room again. What was going on in her mind? I wondered. I looked up at Dr. Sigrand. He was staring at me. Strange. I looked down at the paper and saw what other sounds Martin could make.

> *ja—yes*
> *na—no*
> *oja—happy agreement*
> *chchch—ringing, telephoning, anything connected with bells.*

Dr. Sigrand said, "For the moment Babs's mother is out of the picture. We mustn't risk letting her know aything about this"—and now his voice was blatantly scornful—"so shortly after her face lift, even if she is of the opinion that brain-damaged children should be killed. She might ask us to kill Babs because there is the danger that Babs will come out of this with brain damage. But we don't kill our patients. You and Madame Moran will have to meet us halfway and take our position into consideration. After all, we do the same for you." And all the time, as the man spoke, he seemed to be fighting tears. "On the other hand, we have our rules here. Babs can't decide how she is to be treated. She is not in a position to give us the authority to do what we feel has to be done. Somebody else has to do that, Monsieur Norton." I closed my eyes and thought, This too? "I see you understand, Monsieur Norton. We can keep Babs here and do the right thing for her only if there is someone willing to take the responsibility."

I? I responsible for Babs?

"Someone who is willing to give us the right, legally, to act as we see fit, whom we can reach at any time in case we need permission for special forms of treatment."

"What special forms of treatment?"

"Various kinds. So . . . you are not available?"

I was trapped.

"What do you mean—not available? Of course I'm willing to take on the responsibility!"

A short laugh. "Then please fill out the form, Dr. Reinhardt."

I looked at her. She moved the typewriter in front of her, took a form out of a drawer and put it into the machine, and began to type. "Name ... Norton ... first name?"

"I can't remember. What's my first name, Herr Doktor?"

"Paul."

"Paul," said Dr. Reinhardt as she typed the name. "And your real name? We have to have it too. Philip Kaven. Do you have your passport with you?"

"Yes." I gave it to her. She typed the number and place of issue. I went on reading the paper on Martin.

> gogo—hen
> guga—bird
> gdgd—hello
> aga—thank you

When he purses his lips as if he wanted to kiss somebody, Martin wants something. When he lays his head on the table or between his legs and won't look up, he is offended.

"Name of Babs's mother? She's German, isn't she? And Moran is her stage name?" asked Dr. Reinhardt.

"Susanne Mankov. Born in Berlin. May 25, 1935."

Dr. Reinhardt typed. I read, *When Martin sticks out his tongue he is hungry or thirsty.*

"Residence?"

I gave Sylvia's residence and read, *When Martin points to the floor he usually means the subway or a tunnel or underpass.*

"Presently at Dr. Delamare's clinic," Dr. Reinhardt said, and typed.

"Listen ..."

"Nobody's going to find out about it. Our files remain under lock and key," said Dr. Sigrand.

"Where are you staying, Monsieur Norton?"

I told her. She typed. I read, *When Martin grabs his shoulder with one arm he means school.*

Dr. Reinhardt spoke and typed, "With this signature I

agree to all points mentioned above." She said, "Here we need your right name." She entered it. "Babs ... that's Barbara, isn't it?"

"Yes."

"Barbara Mankov. Born ... when and where, Monsieur Norton?"

"September 5, 1962, in Beverly Hills."

She typed it, and I went on reading Martin's mother's letter, like an idiot, but I was so stunned with rage and helplessness, I didn't know what I was doing. *When he stamps his feet, it means gymnastics.*

"There," said Dr. Reinhardt. "And now the date of arrival." She typed as she said, "November 25, 1971," and I read, *Dear Frau Doktor, if you don't understand what Martin is trying to say, please write it in a note for us.*

35

Dr. Reinhardt must have noticed that I was staring at the letter, because she said, as she took the form out of the typewriter, "That's from my Nürnberg office." She handed me the form and a pen. "Please sign the original and the copy, with your correct name. On this line."

My hand was trembling so, I had to support it with my other hand as I wrote. And with that, I told myself, you've written your death sentence, come what may. No, I thought, not come what may. Babs may die. Or Babs may make a complete recovery. Then it wouldn't be a death sentence. But if Babs pulls through and is left like this boy Martin ... hold it, Kaven! I thought. Why should that be your death sentence? If Babs ends up like this boy Martin, you can still clear out, and ... Oh no! That's something you can't do, Kaven. You're in this up to your neck, whatever happens. A death sentence therefore after all. And yet, I thought, it's two to one it'll be all right. All could go well if the doctors did the right thing, or if Babs departed this life. In either case Sylvia would have to see me as the most selfless hero.

Dr. Reinhardt handed the form to Dr. Sigrand, who only

nodded and left the room. While the door was open I heard a man's voice. "Three of the hostages have heart conditions, two have diabetes, and none of them . . ." Dr. Sigrand shut the door. I looked at Dr. Reinhardt and for the first time saw her face clearly.

Words fail me today as they did then, when it comes to describing Ruth Reinhardt's face, all the more so since on that day I thought and felt so different. I can only assure you, your honor, that on that particular morning nothing was of greater indifference to me than the face of Dr. Ruth Reinhardt from Nürnberg, and what I have to say about it today, in spite of the great change that has taken place in me since then, must remain inadequate.

Ruth Reinhardt has chestnut-brown hair which she wears short and chestnut-brown eyes with extraordinarily long lashes. Her skin is light and clear. A large mouth and high cheekbones give her face a Slavic feel. She has beautiful teeth, small ears close to her head, and a short straight nose. She has a most disciplined face, very alert, extremely intelligent, with an expression of tolerance and empathy. A sad face, your honor, like the faces of those who have seen and experienced much suffering; yet a strong face. I have never seen her laugh when conversing with adults, but with children she laughs often. As I write this, in the year 1973, she is thirty-five years old and unmarried. According to what she told me later, she has had affairs with men from time to time, if the man pleased her. Not from time to time however, but constantly, she has been searching for knowledge and truth. She has no children, but once she said to me, "All the children they bring to me are *my* children! Every child who recovers makes me richer and happier. Every relapse or death makes me unhappy and poorer, and it makes no difference to me if I am dealing with fairly normal children or with children who force me to close my eyes for a moment when I see them for the first time."

Ruth Reinhardt is not beautiful in the conventional sense, like Sylvia Moran, but she has one thing no other woman can match—her laughter. She has the most marvelous laugh I have ever heard. But only for children. For sick children. Her laughter has such power that the poorest of her poor, the spastics, the cretins, laugh with her.

You may have noticed, your honor, that I am writing this

report in two very different styles—as I have written just now, and then, at times, impertinently, rudely, cynically, even dirtily. Apparently I can't stick to the latter, which is really more my style, when speaking of those who live in the dark, or of those tireless, selfless creatures who don't know the meaning of the word "discouragement," about whom I knew nothing and only began to come into contact with now. About them I write differently—no, it writes itself differently. After meeting Ruth Reinhardt I met many others like her, but she was the first. But I am writing according to how I see things today: Ruth Reinhardt is a woman who gives everything away. It makes no difference to her who the recipient may be; the only thing that matters is the giving, and in her case that means helping. It also means that she gives herself. To the end of my days I shall think of Ruth Reinhardt as a woman who always gives more than is good for her, and that until the end of *her* days. And with this, your honor, I'm afraid I've given you a very incomplete impression of the woman I sat opposite to that morning, November 25, 1971, in the Hôpital Sainte-Bernadette in Paris.

36

"Thank you, Dr. Reinhardt," I said, when Dr. Sigrand had left the room. "What has the man got against me? I never did him any harm. Why does he treat me like that?"

Ruth Reinhardt said, "Doctors are human too, Monsieur Norton. Dr. Sigrand has a son, a spastic child. For years he hoped against hope that his son's condition would improve, even if only a little. Two years ago he realized that his son's condition was hopeless."

"I'm sorry to hear that," I said.

"Just try to imagine it, Monsieur Norton." She was toying with the little lamb again. "Dr. Sigrand is the director of a clinic that helps children like that. Some leave here healthy, some with their condition vastly improved, and he has a child that has to remain a helpless creature."

"I understand."

"No, you don't understand, Monsieur Norton. Six months ago Dr. Sigrand found out that his wife was deceiving him with another man, that she hated her retarded son and was beginning to neglect him. This other man was a haven for the poor woman—"

"Poor woman?"

"Of course, Monsieur Norton. The woman was poor, poor and desperate. One must never judge anyone quickly. It must have been dreadful for her when her husband accused her. She went to pieces. She said she couldn't stand the child any longer and yes, there was another man. And she left Dr. Sigrand and went to live with her lover. They were divorced. The court gave the child to Dr. Sigrand. Every night, when he's through with his work here, he goes home to that child."

"Now I understand."

"You still don't understand," said Ruth Reinhardt. "Madame Sigrand's lover was a much younger man than Dr. Sigrand. A wealthy, spoiled young man. He belongs to— I believe you call it the jet set. He inherited a fortune. Madame Sigrand lives with him now, sometimes in Paris, sometimes on the Riviera. She and Dr. Sigrand have no contact whatever with each other. Her lover has always lived on other people's money, and always will."

"Like me."

"I didn't say that. I only wanted to explain to you why Dr. Sigrand—a wonderful human being—treats you the way he does. If this thing with his wife hadn't happened, he would never have been so insulting."

Just then there was a short rap on the door and it opened. A doctor stuck in his head. "Ruth! The terrorists have just announced they'll start killing the hostages if they don't get some food—" He stopped. "Oh. Sorry. I didn't know . . ." and the door closed.

Ruth Reinhardt didn't seem to notice the interruption. She leaned forward. "Let me tell you something, Monsieur Norton. Most people have no understanding in this area." She paused for a moment, then went on. "By understanding I mean that people simply don't know how to behave with these retarded children. Don't look so startled. We are going to do everything we possibly can to see that Babs recovers, but your reaction so far has been typical. People's discomfort is nothing more than the result of an overwhelming embarrassment. They may feel great compassion for a handicapped

124

child, but they don't know how to behave. Do you understand me?"

"Yes, Frau Doktor." Now we were speaking German.

"They either stare at the child because they've never seen anything like it, or they have seen something like it before and know they shouldn't stare. Both are unnatural reactions and are seen immediately by the parents of the child as rejection."

"I understand."

"In my lectures I always stress that people should be taught how to behave naturally with retarded children. I know that's easier said than done, because a lot of these children look so strange and behave so strangely, sometimes even repulsively. It's a dreadful problem." She sighed. "But I think it's the only way. Why are you looking at me like that, Herr Norton?"

For the first time in my life, your honor, I was genuinely moved. I had never been deeply touched, not even by the death of my parents. I said, "Because you make it all so clear, Frau Doktor."

"Good," she said. "So there you are—revulsion, embarrassment, rejection, and it all adds up to a feeling of utter helplessness, and that in turn is the result of guilt, because they simply can't grasp the thing. So they feel guilty and react negatively, brusquely, crudely . . ." She was looking at the toys scattered around her office and her voice became gentler. "Very often, though, it's nothing more than thoughtlessness." She lowered her head. "And so many parents are punished. Marriages break up—as with Dr. Sigrand—the feeling of guilt becomes unbearable, so does the despair. Have you any idea how many parents of retarded children become alcoholics? How many commit suicide? Especially when they reject their own children and want to get rid of them or hide them? None of these parents go unpunished, unless they find their way back to their child."

She rose and began to pace up and down between the toys, her hands in the pockets of her white coat, a stethoscope slung around her neck. "We have to reach the point, Herr Norton, when our society will be so open that it is ready to integrate these people who will never be in a position to achieve as much as those who are healthy."

My God, I thought, all this was what Sylvia said in Monte Carlo, written by Rod Bracken, and I am *living* it!

"Our world," said Ruth Reinhardt, "will only be complete when there is room for the old and the helpless, for brain-damaged and retarded children, for the blind, the deaf, for those with psychiatric disorders, alcoholics . . . all the rest. Only then will we have a good world, when the healthy man realizes: I don't have myself to thank for the fact that I am healthy. I could be retarded, like this child here. It is my duty to understand this sick child, not only here," and she pointed to her heart, "but here too," and she pointed to her forehead. "And that is my hope. But this hope requires a complete reversal of our thinking. We have to get rid of the idea that only the person who earns or achieves something rates as a human being. That attitude is inhuman and unworthy."

"Yes," I said. "But how . . . how about Babs? I have the feeling her condition is very serious. Am I right?"

"You may be right, Herr Norton. I don't want to lie to you. Babs is very ill. I have told you that we will do everything in our power to help her to recover. But . . ."

"But the chances are against it."

She looked straight into my eyes, silently, then slowly she lowered her head. I said, "Thank you."

"For what?"

"For telling me the truth."

37

The storm was still raging over Paris, the sun was gone, the sky was black. In the courtyard below I could see the bare trees. Ruth turned on the desk lamp and said, "You are a product of your environment, Herr Norton. I would never presume to criticize your life-style with Sylvia Moran."

"Today, when Dr. Sigrand woke me up, you said you were pleased to meet me."

"And I was."

"Why?"

"Because you brought Babs here. Because you stayed and slept all night on the bench and didn't try to run away from the situation."

"But I couldn't do that!"

"People are capable of the greatest evil and the greatest good. You stayed with Babs, Herr Norton, and that pleased me. That's why I was happy to meet you. Because after everything I'd read in the papers, I had a quite different opinion of you."

"I can imagine that."

"All of us would react differently if we knew more about our fellow men. I decided to tell you what I thought of Sylvia Moran and her behavior in that dressing room in Monte Carlo when we were alone."

I stared at her.

"What Sylvia Moran said in front of the cameras was written for her, wasn't it? She spoke like the great actress she is. And why did she agree to the whole thing in the first place? Because she had been persuaded that it would be great publicity. And Sylvia Moran is in show business. Why shouldn't she do what her advisers tell her to do? What do you really know about Sylvia Moran, Herr Norton?"

"Well . . . I'd say just about everything."

"I can't see it that way. Do you love her?"

"I . . . of course I love her."

"Of course you *don't*. And never did. And never will. In your position, love is impossible. So you don't know her at all, at least not the things that count, not the real Sylvia Moran."

"And you do?"

"I think I can imagine what she is really like pretty well," said Ruth Reinhardt. "She is a legend and a commodity, and for those reasons if for no others, an exceptional woman. The world—and you too, Herr Norton—know only what is visible, the role she has been playing all her life, the role she has to play as a big star. How can I make it clearer?" She paused, then went on. "I, you, the whole world see only a picture of Sylvia Moran, what's plastered outside movie houses, in magazines, or on television screens." And I thought, startled, She's right! "Sylvia Moran is no longer in a position to be herself. Dr. Sigrand was unfair to her, and I have explained the reason for that to you."

I don't know what came over me, but suddenly I found myself saying to a woman I scarcely knew, about a woman with whom I lived, "But surely what Sylvia said in that dressing room was absolutely repulsive!"

And Ruth Reinhardt replied, "Some people behave repulsively because they are unhappy."

"You can excuse her outburst?"

"Excuse it and understand it, Herr Norton. Sylvia Moran was practically forced to make that speech. She wasn't even asked to approve of what she had to say. Who knew if it was her opinion or not? And don't forget—at the time Babs was a healthy little girl."

"And now Babs has an illness that may leave her in the condition Sylvia found so repulsive."

"Sylvia Moran is a star. She has to do as she is told whether she likes it or not. Isn't that a terrible fate? What happens if she refuses to do what her studio or the manager tells her to do? Then she has to fear for her career, which must go up, up, up. Then she has to fear a drop in her popularity, fewer good parts, and what else, Herr Norton? You know more about it than I do. Sylvia Moran is in a dreadful position, and yours is considerably worse."

So you see, your honor, that was when I first came in contact with that other planet, with those who live in the dark.

"Sylvia Moran came to the end of her rope in that dressing room," said Ruth Reinhardt. "She was ashamed, because the degree of her dependence, in spite of her fame, may suddenly have come clear to her. The more famous you are, the more dependent you are. And people who feel ashamed become aggressive. That's what happened to Frau Moran. I can understand that someone like Sylvia Moran, whose very existence depends on a very definite image, suddenly can't stand the thought of retarded children—out of superstition, perhaps, the fear of precipitating something disastrous. And then consider the fact that your livelihood too depends on Sylvia Moran's image. Forgive me. I'm only facing the facts. I haven't insulted you, have I?"

"Not at all." And she hadn't. Not this woman.

"And you also have to face the fact that she *really* loves you, in spite of the fact that you feel none for her. A woman whose life depends first and foremost on her appearance and on the appearance of her child, a woman with a highly complicated life-style—all this may have come clear to her in Monte Carlo. *I* can't condemn her, and, as I just said, you don't love her. Therefore you really know nothing about her." She lowered her head. "Who knows anything about another person anyway, however much love there is between them?"

38

Tanks. Heavily armed soldiers in battle dress. An empty street. Those were the first things I saw when I stumbled into the salon of Suite 419 in Le Monde at about a quarter to twelve on November 25, 1971. I had driven from Neuilly back to the city, dizzy with exhaustion.

The man at the desk had told me that the key for 419 wasn't on the board. Mr. Bracken and Dr. Wolken or the governess was probably in my suite, perhaps all three. This had surprised me, but I hadn't said anything. When I got to the door of 419, it was locked. The key, I could tell, was in the lock, so I knocked. I had to knock several times until Clarissa finally opened up. She looked at me as if I were a ghost. She was trembling, her eyes were red, and she stepped back as if she were afraid of me. Behind her I could see the television screen—tanks, heavily armed soldiers in battle dress. "What in hell's the matter with you?"

"I must have fallen asleep."

"What are you doing here, anyway?"

"Mr. Bracken said I should stay here and lock myself in and not open to anyone unless I recognized the voice. I turned on the television to distract myself and . . . and I must have fallen asleep."

She walked back into the room, and she flung herself into a chair, weeping. "Clarissa! Where's Bracken? Where's Dr. Wolken?"

"They've gone after the men."

"What men?"

"The ones who got hold of me." Sobs. "Horrible creatures!"

I grabbed her by the shoulders and shook her. I was so exhausted, everything I looked at flickered. I shouted, "What horrible creatures?"

"Meanwhile traffic in the city . . ." I turned off the television and yelled at her again. "For God's sake—talk!" And then she told me everything.

"The three of us slept here last night, Mr. Kaven, and in

the morning, after your call from the hospital, we were terribly upset, and Mr. Bracken said he'd have to call Mr. Gintzburger right away, since it was such a serious matter." Joe Gintzburger in Hollywood, president of Seven Stars. It was the right thing to do. "He didn't want to put the call through from the hotel so he went to the main post office." Clarissa began to sob again.

"So? Then what?"

"Dr. Wolken had fallen asleep on the couch over there, so I went to my room because I wanted to lie down too, and there these three men. . . ."

"What three men?"

"A photographer and two reporters. They must have come straight up from the lobby. In the morning there's so much going on, it's easy to slip through."

"How did they get into your room?"

"I forgot to lock it. They said they knew the room I was in because we always have the same ones."

"And you forgot to lock it?"

"Yes."

"Idiot!"

She began to cry again, and I said, "I'm sorry. I didn't mean it, Clarissa. My nerves are shot. What next?"

Suddenly she clutched me, clung to me. "What happened next?" I asked, gently now, and stroked her hair. Perhaps I could get her back to normal.

"They asked me what was going on here. I told them nothing unusual." Now she was talking fast. "And they told me not to talk nonsense, of course something was wrong and they'd get it out of me. 'You can depend on it, baby'—that's what they said." She drew a deep breath and went on. "They asked me where Babs was and where you were, and why Dr. Wolken was sleeping on a couch in 419, and why only one bed had been slept in and the curtains were drawn and the bedside lamp was standing on the floor . . ."

"Just a minute. They were in 419 too?"

"Yes. I didn't lock the door."

"Why not?"

"Because Dr. Wolken couldn't have left when he woke up."

"He could have called you! Oh dear God!"

"That's right. He could have." She began to cry again. "I didn't think of that."

"How did they get the idea that something was wrong here?"

"They said somebody in the stockroom had seen an ambulance last night, and had seen you, Mr. Kaven. He called the newsroom. They pay fifty francs for information like that. So they came here first thing in the morning."

"So? Go on."

"They went on and on, asking questions. And I began to cry and they took a picture of me. The photographer took pictures of everything!"

"Of what else?"

"Of everything in 419. Of Dr. Wolken asleep. And the bed. And the lamp on the floor. And of a hypodermic that got left behind. They wouldn't give up. They were here almost an hour."

I was massaging her back gently. "And what else did you say?"

She sat up very straight, looked at me with her tear-stained face and said, calm suddenly, "I didn't betray anything, Mr. Kaven. I swear I didn't, by all that's sacred to me." Clarissa was religious. When she said anything like that you could believe her.

"Good girl," I said. "Thanks."

She looked at me, her face close now, still trembling, and suddenly she pressed her lips against mine. So it was true— Clarissa was in love with me.

I was to repulse her, your honor? At this point the one thing I didn't need was an enemy. So I kissed her, doing my best to make it short, which wasn't easy, but finally I managed to free myself. Sitting beside me on the sofa, she assured me over and over that she hadn't betrayed anything. And I believed her. I also believed her when she said, "I never did anything like this in my life, Philip! Never! But I've loved you from the moment I set eyes on you. It's been terrible for me, Philip! Horrible!"

"Kaven. That's my name: Kaven," I said. "It's a beautiful thought, Clarissa, that you love me, but you realize, I'm sure, that it's impossible. I belong to Sylvia, heart and soul." That's what I said, your honor. It worked.

"Of course," she said. "I realize that. I always have respected your feelings for Sylvia. Please forgive me for what just happened, Mr. Kaven. I'll never betray myself again, I swear I won't, however miserable I may be."

"All right, my dear. And now what about those reporters?"

"Mr. Bracken came back from the post office. He found Dr.

Wolken asleep and woke him up. Then they came to look for me and found me with the three men. Mr. Bracken sized up the situation right away, and so did the three men, and they ran off, Mr. Bracken and Dr. Wolken after them."

"Do you know what paper they represented?"

"No. They didn't tell me. Mr. Bracken said he had to catch them in the hotel or on the street, anyway before they got back to their office."

"And when was that?"

"About an hour ago."

"What did you do then?"

"I was scared to death. I went back to 419 and watched television, the terrorists in The Hague, to distract me."

"And fell asleep. Well, that's neither here nor there. The main thing is that Bracken catch them. And that Babs survive."

I shouldn't have said that, and it turned out to be a cardinal error. But I was so terribly tired, your honor, I didn't know what I was saying.

"What do you mean, 'survives'? Is it that bad?"

And then I made my second mistake, worse than the first. I told Clarissa the truth, everything Dr. Reinhardt had told me, and Clarissa began to cry again.

"Stop crying!"

"I can't," she sobbed.

"Goddammit, you can!"

"No, no! I love Babs so much. If something happens to her ... if she ... if she ... and her mother in the hospital, knowing nothing about it ... and never sees her child again before she ... before she ..." She couldn't bring herself to say the word "dies."

The telephone rang. I answered it.

"Monsieur Kaven?"

"Yes."

"This is the desk clerk. I'm terribly sorry, but it all happened so fast and there's so much going on down here—an American tourist group ..."

"So?"

"Two men came in and asked the operator for your room number and I'm sorry to say she gave it to them. They've left, but we don't know where they are. They may be on their way up to you. If you want me to alert our staff or the police ..."

"No! Don't call the police!" That was all we needed right

132

now! "Don't alert anybody. I know the two men. I'm expecting them."

I put down the receiver and told Clarissa, "Get to your room! Fast! And this time lock the door. And open it only for one of us. Got that?"

"Yes. But why? What's happened now?"

I dragged her out of the salon, opened the door to our suite and practically threw her out into the passage. It was still empty. "Get going," I said. "Run!"

She ran. I could see her go into her room and hear her lock the door.

39

I knocked the first one down as soon as he walked into the foyer. He was the smaller one. He was holding a camera in his hand and had another slung around his neck. He had a harelip. I closed the door behind the second one and swung at him, hitting his jaw. But he only shook himself like a wet dog and jumped me. I fell back into the salon, and he got in a few good blows, after which it was my turn and he went down. He was up again in no time, ready to kick me where it hurt most, but I was too fast for him. I rolled out of reach and got up and punched him below the chin, hard as I could. It lifted him off the ground and he fell back, taking a small table and lamp with him. I fell on him and pummeled his face until a tooth fell out and he spat blood in my face, the pig, after which he got me by the throat and choked me until I turned black and fell down. Then he was on top of me again, pounding the life out of me. For a while things went back and forth like this, but then Harelip joined us and I was in big trouble. In the end they had me laid out on the floor, one of them working on me at the top, the other lower down, and it hurt, hurt terribly, and suddenly I passed out.

40

I thought I was going to choke. I gasped for breath and vomited some liquid. It burned, but I was conscious again. I was still lying on the floor, and Bracken was kneeling beside me with a bottle of cognac, and Dr. Wolken was standing beside him. When he saw I had come to, he bowed, his expression serious.

"We sure got here at the right time," said Bracken.

"Guess so," I said. "Where are the two goons?"

"Slowly, slowly," said Bracken. He looked disheveled, and I told him so.

"Look who's talking," he said. "Take a look at yourself, man. You can throw out the suit. It's covered with blood and God knows what else. And your face. No. You'd better avoid mirrors for a while."

He helped me to sit up. Every bone in my body ached. "You came in the middle of it?"

"Yes. And we did a good job on the two motherfuckers. Both of us. Dr. Wolken too. That man can fight. He beat one of them to a pulp."

"The little one?"

"No. The big one," said Bracken.

"Herr Doktor!" I looked at him with honest admiration. "You finished him off? I don't believe it!"

"Please, Mr. Kaven," he said, squirming with embarrassment.

"And then you called the flics?" I asked Bracken.

"Would have liked to," he said. "Unfortunately we had to lay off the two for a second and they got away."

"Got away?"

"And how! I phoned downstairs, but nobody'd seen them. They must have gone out the back way. The little guy lost his camera. There it is." Bracken pointed to it on the table.

"Harelip?" I asked.

"Yes. An Italian. The other was French."

"All right," I said. "That takes care of those two. What about the other three? Did you get them?"

Bracken laughed. "Did we ever!"

"Where?"

"At the Métro station, Place de la Nation. God, man, were we lucky! We almost lost them. They took the Métro. We just managed to get on the same train when they spotted us. They got off fast and disappeared in the *pissoir*. That's where we finished them off. I hope they're still laid out there, in their own piss."

"All three? The two of you?"

"You have no idea what a fighter Dr. Wolken is. Want the bottle? Good idea. But take it easy."

I drank and began to feel better. "Dr. Wolken took on two," Bracken went on, "and flattened them out in the *pissoir*. Never seen anything like it." He still had his coat on. Now he took five rolls of film out of his pocket, three unused and still in their boxes. "I took everything off the fucking photographer," he said. "He's got nothing from here. So . . . how're you doing?"

"Just fine," I said, and that's the last thing I remember saying. I don't think I ever slept so soundly in my life.

41

I opened my eyes. Bracken was standing beside me. I had no idea where I was, what day it was, what time. Then I saw that I was lying naked in the bed Babs had lain in. The table lamp was on.

"Well, at last!" said Bracken. "Do you know how late it is?"

"No."

"Five. You've slept four and a half hours. But you've got to get up now."

"Why?"

"You said you had to go to the hospital to see Babs. And you've got to see Sylvia too." I groaned. "Pain?"

"No."

Of course I was in pain, but that wasn't why I had groaned. I had groaned because all our misery had returned. I got up.

"I took off your clothes," said Bracken. "Sent everything to

135

the cleaners. I washed the blood off your face. Say you walked into a door."

I went to the bathroom and looked at my face in the mirror and was relieved. It could have been worse. My left eye was blue-green and swollen and I had a hefty bruise on my right cheek. My body looked terrible, but I wasn't going to run around naked. I took a bath, and Bracken came in and sat down on the edge of the bidet. "You know, Rod," I said, "when you want to, you can be a pal."

"If you're sitting in the same shit, the best thing you can be is a pal."

"What did Joe say?"

"Shitting in his pants, of course. You know what a rat he is."

"What did he say?"

"First of all he cursed Sylvia for her little dressing-room monologue in Monte. He knows about it. We had to tell him so he wouldn't drop dead if our blackmailer friend ever decides to contact him. Then he cursed me."

"Why you?"

"Don't know. To let off steam, I guess. He also cursed you and Babs. Can't imagine why. With Babs I can understand it. Inconsiderate of the brat to come down with meningitis. Then he said that as far as he was concerned, if this thing leaked out it would be finis for Sylvia; she wouldn't get a job anywhere in the world." He burped. "I let him talk. He has to be in the know; he can say what he wants. In our position the only thing that can help is chutzpah."

"Chutzpah and caution."

"Chutzpah and caution," he agreed.

"And what else did he have to say?"

"Well . . ." He hesitated.

"Go ahead. Give it to me."

"When I spoke to him first he didn't know what to do. Said he had to talk to his lawyers and the VIPs and the PR people, all the assholes. I was to call him again in two hours. So I did."

"And what did he say?"

"You won't like it."

"Tell me what he said!"

"Okay. He said that from here on in the reporters wouldn't leave you in peace. They'd be on your neck day and night. If you go on staying here, they'll watch you every step you take."

"I know."

"So Joe said you'd have to clear out."

"What?"

"You've got to get out of Le Monde. Pronto. As soon as you've got your clothes on. And take Babs along with you."

"Are you out of your mind?"

"Sane as I'll ever be. Joe told me to tell you. And that's an order. I've packed three suitcases for you and two for Babs. Clarissa and Dr. Wolken helped me. They're okay. We can depend on them. And you take off with Babs. First flight we can get to Madrid."

"Now look here, Rod! Babs is dying and I . . . you *must* be out of your mind! Joe too, the idiot!"

"That's what you think. It's all been meticulously planned. I've spoken to your old friend, Président Directeur Général from Le Monde . . . what's his name?"

"Pierre Maréchal."

"Right. I told him Babs had an allergy and that you were flying to Madrid with her today."

"Why Madrid?"

There was no stopping him. "I told Pierre Maréchal that a nurse was flying with you. I said that the nurse was taking Babs to the doctor again, so that takes care of Babs. You're to attract a lot of attention in the lobby when you leave, so that everybody knows you're flying to Madrid."

"For God's sake, *why Madrid?*"

"Shut up! Let me finish. Your friend Maréchal has offered us a car from the hotel. Two reliable men. They'll take your suitcases to the airport."

"But what am I supposed to do in Madrid?"

"Maybe *you've* lost your mind. Sylvia's next picture's going to be shot in Madrid. Remember? And you've got to attend to all the necessary preparations."

"Dammit, Rod—you know I don't have the foggiest idea how to go about anything like that!"

"And you're not going to have to go about it!"

"But you just said I had to fly to Madrid. When I get there I've got to go through passport control, customs. I'll be on the passenger list. And I've got to register at a hotel. Within hours the reporters will know where I am!"

"If you fly to Madrid, you fly on Sylvia's plane and you're not on any list. Did they ever make you go through passport control or customs when you flew in Sylvia's plane?"

"But I have to register. Always had to. And Babs had to register. And they'll see us." I was dumbfounded.

"Idiot! You're not going to fly to Madrid with Babs!"

"But you just said—"

"How could you possibly fly to Madrid, ass? Babs can't be moved and we need you here. Both of you stay in Paris. Only the plane takes off for Madrid, *without either of you!*"

Everything began to swim before my eyes.

"You stay in Paris," Bracken was saying. "We have to work out a way for you to keep in touch without Sylvia's noticing anything. They mustn't get ideas at the hospital. You'd better put on an absolute-despair act there."

"No problem. But where the hell am I supposed to stay in Paris?"

He looked at me silently for a moment, then he said casually, "You've got a little pussy here in Paris, haven't you?"

"Shut up!"

"But you have! Don't tell me you haven't! Because we need her now. A gal that's nuts about you will do anything for you. Come on, Phil! I won't tell a soul! Ever!"

"I have someone, but I don't know whether she'll want to take me in. I've got to call her first and ask."

"Then ask her! On the double! Get going!" He handed me the towel, I got out of the bath and dried myself, then I slung a second towel around me and walked barefoot into the salon and dialed Suzy's beauty parlor. I was lucky. She was still there. A scream of joy when she recognized my voice.

"Listen, *mon petit chou*," I said, Bracken behind me, "could I possibly move in on you for a while? I'll tell you later why. Can't do now."

"Are you on the lam, *mon petit chou?*"

"Yes and no. It's a complicated story."

"Then come. Come right away. Tonight. After eight." I could hear her laugh. "You lucky dog!"

"How come?"

"My little count is flying to Acapulco at seven. How about that? *Chéri*, we're going to have ourselves one wonderful time!"

"But I have luggage. Five pieces."

"Have them sent to me here. We're open till seven. I'll get them over to my place."

"Thanks."

138

"So when are you coming?"

"Tonight. But it may be late."

"I'll be waiting."

"Thanks again."

"Don't thank me. I'm so happy you're coming. So, until onight. As late as you like. I'll be waiting."

I hung up. "Well?" said Bracken.

"A-Okay."

"Fine. We'll keep in touch by phone. You go on visiting Babs and Sylvia. She mustn't know a thing about Babs, of course."

"Of course."

"Where does the girl live?"

"Quite a distance from here."

"I asked where she lived."

"And I told you—quite a distance from here."

"Okay. So don't tell me. The main thing is that you don't have to hide out in the city. Telephone number?"

"I'll call you tonight and let you know."

"Right. I've put out a suit and underwear for you. All you have to do is get dressed."

I held my head in my hands and stared down at the desk. Things were getting worse by the hour, but Joe and Rod were right—this was the only way out, if there was a way out at all! A thought occurred to me. "And what about Clarissa and Wolken?"

"They stay here. No reporters are going to get anything out of them. I'll be here too. I've got to stay in case ..." He stopped.

"Yes," I said, "in case ..."

"Babs is in bad shape, right?"

"In very bad shape."

He said something unprintable.

"But how do I get the damn suitcases back from the airport?"

His smile was smug, "I got in touch with another dear friend of yours—Lucien Bayard. He's going to get hold of some friends who will bring your luggage back from the airport. They won't squeal, not for a million, says he, and he'll take care of them financially. They'll bring it to wherever you want in a small van. You only have to give the gentlemen your address. They'll take you along too. Drop you somewhere near the Hôpital Sainte-Bernadette. Not too near."

139

I groaned.

"I know," said Rod. "You're hating every minute of this, all this fuss over the brat. How about thinking of yourself for a change?" That did it! "The men will take your stuff to your pussy, right?"

"Yes. And you'll find out where she works," I said. "The telephone number's all you need."

"And why not? We're both in the same shitty boat, just as you said last night. And however much we hate each other, right now we've got to stick together. That's clear to me. To you too, I hope."

"To me too," I said. And then my eyes dimmed.

42

Overcome anger with warmth
Requite evil with good
Conquer the miser with gifts
Conquer the liar with truth
Conquest breeds hatred because the conqueror
is unhappy
Nobody in the world can stop hatred with hatred.
Hatred is dispelled by love.

Guatama Buddha

In the morning I had seen the back of a picture frame on Dr. Ruth Reinhardt's desk and had taken it for granted that there was a picture in it. Now, in the evening, I was sitting alone in her office and I had turned the frame around. No picture. A piece of paper with the above lines printed on it. "Hatred is dispelled by love. . . ."

After a spectacular farewell performance in the Le Monde lobby I had actually driven to the airport in a hotel car with all my luggage. Lucien Bayard's friends had picked me up there in a small van, as arranged, and had dropped me in Neuilly, not far from the Hôpital Sainte-Bernadette. By this time my suitcases, Babs's two included, were at Suzy's salon.

I gave the man at the gate my false name and told him that

wanted to see Dr. Ruth Reinhardt. He used the phone. "She's not in her office, monsieur," he said. "They'll call you."

They had a paging system in this hospital too, and every doctor carried a beeper the size of a pack of cigarettes. After a while the gatekeeper told me, "Dr. Reinhardt is with a critical patient. She wants you to wait in her office. You know where it is? She'll come as soon as she can."

So I took the elevator to the fourth floor, walked along the corridor with the administration offices, past many open doors, doctors, orderlies and nurses. I was wearing my dark glasses. All the talk I could hear was concerned with the terrorists and hostages in The Hague.

Ruth Reinhardt came into her office in a few minutes. There were dark circles under her brown eyes; she looked exhausted, but her handshake was as firm as ever.

"Excuse me, Herr Norton, but it was an urgent case."

"Please don't mention it, Frau Doktor." Embarrassed, I put the frame back on the desk. We sat down. "Buddha," I said. "The lines are beautiful. Are you . . . I mean . . ."

"You want to know if I am a Buddhist?" Such a serious face. She passed a hand across her forehead in a tired gesture. "I'm very interested in Buddhism. What's the matter with your eye?"

I couldn't lie to this woman. I told her everything that had happened. "So I had to leave the hotel. I'm staying with a friend."

"I think that's very sensible. Of course I'll need your friend's telephone number."

"How is Babs?"

"She's not doing well, Herr Norton. Unfortunately. Not at all well."

"Hm."

"I know what you're thinking, Herr Norton."

"I don't think you do."

"Oh, but I do." And I knew that she did. I said quickly, "You've been on duty since last night. You're dead tired, Frau Doktor."

"This is the long shift. For Dr. Sigrand too. Ordinarily I would be off duty now, from nine until nine tomorrow evening."

"What do you mean, 'ordinarily'?"

"I'm staying in the clinic. Dr. Sigrand is too. When we have a serious case like Babs, we sleep in the clinic. Don't look so upset. I can sleep anywhere, on a cement floor if necessary.

141

Now come with me and we'll go to see Babs." She rose wearily. The little lamb fell to the ground. I picked it up "Thank you," she said. "The children love to play with it."

I nodded, and we left the room. In the passage I could hear a loudspeaker: "A special committee of twenty-eight men has been formed to deal with the taking of hostages, acts of terror, kidnapping and organized crime. We are switching you now to the international airport at Schiphol. Pierre Renoir, are you ready?"

The voice faded. We had reached the private patients' wing. Ruth Reinhardt opened a door and I entered Babs's room, the same room I had been in before. But it wasn't dark now; the lights were on. I could see Dr. Sigrand and a nurse leaning over Babs. He was putting a hypodermic syringe into a dish the nurse was holding for him. He looked gray, gaunt, worn out, like an old man. He nodded at me. He was too tired to hate me.

I saw Babs and was horrified. Her spotted face was swollen and red, her right ear was bandaged. Her eyes were open, the eyeballs rolled up so that practically all you could see was the whites. Her body was twisted sideways. She had drawn her legs up to her stomach, but askew, in different directions. Sigrand was talking softly to the nurse, who nodded and withdrew.

"What did you just give her, doctor?"

He didn't look at me once during the entire conversation, which took place in French. "Something to take care of the spastic attack."

"What do you mean, 'spastic'?" Babs moaned. "Why is she moaning?"

"Because she is in pain."

"I want to know . . ."

"A spastic condition is an indication that there has been an increased tendency toward convulsions," Ruth Reinhardt said softly. "The meninges, that is to say the brain membranes, are inflamed and the tension is unbearable. And the nerve roots are irritated, causing great pain. That's why Babs can't relax. You understand?" I nodded. "That's why her legs are twisted like that."

"Hills," said Babs. Her voice was hoarse.

"What?"

"Santa Monica," said Babs.

"It doesn't mean anything," said Ruth Reinhardt. Mean-

142

while Dr. Sigrand was covering Babs gently, wiping away the sweat that was pouring down her face. Her breathing rattled in her chest.

"Babs!" I said.

"Be quiet!" said Dr. Sigrand.

"She can't hear very well, Monsieur Norton," said Ruth Reinhardt. "Perhaps not at all."

"An hour ago her temperature was 106.6. She is disoriented," said Dr. Sigrand.

Just then Babs vomited. Dr. Reinhardt jumped forward and rang a bell. Dr. Sigrand raised Babs's head. She began to scream horribly. "Why is he holding her head?"

"Because otherwise she might choke." Babs was still vomiting.

The door flew open. The nurse who had just left ran in. With warm water and damp cloths the two doctors and the nurse cleaned Babs up. Another nurse brought fresh linen. They changed Babs's bed. She never stopped screaming. Right then no one was paying any attention to me. I had turned away. I couldn't bear the sight of the World's Greatest Little Sunshine Girl any longer.

"Make up the cot over there," said Dr. Sigrand, gesturing in the direction of the corner of the room where a cot was standing. "I'll be sleeping here tonight."

"Yes, doctor," said the nurse, and left with the dirty linen.

"Will she make it?" I asked Ruth Reinhardt.

"You can see—we're doing the best we can."

I walked over to Babs, revulsion choking me, and knelt down beside her. I really don't know any more, your honor, whether my feelings at the time were compassionate or whether I was just putting on an act. "Babs."

No answer.

Louder, "Babs!"

"Don't, Monsieur Norton," said Dr. Sigrand.

Still louder, *"Babs!"*

Babs howled as if possessed and sat up, her foul breath close to mine, and she struck me—little Babs who loved me so much, your honor, struck me as hard as she could in the face. It hurt so that I let out a cry. Then she back back gasping and started to scream again.

"Get out!" said Dr. Sigrand.

Ruth Reinhardt took my arm and led me to the door. "Come with me, Monsieur Norton."

143

"I don't want to."

Babs was still screaming. "Get him out of here!" hissed Dr. Sigrand.

"You *must* leave now!" Ruth Reinhardt was still holding my arm, and I was astonished at the strength with which she pushed me out of the room. The door fell shut behind us. "Dr. Sigrand told you that Babs is completely disoriented."

"And she isn't reacting to the antibiotics, and . . . and . . ."

"The immune globulin."

"And all the other stuff he's given her."

"Maybe she will soon."

"And maybe she won't."

Ruth Reinhardt was silent.

"And what happens then, Frau Doktor, if she never reacts to anything that's given her? What happens then?"

"We have other possibilities."

"What other possibilities?"

"You wouldn't understand. Of course we have to anticipate complications."

"Anticipate complications? What do you call what's happened until now? Wouldn't you call all this 'complications'?"

"No. There are no complications. Yet. What has happened until now is all part of the natural course of this particular illness."

"Is that so. Well . . . fine!"

"It isn't fine," Ruth Reinhardt said quietly.

"I . . . I didn't mean it like that," I said. "I'm terribly, terribly upset. I . . ."

"I can see what you are, Herr Norton. Please come back if you want to. I don't know if we will let you see Babs, but we'll give you information. *I'll* give you information, Herr Norton. And I'll never lie to you."

I bit my lip. "I know that, Frau Doktor.

"You can call anytime."

"You've got to get some sleep."

"I shall. Right here in the hospital. You may call me during the night, and if . . ."

One of the nurses came out of Babs's room. "Frau Doktor, please come quickly. Dr. Sigrand needs you."

"I'm coming," said Ruth Reinhardt, and went in. She hadn't even said goodnight.

I don't know how long I remained standing in front of the door to Babs's room, perhaps a minute, perhaps a quarter of an hour. Finally I left and walked through the passage again, with its many offices and open doors, and heard the voices of television reporters. "And this is a member of the special commission, his back turned of course, his voice electronically distorted . . ." On down the passage. "We offered them a Douglas DC-8-62 . . ." Nine o'clock. "The Japanese wouldn't accept it . . ." I began to run.

When I got outside it had stopped raining. I walked from one hospital to the other. Rue Cavé was only twenty minutes away.

43

I found Sylvia in bed, but now the lamp on the bedside table was lit. Her head was still bandaged, but her mouth and eyes were uncovered. Her eyes looked terrible, swollen, tearing, the skin around them blue, black, green, the way they always are after a face lift.

"Pepito! At last! I've been longing for you." Today her voice was clear.

"I couldn't come earlier, Silky. I . . ."

"Kiss me!"

That's what she said, your honor; that's what she demanded. No self-pity now, I told myself, and kissed her on the mouth, in the course of which I noticed that her eyes were not only swollen, they glittered with an unholy excitement. So what, in God's name, had happened here? I heard a door open and turned around. Rod Bracken was coming out of the bathroom. He looked like a madman.

"What's the matter with you two?" I said.

"Clarissa!" said Bracken. "The bitch—"

"What about her?"

"She was here this afternoon."

"Here?"

"Here! To see Sylvia, idiot!"

"She could never have gotten past the gate!"

"And how, she got past the gate!"

"How?"

145

"She called Sylvia and said something had happened that she ought to know about. So Sylvia contacted Dr. Delamare and gave him an exact description of the bitch, and they gave her a number, and they let her see Sylvia. The damn fool! I could wring her neck!"

"Shut up, Rod!" said Sylvia.

"Then, after Clarissa left, Sylvia tried to reach you. You were gone. Then she got hold of me. I had to come here at once. She arranged it so they'd let me in too."

I sat down in a chair beside the bed. Rod was pacing up and down the room. Sylvia was weeping with her swollen eyes. And my luggage and Babs's luggage was at Suzy's place. And Sylvia's private jet was in Madrid. And Babs might be dead by now. No—until now our luck had been lousy. Why should it suddenly change?

"My poor darling Pepito!" Sylvia, still weeping. "Rod told me how they beat you up. When I think of all the things you put up with to help me. God, how I love you!"

"Forget it," I told her. "I've just come from the hospital. Babs is better."

"No," she sobbed. "I don't believe it. My child, my darling, my little Babs—she's terribly ill. Clarissa told me."

"Forget Clarissa! Was she in the hospital? Has she seen Babs? Has she spoken to the doctors? She's hysterical. Babs *is* better, I'm telling you, and I've just come from the hospital."

"Lies!" she sobbed, and I couldn't stand the sight of her. "And we've got the press on our necks. They'll hunt you down, and Babs, and me . . ."

"They will *not* hunt us down," said Bracken. "I told you how I've taken care of them."

Suddenly Sylvia was raving. I'd never seen anything like it. That was the night when I realized that I knew nothing at all about women, above all about mothers. Sylvia Moran, your honor—I have said dreadful things about her, but now I have to report on how she behaved that night. It was no motion picture, there were no cameras.

"I want to see Babs!" she screamed suddenly and so loudly, Bracken and I were shocked. I said *sotto voce* to Bracken, "Does anyone here know the truth?" He shook his head. Sylvia was still screaming. "I want to go to my child! I must see her! I must!" And all this with her head swathed in bandages. The tubes, thank God, had been removed. She was struggling for breath. "She's my child, and my child's in trouble! Don't stare at me like that, you fools! What do you know about children? Babs . . . Babs . . ." And so on. Impossible to stop her.

Bracken whispered in my ear, "She's still very weak. It won't last long. Then I'll talk to her." His voice was hoarse. He'd got there ahead of me and had already been treated to one scene like this. "The doors are padded," he croaked. "You can't hear anything outside."

We had to listen to Sylvia's ravings for a good ten minutes. Bracken had underestimated her strength. All in all, it was a very touching scene, your honor, but it could have spelled the end for all of us. Heartbreaking, yes, an outburst of pain and love, but in vain, all in vain.

When Sylvia paused for a moment, Rod gave me a sign. It was my turn. I thought of everything Ruth Reinhardt had said about how well she understood this woman. I pulled my chair up to the bed and tried gentleness. "My poor Silky. Of course it's dreadful for you. But we can't take you to see Babs. You must realize that."

"I can see her! I can!" But softly now. "I really can."

"No, no," I said. "Think of the reporters."

"I don't give a damn about the reporters."

"But they decide your future. Think of your future, Silky."

"I don't give a damn about my future either!" Tears again, obscenities from Bracken. "Babs! Babs! It's all my fault!"

"*What?*"

"It's my fault that Babs is so ill."

"It's *not* your fault! Have you gone crazy?"

She was wringing her hands. "It *is* my fault! Meningitis! Encephalitis! Do you know what it means?"

"What?"

"It's God's punishment for what I said in Monte Carlo. It's my fault! Mine! Mine!" And she was screaming again.

"Stop screaming!" said Bracken, his face purple with rage, but I knew his rage sprang from fear, knew it because I felt the same way. "Think of your face!" he said. "Every distortion can be harmful! I'm telling you—you cannot go to Babs. How do you propose getting there? On a stretcher?"

From then on Bracken and I took turns. When you're fighting for your life, you become brutal.

"If it ever leaks out—about your face lift and Babs—you can give up!"

"And your career is your life, isn't it?"

147

"Think of *The Chalk Circle!*"

"The picture you've been waiting for all your life!"

"I called Joe. He says if any of this leaks out, any of it, nobody'll touch you with a ten-foot pole!"

"You're not only under contract for *Chalk Circle* but also for three other films!"

"You have your own company now!"

"What do you think the banks will say who've given us credit?" And so on and so forth, Bracken and I, fighting for our lives.

"We've signed contracts. You know the paragraph about penalties for reneging. You couldn't begin to pay them. You've got to do as we tell you, and we're telling you—*stay here!* Phil will keep you informed. He's rented a studio from a friend who's away so that the reporters don't hound him." He got that in neatly.

"And every day I'll bring you better news about Babs," I said, and could see Babs, vomiting, screaming, in that hideous position, and could hear Ruth Reinhardt's voice, "She isn't doing well, Herr Norton," could hear Dr. Sigrand's voice asking them to make up his bed on the cot in the corner of Babs's room, thought of the scream of rage with which Babs had struck me, and said, "The medication is working, word of honor, Silky. That's why I came here as fast as I could, to assure you that everything was going to be all right."

"Your profession is merciless, Sylvia," said Bracken. "The least mistake and you're out." And he went on to tell Sylvia how quickly her resources would be gone if she wasn't sensible now.

"Sensible?" she sobbed. "When it's all my fault and God's punishing me?"

"Yes—sensible," Bracken said. "You can't do a thing for Babs now, but you can ruin yourself. For the rest of your life. Clarissa and Wolken are staying at the hotel. Officially Phil has just taken off for Madrid to make all preparations, taking Babs with him. When she's okay again, they 'return,' but right now we've got to lay low. Have you any idea how I'd like to fire Clarissa at this point? But then she'd talk, and that would be dangerous."

"Clarissa loves Babs," said Sylvia. "That's why she came to see me."

"Of course she loves Babs. She's a great gal!" He sat down on the edge of the bed, and I knew exactly what he was going

148

to say. "Look, Sylvia. Right now, and in the few days that lie ahead, the only person who can help us out of this mess is Phil. He can look in on Babs every day and come straight from her to you. The doctors trust him. He's the only one they'll let in. And he knows how to keep the thing secret. He's the only one right now who can protect your career, and Babs. Am I right, Phil?"

"Absolutely."

She capitulated at last. "What would I do without you, Pepito? I'd be lost."

"But you have me, Silky, and I love you, and I love Babs. You know that, don't you?"

The tears were coursing out of her eyes onto her bandages. "I know that, Pepito, my beloved Pepito."

Bracken looked at me, I looked at him. We'd weathered the storm. For the time being. That was quite a look that passed between us, your honor.

"You're right," said Sylvia. "There's nothing else we can do. I thank both of you for standing by me." And she really believed what she was saying. Poor Sylvia! I drew a deep breath to control my heaving stomach. She still smelled nauseatingly of anesthetic, but I kissed her on the mouth and bit her lower lip gently. She liked that.

"You're the best guy in the world," she said. "And you too, Rod. You're the two best guys in the world, and I love you both."

I said, "I'll go back to the hospital again." Nothing was further from my mind. Suzy was next on my agenda. "Just to make sure. When I left, Babs was fast asleep. And tomorrow I'll come to see you again, Silky."

"Thank you, Pepito. Thank you. I shall never forget what you are doing for me," and the tears kept rolling out of her swollen eyes.

44

In the corridor, I said goodbye to Bracken. He had to get back to Le Monde fast to prevent any further disasters; I had to get to Suzy, to her apartment, to my new home, without being recognized.

Sister Hélène was still substituting for the worldly nurse. When I pushed back the heavy curtain, she looked up. "Oh, monsieur, you have seen madame?"

"Yes, Sister Hélène."

"She's much better today."

"I know, and I'm delighted."

"I am too, monsieur. Madame has already had one visitor today."

"I know. Dear Sister Hélène, would you be so good as to connect me with Dr. Delamare?"

"Is something wrong?"

"No, no. I only want to tell him something, confidentially."

"I see," said Sister Hélène. "Dr. Delamare has gone home. I'll give you his number. You can call from the phone booth at the end of the corridor."

I had thought it over for a long time, and had come to the conclusion that it was the right thing to do. I told Dr. Delamare nothing about Sylvia's tirade in Monte Carlo, nothing about my own worries. I said only that Babs was in the Hôpital Sainte-Bernadette with meningoencephalitis, and that Sylvia had found out about it from Babs's hysterical governess. "Of course Madame Moran got terribly upset," I said. "She wants to go to her daughter right away."

"But that's impossible!"

"I know. And I was able to calm her down. I'll look after Babs and keep Madame Moran informed daily."

"Very sensible decision, monsieur."

"I just wanted to ask you, doctor, to see to it that Madame Moran gets some special attention. She may be prone now to restlessness and great anxiety. I am sure you have medication for such cases, to calm the patient . . ."

"Yes, of course. A tranquilizer. As soon as you hang up, I shall call the hospital and give the station my orders."

"Thank you, Dr. Delamare."

"I'm terribly sorry for you. You've got a lot on your mind already, and now the child has to fall ill. I do feel for you, monsieur."

"Thank you, Dr. Delamare."

45

"Crazy!" said Suzy. "That's what you are—absolutely crazy!"

She was sitting on a shocking-green plastic beanbag chair in her crazy living room, and she had on a black transparent robe, nothing underneath it. She had received me half an hour ago, radiantly happy. Now she wasn't radiantly happy any more; she was upset. And she was smoking. It was close to midnight.

She had been smoking and drinking Calvados ever since I had arrived. I was sitting opposite her on a shocking-pink beanbag chair. Between us there was a bright-yellow plastic table, fat, round. It looked like an enormous Babybel cheese. As already mentioned, Suzy's decor was wacky. Even the rugs were made of a peculiar stiff plastic weave, and there was a complicated stereo system. The whole thing must have cost a small fortune.

Your honor, what else could I have done? Suzy as good as raped me on arrival, then she peppered me with questions: Why had I moved in on her? Who was after me? What had I done? And finally, in terror, "Did you shoot a flic?"

"It has nothing whatsoever to do with the police," I assured her, and she switched immediately from fear to enthusiasm. "Then everything's fine! Then I don't give a damn what's up! But if you'd done in a flic, then nobody could help you. But this way . . ."

"This way you can?"

"And how!" she said proudly. "You have no idea how many of them I know. Not the small fry but the big shots. I've done them so many favors, they'll do anything for me. If you want an apartment with a no-search guarantee, then take mine. If they're looking for a guy, they don't look here. Anyway, not right away. I'm last on their list. That's a promise. And that gives you all the time in the world to scram. I can get you forged papers too, a stolen car with the license changed . . ."

"Suzy! I *haven't* done anything!"

"The concierge gave me such a funny look when your stuff came, such elegant luggage! But he can kiss my ass!"

"Suzy!" Finally I yelled at her, and that shut her up. "Get us something to drink," I said. "You're going to need it. I'll tell you all about it."

So I told her everything, and when I was done, Suzy said, "Crazy! That's what you are. Absolutely crazy!"

"Why am I crazy?"

I couldn't think straight any more; perhaps Suzy could. She was a sensible woman, and she was experienced. So, let's listen to what she has to say, I thought. "Why am I crazy?" I poured myself another Calvados.

"Because you keep on playing their filthy game!" said Suzy.

"I've got to go on playing their filthy game."

"You don't have to," said Suzy, drawing her legs up. "Nobody has to!" She was drinking Calvados too. She leaned forward, her baby voice suddenly serious. "Okay, let's say the brat dies. But there's no guarantee that she will. And if they manage to pull her through?"

"Then everything's okay too," I said, and drank Calvados.

"Let me finish."

"Sorry, *mon petit chou.*"

"So . . . if they manage to pull her through but she's never right again—I mean, blind or mute or deaf, or she ends up like one of those moron kids—what does your future look like then? I love you, *mon petit chou.* You're the first man I've ever really loved. Don't laugh! *Please don't laugh!*"

"I'm not laughing."

She lit another cigarette. "And do you want to know why I love you, why you're *numero uno* in my life, and why I know I'll never love another man again?"

"Why?"

The robe fell open and off her shoulders. She sat in front of me, naked, between us the Babybel table. "You've told me everything, and that was wonderful of you. You trust me."

"Now don't start crying!"

"But I've got to! I can't help it! Give me your handkerchief."

I gave it to her. She blew her nose, then she wiped away her tears. "Thanks. And now I'll tell you why I love you so much, but you mustn't get mad. I'm so afraid you'll get mad."

"You needn't be afraid. You can say anything you like."

"That's the wonderful thing about both of us," she said. "We can tell each other anything, we can do anything we like with each other, and we know all about each other. That is to say—you don't know everything about me but I know all about you, my darling. I always shriek so that I won't hear it . . ."

"Hear what?"

"The awful things you say about yourself. But at the bottom of my heart I know, of course, that they're true."

"What do I say?"

"That you're a piece of shit," said Suzy. So I drank some more Calvados. "Now you're mad."

"Not at all, pet. You're absolutely right, so why should I be mad? Ridiculous!"

"Thank God. But I'm not finished yet, *mon petit chou*. The important thing is that I'm just as much a piece of shit as you are. That's why we understand each other so well. That's why you're the first man I've ever loved."

"Just a minute," I said. "Why are you just as much a piece of shit as I am? You work hard, you have a beauty salon on Avenue Charles Floquet, near the Eiffel Tower, swanky neighborhood; you have five attractive girls working for you, you've achieved something in life . . ."

She interrupted me. "Phil! Don't tell me you haven't noticed it! A man like you?"

"Noticed what?"

"My five attractive girls," she said.

"What about them?"

"They're five attractive prostitutes. No . . . I can't believe that you didn't realize it."

"Well, I didn't," I lied.

"My sweet *petit chou*. There isn't one of them who wouldn't take you on if you paid. Only none of them dares. Because they know you belong to me. If they knew you as I know you, *they'd* pay *you*! Until now business has been first-rate. The johns picked up the girls, they arranged to meet somewhere, they did their stuff, then they paid me. Not one of them has

153

ever cheated me. I'd lay my hands in the fire for every one of my girls."

"So if that's the way things are going, what's the trouble?"

"They can't keep going any more. It's got around what cute pussies they are, the johns come back, new ones turn up. We're earning ourselves silly, but one more month like the last one and I can close up shop. Then my five little pussies will collapse. Finis."

"So there you are," I said. "Everybody has his problems."

"I thought I'd work right along with them. I'm no better than they are. Everybody is equal before God, isn't that so, *mon petit chou?* But what good would it do if I let the johns screw me too? At last we have money to burn and have to throw in the towel."

"You're going to be a countess," I said. "Then you can forget all about it. Then you can sell the place."

"Let me tell you something—since I've known you I can't stand the little runt. I get the shakes when he touches me. The sight of him makes me want to throw up!"

"Come on!"

"It's the truth. Have you any idea how glad I am that he's in Acapulco? But he'll come back and you'll go away and I'll be a countess, and then what?"

I drank some more Calvados, and so did she.

"I talked to the girls the other day," she said. "Put my cards on the table. I have enough money to open another salon, and there are plenty of pretty girls running around Paris. I could get hold of some specialists . . . you know what I mean. And we'd be rich. Don't you think so?"

"I'm positive."

"But there's one problem."

"What?"

"I wouldn't be able to run both places. That would be too much for me—to keep track of the girls, the books, the johns. If I opened a second salon I'd need a man to help me. A man like you."

I was silent.

"I said a man like you," said Suzy.

"I heard you."

"So what do you think?"

"Well . . ."

"Look," she said eagerly, "it's all so simple. You walk out on the old bag. You walk out on Babs . . ."

154

"If only it were that simple."

"You have no idea how simple it is! Do you realize what my clients are like? No ordinary gents, I assure you. I told you—cream of the crop. I saw to that. Top-ranking guys in the police department. There'll be a scandal when you disappear, naturally, but finding you will be a different story. They'll never find you! You didn't give anybody this address, did you?"

"No."

"And when you called me from the hotel you didn't call me by name. I noticed that."

"I know I didn't. Somebody else was there."

"Voilà!"

"But what about the men who brought my luggage from the airport?"

"I fixed that," Suzy said triumphantly. "I didn't put in an appearance. I have a little apprentice, dumbest girl you can imagine. The men didn't exchange more than three words with her. When they start looking for you she'll say the luggage was picked up right afterward."

"By whom?"

"By somebody. The girl can't remember anything. And you? You get absolutely foolproof papers. You speak French like a Frenchman. We give you a different haircut, a mustache. In a few weeks it'll be forgotten. I'm rid of my count, you're rid of the old whore and the brat, not that I don't feel sorry for the kid, *mon petit chou*, but I have to think of us both, and one thing I can promise you: *I'll* never treat you like she did, the old bag who has to have her face lifted in her thirties! *You'll* wear the pants in my house. Things will be done *your* way! And then you won't be a gigolo any more. I'll be the best wife in the world to you . . . don't be afraid, you won't have to marry me, but I'll be the best wife in the world to you just the same. Only stay with me. Not a bad offer, is it?"

Well, your honor, by now you know a thing or two about me and you'll probably be able to come to your own conclusion as to what my reaction to her proposition was. Something I'd always wanted—suddenly to be somebody else. To be able to write finis to playboy Kaven.

"I asked you if you didn't think this was a good offer," said Suzy.

"It is a good offer," I said slowly. "Not bad. Not bad at all."

She jumped up and fell into my lap and threw her arms around me and kissed me wildly and grabbed me . . . I don't have to go into details, your honor.

"If Babs survives," I said, staring straight ahead, "and ends up mute or blind or an idiot, I can hang myself," whereupon Suzy became ecstatic.

"You see! You see! What did I tell you? Oh, *mon petit chou*, I'm so happy!"

She kissed me all over my face, and I said, "Ouch!" when she covered my bruises with her kisses, and that startled her, and she blew on them and kissed them gently. "And now we'll get drunk," she said, "and put on some music, and then we'll do it, all the sweet things . . ."

I said, "To get drunk isn't a bad idea."

She jumped to her feet and danced naked through the room, and then we drank and played records—Gershwin, Cole Porter, Glenn Miller—both of us loved the old melodies. And we chatted and fondled each other and procrastinated about going to bed because however much Suzy wanted it she liked to drag things out as long as possible and then it was always exceptionally exciting. Suzy made coffee so that we shouldn't be too drunk and then, around five in the morning, we went into the bedroom and Suzy undressed me. When I was naked, a new record dropped into place on the stereo and the next thing I heard was John William's voice, *"Ô Dieu, merci pour ce paradis qui s'ouvre aujourd'hui à l'un de tes fils . . .*

I sat down.

"What's the matter, darling?" Suzy sounded startled.

"Pour le plus petit, le plus pauvre fils . . . merci Dieu, merci pour . . ."

By that time I'd reached the record player. I lifted the needle off the record and almost ruined the player getting the record off the turntable. Suzy watched me, horrified. At last I had the record in my hands and smashed it on the hard back of a chair. It broke in half. I broke the halves in two and cut my right hand, which began to bleed, then I flung what was left of the record into a corner. And all the time Suzy watched me without saying a word, then she looked down at the floor. But now she didn't cry. She was much too sad to cry. She got up and fetched iodine and gauze and cleaned up my cut hand. Then she said, "Babs—yes?"

I nodded.

"You want to go to the hospital?"

I nodded.

Suzy, in the saddest voice I had ever heard: "I'll make some strong coffee for you. And you've got to eat something."

"I couldn't eat a thing."

"But you must. Get dressed. You'll find everything you need in the bathroom."

So I washed and got dressed and went into the kitchen, and Suzy breakfasted with me. She was still miserable, but every now and then she tried to smile at me and I tried to smile at her. The coffee was wonderful, hot and strong. "I do love you so much, *mon petit chou*," said Suzy.

"And I love you."

"And I meant what I said, about my plan."

"I did too."

"But now nothing will ever come of it."

I said nothing.

"You see?" said Suzy.

I said, "I'm sorry."

"Don't be sorry. You can stay here as long as you like, as long as you need me." She said, "me," not "my place." "And nobody will ever find out that you're here, I promise you—except for the people you have to tell."

"Thank you, Suzy."

"Shall I call a taxi?" she asked, and wiped the back of her hand across her lips.

"No," I said. "That's too dangerous. And it's still very early. I'll walk for a while. What's the time, anyway?"

"Almost seven. Put on your glasses."

I put on my dark glasses. We walked into the foyer, and Suzy helped me into my coat. And kissed me. "I'll put your things away in the meantime," she said. "I'll hang up Babs's things too or they'll get crushed. You have the keys?"

"Yes."

"So you can come and go as you like. I have to go to the salon soon. But come back as soon as you can. You need to sleep."

"Yes," I said. "Thanks."

"Don't thank me. I've got to talk to my friends at the police station too, so that they don't look for you here."

"You don't have to do that. Officially I moved out of the hotel yesterday, with Babs. We flew to Madrid. I thought I told you."

157

"That's nice," said Suzy, and turned her head away.

"Don't cry," I said. "Please, *mon petit chou,* don't cry."

"Who's crying?" said Suzy, looking at me and rubbing her eyes. She had lit a cigarette. "I got smoke in my eyes. It's all right now. I'm glad you're going to stay with me, for a while anyway. Maybe only for one more night. Who knows? It would have been nice, though, if we could have gone ahead with my plan. But I realize that's impossible now. Because you're never going to get out of the trap you're in."

"We'll see."

"No we won't," said Suzy. "If there was any chance of your getting out of it, would you be going to see the child now?"

It was 7:10 on November 26, 1971, a Friday.

46

Babs. The Word's Greatest Little Sunshine Girl. There she lay, sweating, blisters on her lips, red spots all over her body. She had pulled her nightgown up to her neck. Suddenly she let out a cry and stretched her arms and legs straight up into the air, stiffly, and her whole body began to shake jerkily, spasmodically. Her breathing rattled in her chest, she gasped, wheezed, couldn't seem to get enough air. She began to toss from side to side. The pupils of her eyes were rolled up, one eyelid sagged, the rims of her eyes were inflamed. I could see it all by the weak light of the lamp.

There was foam on her lips, although her teeth were clenched so firmly that she was grinding them. Two nurses, Dr. Sigrand and Dr. Reinhardt were working on her. I stood to one side. The three women had to hold the struggling child down so that Dr. Sigrand could give her an injection. It was 8:15 A.M. I had had to walk several kilometers before finding a taxi. I had arrived ten minutes before.

Dr. Sigrand was the first to turn around and notice me. His face was gray with exhaustion. I saw the disheveled cot on which I felt sure he had slept very little. His eyes were bloodshot, his face was unshaven. When he saw me he said simply, "You?"

"Yes. It's me."

"Why have you come?"

I didn't want to say why, but I did. "I was terribly worried about Babs."

"Why didn't you call?"

"That wouldn't have been the same. I wanted to see her."

This was the moment, although I only realized it later, when Dr. Sigrand lost his aversion to me. From then on he treated me like a decent human being. Ruth Reinhardt gave me a brief, serious glance, then turned her attention back to Babs. She looked like an old woman. She probably hadn't slept all night either.

"If only you had called earlier," said Dr. Sigrand.

"Why?"

"Because we'd have told you to come straight here. But you forgot to give us your telephone number yesterday, in all the excitement. We called Le Monde. Monsieur Bracken didn't know where you could be reached either." Babs screamed, and Dr. Sigrand turned quickly to attend to her. "He's looking for you too."

Dammit! I'd forgotten all about Bracken.

"That's why it's so strange that you came now of your own accord," said Ruth Reinhardt.

"Why strange?"

"Because we need you ..." She couldn't finish the sentence, because Babs began to scream again, her arms and legs shot up, and she seemed to be suffering from something that looked like an attack of epilepsy. I don't remember being so horrified in my entire life. I am not a very courageous man, your honor, but I think the bravest man would have been shaken if he had seen what was happening to Babs.

I felt nauseated and got out of the room fast, saw the door to a toilet, tore into it and vomited into the washbowl. As I was rinsing my mouth, I saw myself in the mirror. I looked ghastly. I stank of Calvados. Suddenly I felt weak at the knees and had to sit down. I must have sat there on the john for about fifteen minutes, staring at a poster that said, "Long Live de Gaulle!"

47

At last I felt strong enough to go back to Babs's room. Only two nurses were there. "Monsieur Norton . . ."

"How is she?"

"Not good, monsieur," said one of the nurses. "Dr. Reinhardt and Dr. Sigrand are looking for you everywhere. They have to talk to you."

"Talk to me?"

"Yes. It's urgent. I'll have them paged. Please wait in Dr. Reinhardt's office." They were very friendly. "Can you find it all right?"

I nodded, left the room, and walked quickly down the quiet passage to Ruth Reinhardt's office with its many primitive, colorful toys and with the little wheelchairs in the corner. And there was the little lamb on her desk, the frame with the Buddha verse. It was still dark outside, and the lights were on. I walked up to a filled bookcase: N. W. Faber, *The Retarded Child*. L. Charmichael, *Manual of Child Psychology*. Hundreds of books. German and English, a few in Russian among them, a row in French a little lower down. Then I was staring at one in particular; R. Reinhardt, *Clinical Treatment and Therapy for the Brain-Damaged Child*. So Ruth Reinhardt had written a book. I took it off the shelf. It had a dedication: "Dr. Bruno Bettelheim. My teacher. With admiration and respect. R.R."

I heard steps and put the book back quickly. The door opened. Ruth Reinhardt, Dr. Sigrand and a nurse walked in. The nurse carried a tray with a metal pot on it, three cups and a sugar bowl. She put the tray down and left us.

"There you are, thank God!" said Sigrand. He fell into a chair, groaned, stretched out his legs and rubbed his eyes. Ruth Reinhardt was looking at me. "Will you have some coffee?"

"I'll be glad to." She poured. "You've written a book, Dr. Reinhardt," I said.

"Yes, Monsieur Norton." For the first time she sounded shy. Then we were sitting around the desk, drinking coffee. I saw that Dr. Sigrand's hands were trembling. He looked close to collapse. Without looking at me he said, "I apologize for the way I behaved to you, Monsieur Norton. But I think you should know . . ."

"He knows," said Ruth Reinhardt.

"Well then . . . You came here of your own accord, because you were so worried about Babs. That's a quite different story. Now . . ."

"Don't continue, Herr Doktor!"

He nodded and we drank our hot coffee, in silence for a moment. Then Ruth Reinhardt spoke. "I'm afraid we have some hard things to tell you, Monsieur Norton." I could only nod. "We have tried penicillin, various antibiotics, immune globulin, cortisone derivatives, and so on, but nothing has worked for us."

"And now we are faced with increasing tetanic spasms."

"With *what?*" It was a day that didn't seem to want to grow light.

"What you just witnessed."

"It looked like an epileptic fit."

"But it isn't epilepsy, Monsieur Norton," said Dr. Sigrand, whose attitude toward me had changed so much. Now he spoke to me as if to a friend. "It is all connected with the inflammation of the brain membranes and the brain."

"The grinding of the teeth," said Ruth Reinhardt. "The positive signs in the pyramidal tract . . ."

"All much too complicated for the layman," Dr. Sigrand interrupted her. "The only thing we can say is that with all our expertise, we have come to the end of our resources. Three hours ago the lab gave us bad news. We had been expecting it. Babs does not have a clear-cut case of meningoencephalitis. There are complications."

"What complications?"

"The presence of a virus, as well as the usual bacteria. That's why none of the medication works."

"What happens next?" I asked. "Nothing?"

"There is something," said Ruth Reinhardt, staring at the little lamb. Then she looked helplessly at Dr. Sigrand.

"Something that very probably could keep Babs alive," said the doctor.

"But you're not a hundred percent sure?"

"No. I'm not a hundred percent sure."

"So what am I supposed to say?" I asked.

Ruth Reinhardt said, "I'm afraid you're going to have to say something, Monsieur Norton. And unfortunately you're going to have to say it right now. You see . . ."

"You see," said Dr. Sigrand, "we can control the bacteria, but that doesn't get us anywhere if we can't contain the virus. That's the most important and urgent thing we have to contend with now, to stop the devastation caused by the virus."

"And you've got something that can do it?"

"We have a drug that can do it," said Ruth Reinhardt.

"So what is the problem?"

"The drug is still being tested," said Ruth Reinhardt.

"Oh, I see."

"I don't think you do, entirely. Drugs like this often have to go through years of clinical research. We've used it a few times, and nearly always with good results."

"Nearly always?"

"Yes, Monsieur Norton. In most cases the drug works miraculously. But not always. In a few cases . . ."

"I understand."

"It's the only drug that can possibly keep Babs alive," said Dr. Sigrand. "But we need your written permission. You have to give your consent or we can't go ahead."

"And if I give my consent, and things go wrong?"

No reply. I looked at Ruth Reinhardt; she looked at me and said nothing. I looked at Dr. Sigrand; he looked at me and said nothing. Then he shrugged and said, "If we *don't* use the drug, I can guarantee that Babs won't live through the day."

When you hear somebody say something like that, your honor, all sorts of thoughts flash through your mind. My first thought was: If Babs doesn't survive the day, wouldn't that be the solution? But then, your honor, something happened that I don't understand yet, something absolutely baffling, considering the man I was at the time. I think there is only one explanation for it: Since I had met this woman, Dr. Ruth Reinhardt, something seemed to be wrong with me. That has to be the explanation for everything I did from then on, including the next thought that came to me; my second thought was: Who am I to condemn this child to death? Or any other child? Or any living creature on this earth?

With a voice that didn't sound like my own, I said, "I give my consent. Do whatever you see fit. Use the new drug."

Ruth Reinhardt placed a form in front of me. I could see that everything relevant had already been filled in, and I signed. And with this signature I determined everything that was still to happen, and what led in the end to Romero Rettland lying dead on the filthy floor of the foulest hot-sheet hotel in Nürnberg with a bullet in his heart.

PART TWO

Diagnosis

FORTUNE TELLER: You know as well as I what's coming. Rain. Rain. Rain in floods. The deluge. But first you'll see shameful things— shameful things. Some of you will be saying: "Let him drown. He's not worth saving. Give the whole thing up." I can see it in your faces. But you're wrong.

—Thornton Wilder, *The Skin of Our Teeth*

1

The old man lifted the dead child. Tears were pouring down his cheeks. Then he walked away on the dusty road that ran between fields, walked on and on, the dead child in his arms. The old man was wearing a crumpled hat, his shoes were worn crooked, his pants and loose-fitting shirt were tattered. He walked waveringly, uncertain and unsure, but he went on and on toward the blue mountains that rose up in the distance out of fog, into the glare of the sun. It was hot, the ground was parched, but the old man walked on, the child in his arms. Now he was quite small. The picture darkened, and out of the darkness came the words: *The End*. They moved forward slowly, growing in size, until they finally came to a standstill on the screen; then the screen darkened too.

The picture ended soundlessly, even the music had stopped, and the vast auditorium of the Teatro Sistina on the Via Sistina, near the Piazza Barberini, remained dark. It was May 18, 1972, a Thursday, in the heart of the Eternal City. The time, according to the luminous dial on my wristwatch: 10:45 P.M. It was infernally hot in the huge Teatro Sistina. A heat wave, the like of which hadn't been experienced in this century, was plaguing Rome. I was sitting with Rod Bracken beside Joe Gintzburger, in a box. Bracken had said once that Joe had the voice of a Bible salesman, and I had to think of that as the president of Seven Stars whispered to me, "Marvelous! Simply marvelous! And the fact that Alfredo departed this life three weeks ago is nothing short of a miracle. D'you hear, Phil? A miracle!"

"Yes, Joe."

Joe Gintzburger was wearing a tux. He was a little man, rosy-cheeked and slight, a man with the kindest face in the world. Only his mouth was too small. It looked like a hole in his face. "That Alfredo kicked the bucket just before the premiere guarantees us another half million dollars in Italy alone! Dear Lord, I thank you!"

"Amen," said Bracken.

Slowly the lights went on until the whole house was again

164

brightly lit. Flowers all along the bottom of the screen, a fantastic display. It remained totally silent in the big auditorium. And then Sylvia came onstage from the wings. A spotlight picked her up and stayed with her. There she stood, in an evening dress, silk, a muted beige, high-necked at the front, the back bare to the waist, her satin shoes dyed to match the dress. Diamond earrings, necklace, a solitaire ring, the largest one she owned—that was all. Simple elegance. After all, it was a serious event that had brought us here.

Everybody who could rank as "society" in Rome was assembled, not the sleazy Via Veneto–Dolce Vita gang, but those who were rarely seen in public, representatives of century-old aristocratic houses, bank presidents, industrial millionaires from the north, at least two dozen statesmen of various governments. Also present were newspaper publishers, famous actors and actresses, directors and authors, singers, painters, —all of them world-famous.

Oh, I almost forgot the Church! Representatives from the Vatican, substitutes for God's substitute on earth, were also present. The film that had just ended had a lofty theme. The story was by a well-known Italian author who had one great thing going for him: He had been dead more than seventy years, so no rights had had to be paid. He had started out as an anarchist and in due course switched allegiance and become a merciless fighter for the Catholic Church. That was why so many clerics were present. In all fairness, Carlo Marone had seen his chance and grabbed it. Soon I will tell you about Carlo Marone. He was in sole charge of everything. For days he had kept the most prestigious motion picture and television people, the press, even the publisher Olivieri on tenterhooks whether tickets would be available for them for the premiere. And then of course the critics. Only the top-ranking ones, naturally. Flown in from the four corners of the earth. And finally, scattered through the hall, twenty beautifully groomed men and women whom nobody seemed to know.

The moment Sylvia emerged from the wings, there was applause. Applause may not be the right word in this case, but I can't find the right word for what burst out in the Teatro Sistina when Sylvia walked on stage. The Italians are film freaks, and Sylvia is the greatest motion picture actress of our time; the film we'd just shown—*So Little Time*—was magnificent (the last one Sylvia made before the face lift).

The walls of the Teatro Sistina trembled, the floor of the box we were sitting in shook under our feet. It was frightening. They were not only applauding, all these beautiful and mighty people, they were stomping their feet and bellowing Sylvia's name. It sounded like a madhouse. Yes, Marone was quite a guy!

Joe Gintzburger, Bracken and I were of course clapping too. Bracken grinned at me and Joe. Joe yelled over the tumult, "That one in the front, the one in purple—is he one of the Pope's guys?"

"Yeah!" Bracken yelled back. "That's him."

"He's blubbering," said Joe, which was saying too much, but the holy man was wiping his eyes with a handkerchief. "One more million in Italy!" cried Joe, and he wept too.

Sylvia was standing in the spotlight, more beautiful than ever. Dr. Delamare is a master. He earned every bit of the astronomical bill with which he presented us. He worked miracles on a miracle. Sylvia looked divine.

Now Carlo Marone came onstage from the opposite side. I'm going to have a lot to tell you about this man, your honor. At age forty-seven he was the most elegant gentleman in Rome and the idol of every woman in that city. He looked absolutely marvelous, which had been a great asset to him when he had been a pimp. And Carlo Marone wasn't a pimp any more. For years now he had been the foremost distributor of films in Italy, and every film Seven Stars had produced was on his roster. That alone made him a millionaire, in dollars. His castle on the jet-set hill, Pincio, was a museum that was guarded day and night by private police because of its priceless treasures. As I watched him walk up to Sylvia, I recalled the night I had spoken to him in his castle. How time did fly! That had been half a year ago.

Carlo Marone was wearing a bright-red tuxedo and was carrying a bouquet of Baccara roses. First he bowed low before Sylvia, then he kissed her hand. Then she kissed him on both cheeks and on the mouth. He handed her the roses, and Sylvia was moved to tears. She can cry in front of the camera whenever she has to, your honor. There she stood, weeping, and her left eyelid was absolutely level with her right one again. Professor Delamare had attended to that. And her makeup didn't run. Katie and Joe Patterson had seen to that.

The girls now came out of the wings, six pretty starlets, dressed discreetly. They brought more flowers, even orchids.

Suddenly Sylvia was standing in a sea of flowers. The audience was still applauding.

Carlo Marone kissed Sylvia again, they embraced again, then Marone walked off the stage. The girls had withdrawn too. Sylvia lifted one arm. A man in a tux brought a microphone on stage and adjusted it in front of her. Slowly, very slowly, the applause died down.

Sylvia, holding the roses, took a half step forward, to the microphone. She passed a hand across her wet eyes . . . and spoke in perfect, fluent Italian, but hesitantly and stammering a little, as if she was finding her words with difficulty and hadn't learned them by heart on the plane that had brought us here from Paris, as if Bracken had never given her the text he had composed. "Ladies and gentlemen." And now there were flashes throughout the hall, a veritable display of fireworks. "I thank you. I thank you with all my heart. I am proud to be able to stand before you . . . in this wonderful city . . . and to witness your approval of what so many people have created . . . I am only one of them . . ." She couldn't go on because the applause started all over, and again lasted a long time. Joe looked at his watch. Sylvia raised a hand. Finally there was silence.

"Heavenly Father!" said Joe, and his voice trembled. By God, he was crying again. "Two minutes and forty-seven seconds!"

"Meanwhile," said Sylvia, and her voice grew gentler, more hesitant, "ladies and gentlemen, however proud I may be, I am just as deeply sorrowful at this moment, because my partner in this picture can't stand before you with me. He was the genius of the Italian motion picture industry. You know that as well as I do. He gave us one masterpiece after another, this great man, this great actor, my confidant and good friend, whom I shall never forget—Alfredo Bianchi." Pause. Tears from Sylvia's beautiful eyes, a few sobs in the audience. These came from the twenty elegant ladies and gentlemen whom nobody knew. I mentioned them a while ago. Hired by Marone and scattered through the auditorium. Salary for the evening: fifty thousand lire, and worth every bit of it.

"Alfredo Bianchi loved this picture," said Sylvia. "He told me himself that he hadn't had a wonderful part like this in his entire life. And how he worked at it! How many nights he and I discussed everything with the director and script writers down to the minutest detail before we even started with the production. The changes Alfredo demanded, every one of them so right. He said . . ." Sylvia couldn't go on. She swallowed.

"How old was Bianchi?" Bracken asked softly.

"Sixty-eight."

"He said . . ." Sylvia was in control again, but still obviously fighting back tears. "He said to me, 'Sylvia, my girl, this is the film I always dreamed of. I don't think I'll make another.' "

"A miracle that he ever got through it," whispered Bracken. "The old junkie! How many times did he take the cure?"

"Five."

"Hats off to him!" said Bracken.

"He only managed to drag himself through the picture on around-the-clock needles."

"Don't I know it!" said Bracken. "And who saw to it that he never ran out of the stuff? I have to do everything."

". . . and, ladies and gentlemen, what Alfredo said to me has come true, but not the way he meant it, has come true in a dreadful and tragic way, a way that could make one rail against God, even though we know that His decisions are unfathomable and merciful. No, Alfredo, our beloved Alfredo Bianchi, won't make another picture. But he is still with us. He couldn't see this picture tonight, a picture that he—yes, *he*—made so marvelous. He overtaxed his heart in this picture, a heart that beat only for others. He felt it coming but he didn't seem to care. He wanted . . . he *had* to make *So Little Time,* and we who loved him see this film as his last will and testament."

"Wrote every word of it," Bracken whispered to Joe, who was blowing his nose. Joe nodded.

"Six months after we had finished filming, the heart of this great man stopped beating. He has gone to his final rest on Roman soil, at the Campo Verano cemetery, not far from the Basilica San Lorenzo, the cemetery he loved because his father and mother are buried there."

Bianchi, a perennial bachelor, had never married and had no heirs. His entire fortune would go to the Church. Alfredo had suffered because of his addiction. Whenever he had hit rock bottom, he had run to the Church and confessed and done penance. But who knew any of this except us few insiders? And the Church would recommend *So Little Time* worldwide. You've got to be lucky!

"I . . ." Sylvia's voice was unsteady. "I . . . please excuse me, ladies and gentlemen . . ." She paused and regained her composure. "Let us observe a minute of silence in memory of this great man, Alfredo Bianchi."

She lowered her head, the roses pressed against her bosom. Cameras whirred. Slowly, the audience rose to its feet and stood silently; Joe, Bracken and I did too. And I saw Sylvia out there on the stage, and had to think suddenly of all that had happened during the last six months. Yes, your honor, one can remember a great deal in a few moments. . . .

2

The door flew open. A dumpy little woman in a shabby coat burst into Ruth Reinhardt's office. Her hair straggled out from under the hat on her head. It was 8:00 A.M., November 27, 1971, still almost dark, and it was raining. I was sitting at Ruth Reinhardt's desk.

The little woman was out of breath; water dripped from her umbrella. She was terribly excited. "Frau Doktor! How could it have happened? Why didn't you stop it? I begged you to watch her and now Vivian is dead, dead, dead!" The room was so dark, even I found it difficult to see anything clearly. The poor soul stumbled as she ran up to me crying, "Dead! You gave her the new medicine, and that's what killed my little Vivian, and . . ." Then she saw me. "Oh . . . excuse me, please. But this is Dr. Reinhardt's office, isn't it?"

I said, "I'm waiting for Dr. Reinhardt. She's with a sick child. She'll be here soon."

The woman pressed a hand to her mouth and stared at me, then she ran out. And I sat there and was suddenly terribly afraid.

This happened, your honor, as just explained, on the morning of November 27, a Saturday. The day before I had given my permission for Babs to be treated with the new drug that hadn't been thoroughly tested yet. Dr. Sigrand and Ruth Reinhardt had gone to bed. They were sleeping in the clinic. They handed Babs over to a colleague with strict instructions to call them if there was any change. I went "home" to Suzy. She wasn't there. I had just enough strength to call Bracken at Le Monde. I gave him Suzy's number *and* her address, because with the telephone number he could get her address anyway, but also to keep everything on as friendly a basis as possible. It had been Bracken's brainstorm, when Sylvia had begun raving that she had to see Babs, to tell her that I had moved into a friend's studio—you recall it, surely, your honor. In order to avoid any confusion, Bracken said on the phone that we should decide where this studio was. How about the seventh arrondissement, in the Avenue de Saxe, where, if Sylvia wanted to know how she could reach me, there was, alas, no phone? I told Bracken what terrible shape Babs was in and the risk I'd taken, and Bracken was sobered. "You couldn't have done anything else, Phil," he said finally. "All we can do now is hope. And oh yes, there's something else."

"What?"

"The night clerk, Lucien Bayard, says you have a date with him to discuss something important. He doesn't know what to do until he talks to you."

The races next Sunday in Auteuil! Lucien was going to place my bets as he always did. "What did you tell him?"

"That you're away but that I can reach you by phone."

"Okay. Then tell him to go ahead. Whatever he decides to do is all right by me."

"Yes, Phil."

"And don't call me at my friend's place from the hotel. Never call from the hotel anytime, not even when you call the clinic. I'll go see Babs every day, and then in the evening, I'll go see Sylvia."

"What are you going to tell her?"

"That Babs is getting better every day."

"But if . . ."

"Shut up!" I said, and hung up. And that's the last thing I can remember. I must have fallen asleep at once. When I woke up it was 6:00 P.M. and dark. I left Suzy a note on the kitchen table, that I'd be late, she wasn't to worry, and if anyone called up whose voice she didn't recognize, she should play dumb. This time I took a bus and the Métro to the Hôpital Sainte-Bernadette.

Babs was asleep, and she was talking in her sleep. About Beverly Hills, Tokyo, *Winnie the Pooh*. Ruth Reinhardt, Dr. Sigrand and I stood by her bed for a long time. Dr. Sigrand was completely changed; he treated me like a friend.

"And the new medication?"

"We only began giving it to her this morning, Monsieur Norton. We've got to wait."

"Her condition is unchanged?"

"Her condition is worse," said Ruth Reinhardt.

The two doctors had had a chance to get some sleep and seemed stronger. "I've got to go and see Miss Moran." Both doctors were silent. "What shall I tell her?"

"Tell her that, taking all things into consideration, Babs is better," said Dr. Sigrand, and that's what I said when I got to Dr. Delamare's clinic in the Rue Cavé.

"Are you telling me the truth, Pepito?" Sylvia was still wearing a bandage, but her eyes were uncovered, and they wouldn't let me go. I thought how much easier it would have been if her eyes had been kept bandaged.

"The whole truth—honestly!"

"You swear it?"

"Yes."

"Oh, Pepito, if I didn't have you now, I'd kill myself. You're doing everything, looking after everything, just as if Babs were your child."

"Well, in a way she is," I said heroically.

And she said, with a bitterness I didn't notice at the time but that now, when it's all over and too late, burns in my consciousness, "I wish Babs was your child."

"Everything's going to be all right," I said. "They expect miracles from this new drug." If I was going to lie, then I'd do a good job of it. "You'll see—a few more days and Babs will be out of the woods."

"Yes ... everything's going to be all right," she murmured, and fell asleep.

When I got home I told Suzy what had happened. When I finished bringing Bracken up to date on the phone, I found Suzy standing in front of a small table with a lighted candle in a saucer on it. Her lips were moving and she spoke in a whisper. "The poor child. Only God can help her."

"You believe in God, Suzy?"

"Of course."

I said nothing. Suddenly she grabbed me and pressed herself hard against me, sobbing, "I know. I should be saying: What concern is it of mine? Why should I give a damn for Sylvia? Both of them make it impossible for us to be happy together ... even if Babs dies! But I don't want to be happy with you just because Babs has died. She's got to live."

"And be a retarded child?"

"Don't say that!"

"You said the same thing yesterday."

"Oh, that was ... I ... I ... don't you understand, you idiot? I love you!"

"Of course I understand, *mon petit chou.*"

Two minutes later we were in bed and it was absolutely wild, as usual, perhaps more so that night. Finally I fell asleep. Suzy woke me at 6:00.

"What is it?"

"I can't sleep, *mon petit chou.*"

"Well, then at least let me sleep."

"No. You've got to get up."

"Get up?"

"Yes. And go to the hospital. You've got to be there when they make their morning rounds, and they do that at eight. We've got to know how Babs did in the night." She said "we."

So I got up, we had breakfast, and I took a workman-filled bus and then the workman-filled Métro to the hospital.

At the hospital I hurried to Ruth Reinhardt's office and found her as she was leaving. "How is—"

"I don't know. I'm on my way to her. Dr. Sigrand and two other doctors are waiting for me. Please wait in my office, Herr Norton. I'll come as soon as I can."

So I went to her office and sat down at her desk in the dark, and watched the rain streak across the panes. And that was when the stocky little woman burst into the room, breathless, soaking wet, and stammering with excitement. "Frau Doktor! How could it have happened? ..."

3

A few minutes later Ruth Reinhardt came in, and, as usual, she was controlled, her face serious. She touched my shoulder lightly as I jumped up. "How is Babs?"

She looked at me silently.

"Please, Frau Doktor."

She said, and as she always did when we were alone, she spoke German, "It would be very wrong of me, Herr Norton, to arouse any false hopes. That's why I was silent. But for the first time since we started her on this new drug, her condition seems slightly improved."

"But that's wonderful!" I cried, and had the feeling that another man and another voice were speaking.

"I should have said, *perhaps* is slightly improved. The temperature has gone down a little, the stiffness in the neck is less pronounced, the dreadful positions seem to have eased, things like that. But she is still very, very ill. All we can do now is be patient and wait. Will you be patient? Will you wait? Will you . . ." A pause. "Will you stay the way you are if the news is bad, very bad?"

"I don't know."

"You are a different person, Herr Norton, from the one you were when I first met you. I talked to Dr. Sigrand about it. He agreed with me. It is astonishing."

"But I don't want to be a different person."

"That's not up to you, Herr Norton. Things like that simply happen. But let's not talk about it. You were here when Madame Ralouche came in?"

"You mean the woman whose daughter died last night?"

"Yes. She's still terribly upset. Wants to sue me, see me in jail. Then she collapses and cries and begs me to forgive her, and declares that Vivian's death was the most fortunate thing that could have happened to the girl, after which she starts all over again from the beginning. Her husband's on his way here. He wasn't there when Vivian died. He'll be here soon. He knows how to handle his wife."

"Handle her?"

"Dear Herr Norton," said Ruth Reinhardt, "did you think for a moment that Madame Ralouche's feelings were sincere?"

"So what are they if not sincere?"

"Vivian was nineteen," Ruth Reinhardt said. "She was here for thirteen years, sometimes ambulatory, sometimes bedridden. And Madame Ralouche's feelings are the typically ambivalent ones we see so often when a retarded child dies. No child is ever loved as much by its mother as the brain-damaged child, and no mother wishes as strongly—consciously or unconsciously—that her abnormal child should die."

4

Babs lay hunched up in bed. The blue lamp was lit; otherwise it was dark in the room. Her breathing was dreadful—sometimes deep, then for long stretches, she didn't breathe at all. Ruth Reinhardt had told me this was typical. She called it biotic breathing.

We had come here because Ruth Reinhardt wanted to observe Babs for at least an hour after having given her another dose of the new drug. We had moved two chairs to the bedside. While we were talking she continued to examine Babs, took her pulse, listened to her lungs with the stethoscope, noted how she ground her teeth, watched her every movement.

"Babs is sleeping on the borderline of consciousness," she said. "We don't have to whisper. She can't hear us." So we talked, your honor.

I have experienced things with this woman that I shall never forget, certainly not the conversation that took place at Babs's bedside. It began with my asking Ruth Reinhardt why she had dedicated her book to Bruno Bettelheim.

"Because I have him to thank for everything I know about the treatment of sick children, the problems they pose and how ruthlessly they are abused in all societies—capitalist, socialist, by those on the right and those on the left, communists and reactionaries the world over."

"Abused?"

"Yes, abused. There is nothing on this earth that man will not abuse in order to gain power over his fellow men."

"But brain-damaged children?"

"They are victimized too . . . I have learned so much from Dr. Bettelheim."

"And who is he?"

"Dr. Bruno Bettelheim is an Austrian." She was taking Babs's pulse, gently, oh so gently, her eyes on her wristwatch. After a while she went on. "He was born in Vienna in 1903. He studied psychology there, psychoanalysis actually . . ."

"What is her pulse?"

174

"A hundred and twenty."

"Not good?"

"No. Not good. But it should improve. Soon, I hope." She took the little lamb out of the pocket of her coat. "The Nazis forced Dr. Bettelheim to ... shall we say, interrupt his work? He was sent to a concentration camp—Dachau. Later Buchenwald. He was extraordinarily lucky because in the end they let him go, and he moved to the United States, where he became director of the clinic for retarded children at the University of Chicago. The Orthogenic School. I worked there with him for two years, with autistic children. They are the ones who live outside our world, who can't grasp it. They are the ones most seriously damaged." She began toying with the little lamb. "In that area, everything is still obscure, but we are making progress. Does any of this really interest you?"

"Certainly," I said, "considering . . ." And I looked at Babs.

"Babs is going to get well," she said, "I hope. At any rate, I consider it very likely. But so many children never recover, or it takes years for even a partial recovery, and it's a subject nobody wants to talk about unless he wants to use the topic to further some miserable personal goal."

I said, "I have no personal goal."

She looked at me silently.

"You're going to be hurt."

"Please tell me what you're thinking."

"Very well," said Ruth Reinhardt. "The average person tends to face the problem of the brain-damaged child with the attitude: I have my own problems. They know it exists and they think it's very sad, but they don't want anything to do with it. Because they can't grasp what's wrong. And they don't know how to behave with children like that. They feel the government should build homes for these unfortunates and look after them. That's what they're paying taxes for. They know any mother can give birth to a brain-damaged child, or a child can develop an illness that damages the brain, but they don't have any children, or their children are healthy, and they don't want to realize that one day this might change. The average person, Herr Norton, pays no attention to the problem, and when he gets it thrust at him, out of whatever motive, he is irritated. Even well-meaning people feel more often than not that one shouldn't bother with these children, that they should be eliminated."

"I know what's going on in the States," I said, "and in other

175

countries. I've heard about the pro-euthanasia groups. But in Germany I've been told they're quiet about it because they remember the euthanasia crimes of the Nazis."

"I'm sorry, Herr Norton, but you're wrong about that. They just took an opinion poll in Germany. Sixty percent were against prolonging the lives of those unfortunate creatures, and thirty-eight percent—think of it!—thirty-eight percent were for their extinction. The poll purposely mentioned the Nazis' treatment of retarded children, yet scarcely thirty years after Hitler, thirty-eight percent are for their elimination!"

5

Ruth Reinhardt examined Babs with her stethoscope, listened to her heart beat, her ear pressed against the child's back, tapped her chest, took her temperature. It was 105.4. Still, Ruth Reinhardt decided that Babs was a little better. She sat back and went on speaking.

"You may want to know why we make so little progress with our work. As I said before, it is because both the right and the left pick up our cause with great fanfare. They use this dreadful problem to further their own personal and above all political ends. Our world is becoming increasingly divided into two camps, however many shades of political orientation there may be—into the right and the left."

"Those on the right don't put it bluntly and say: We have formed a society that is capable of protecting itself from most normal catastrophes and is also able to create considerable material luxuries, and in this society there is no room for the nonachiever. No. They choose to refer the whole thing to the people, who are always uneasy when confronted with a serious problem, and in the end infuriated. And what do people say? The people say: Why spend money on these brain damaged children? There's nothing in it for us, and we, the people, are against all the fuss made over these halfwits." She was stroking the toy lamb. "And the right does not disagree. The right gives no support to the humane progress

176

of the human race but instead draws attention to," and now her voice was bitter, "a healthy folk sensibility, the same folk sensibility that made Hitler so successful. But it is the duty of every modern nation to do everything possible for these unfortunate children. It should be a matter of course. But it isn't. And why? Because it doesn't make for good propaganda. Help Ethiopia! That makes headlines. So does an earthquake in India. And that's where the right stands. And it's only half the problem.

"On the left," she went on, never taking her eyes off Babs, "we find a lot of people who are ashamed of their proletarian origin. They have never been able to integrate with the middle class, a class they wish they belonged to. Some have even higher ambitions. What a strange weakness! These people really have no reason to feel inferior—they're clever, they're talented, and they have power. In many cases they govern. We have an internationally famous professor here in the hospital; his father was a streetcar conductor. There is no place for social inferiority complexes in our twentieth century."

"Bad," said Babs.

"What did she say?"

"She said, 'Bad.' "

Ruth Reinhardt stroked Babs's shoulder gently as she went on. "So because the people on the left feel inferior, they support the protection of the weak as a reproach to the middle class they despise and envy. They say: I mustn't talk about myself, but I can talk about handicapped people—for instance, brain-damaged children. Thus the whole problem again becomes a political issue. You see?"

I nodded.

"I feel sick," said Babs, surprisingly clearly. "Herr Doktor . . ."

"Yes?" Ruth Reinhardt leaned forward.

"Wouldn't feel so bad if I was the doctor," said Babs. Then she was grinding her teeth again.

"So that's the way it is." Ruth Reinhardt leaned back. "Right and left—all of them are opportunists. And the poor sick children are the ones that lose out. Neither group *really* wants to help them. It is the bitter truth: Retarded children can be cared for, educated and get medical treatment only with money from private sources. They are dependent on the initiative and charity of wealthy donors, on people like Princess Grace, who has done so much good in her tiny country.

You saw that for yourself. And you can find such private initiatives under every regime, right or left. But it isn't enough, it isn't nearly enough. And the greatest tragedy of all is that the victims are those who can't defend themselves and never will be able to defend themselves—the poor and the infirm."

"But isn't there a third aspect to the whole problem, Frau Doktor? I mean, the doctors."

"We doctors are supposed to follow the commandment: Thou shalt not kill. Whatever regime they are working under, doctors have the same lofty responsibility, because in the last analysis, the doctor can't be controlled. He is responsible to the individual alone, that is, the individual is at his mercy and always will be. Under these circumstances we have to demand the highest ethical standards from a doctor. A doctor can do many things that can never be proved against him."

"Yes," I said, watching Babs and her dreadfully labored breathing.

"So a doctor must carry his obligation to his patients within himself, which doesn't mean that every doctor is capable of doing just that." Ruth Reinhardt sighed and went on. "I know of some dreadful cases where doctors, respected doctors, told the parents of such a child about foreign drugs that cost a small fortune but were certain to help, even in absolutely hopeless cases, and these doctors knew it wasn't true. They deceived the desperate parents; they lied to them about possible recoveries and made fortunes that way. I know bad and mediocre doctors, even doctors who were finished, yet who managed to stage spectacular comebacks that way. Now they are worshiped like gods."

"But doctors are only human too."

"But a doctor has a special position in society. It is his duty to preserve and prolong human life and to fight suffering. The more he is exposed to political influences or forces, as was the case, for instance, under the Nazis, the greater is his obligation to his Hippocratic oath, *which is his law.*" Now she was looking at me as she said loud and clear, "A doctor therefore may never kill. The Hippocratic oath—and if you like, the Biblical commandments—obligate a doctor never to participate in killing, even if the patient is mongoloid or spastic. His life must be preserved." Now she spoke with vehemence. "According to all religious and philosophic principles, nobody on earth may agree to the killing of any other human being."

The fact that we sat in the dark as I listened to Dr. Ruth Reinhardt, that serene, wise helper of those who live in the dark, is no invented effect, your honor. Like everything else in this book—*it is the truth*.

"The only permissible euthanasia," said Ruth Reinhardt, "is a mercy killing when the doctor knows his patient is fatally ill and in agonizing pain and frees this patient from his suffering, even if his tortured life is shortened by it. About such cases there is an unspoken agreement between most doctors and theoreticians, philosophers, even priests, that then, and only then is euthanasia permissible. And this because the lessening of suffering also falls under the heading of a doctor's duty. But who among us is the superman, the godlike creature who may decide where the borderline between healing and killing lies?" Ruth Reinhardt drew a deep breath. "When a nation legalizes murder, Herr Norton, where will it end?"

For quite a while there was silence, then she went on. "The problem becomes more difficult when it is a case of keeping someone alive with elaborate technical methods—I am thinking now of some hopeless cases involving children, for instance when a brain-damaged child's breathing is so disturbed that its life depends on a breathing mechanism, and we know that the brain died long ago. Normal life is therefore no longer possible and never will be. Then the apparatus may be turned off, especially if it is needed by someone else who still stands a chance. To that I can agree. But that is passive euthanasia. Those are individual cases that can be clearly and responsibly resolved. Active killing, though, even if the parents want it, is something to which no doctor can agree." Now she was speaking fast, as if a dam had given way, and I found it difficult to follow her. "It would be hubris," she said, "for any human being to say this or that life makes no sense. Who would dare to pass such judgment, Herr Norton?" She didn't seem to expect an answer but went right on. "It is a moot question whether Einstein, with his theory of relativity that in the end led to the atom bomb, really did the world so much good, whether his theory really spelled progress. Isn't it quite possible that a brain-damaged child who may arouse sincere humane feelings in at least a few human beings, that such a poor creature, by its very existence, has done more good than a great inventor? What do you think, Herr Norton? How do we arrive at our science of the measure of things, a measure of their value? And how correct is it?"

"You're right, Frau Doktor."

"I don't know whether I'm right or not," she said, "but I know one thing: It is insupportable—I would go so far as to say it is criminal arrogance when someone says of another person's life that it is meaningful or senseless. Confused and helpless creatures like us can never decide that. And we will never know what importance a human life can have, what extraordinary meaning, just in its utter misery."

6

That evening I took the Métro and the bus to Dr. Delamare's clinic and visited Sylvia. She had been given tranquilizers; Dr. Delamare had seen to that. She spoke slowly, and her speech was slurred, and of course she wanted to know at once how Babs was. And of course I said that Babs was much better. The new drug had already had a good effect on her. "Really and truly, my Silky, you must stop worrying."

"I may?"

"I swear you may, by my love for you, by my life!" Then she told me how happy she was, how much she loved me, that she couldn't imagine life without me, that she would kill me if I ever so much as looked at another woman, etc. We were back to normal. Well, not quite. Bracken and I had told her that I was staying in the seventh arrondissement, in the Avenue de Saxe, at the studio of a friend who was away. But there was no telephone. Unfortunately. Which started her off. "What friend?" "Jack Ronston." "Where has he gone?" "To India." How did she happen not to know this Jack Ronston? She didn't believe a word I said! I was living with a whore, having a ball while she lay there in the clinic and Babs, poor child, was terribly ill in a hospital. So all declarations of love were followed by hysterics.

I let her rave, and went on swearing by everything that occurred to me that I would never deceive her or could even dream of deceiving her. I swore by everything except Babs's life. And the whole thing didn't really upset me. Hadn't I given her a false address? Hadn't I said there was no phone in the studio? That's what Bracken and I had agreed on over the phone; as a matter of fact it had been his idea.

"If you don't believe me, ask Rod!"

"You and Rod are working together!"

Then I looked at her with melting eyes and was sad and said I hadn't deserved such treatment, that she should doubt my love and think I was capable of such a heinous thing as sleeping with another woman, with Babs so ill and . . .

That worked. She was ashamed and kissed my hands and begged to be forgiven. It was only her love that made her so jealous, and unfair, and suspicious. Only her love. So I forgave her, your honor, and thought how unfair her accusations really were. Of course, I had lied to her, and I *was* sleeping with another woman, but I wasn't deceiving Sylvia in the true sense of the word, not with little Suzy. If I was deceiving her—and I was—with another woman, then it was a woman I had never touched, whom I didn't dare to touch, a woman—and this came astonishingly clear to me as we quarreled—whom I had begun to love in a way I had never loved before.

7

After my arrest and imprisonment, your honor, you received several diaries of mine from the police, who had confiscated all my personal belongings. I explained that I could let you have this detailed report only if you let me have these diaries in which I jotted down everything in my own private code. You were good enough to grant my request.

I have just opened the diary for the year 1971, and I shall now describe the events that led up to the catastrophe according to my record of them. Under the date November 27, I find short notes about my visit to Sylvia, the scene she made, as just described, how I calmed her, and how I was horrified to discover that I had begun to love Ruth. Then I see that Suzy cooked lamb stew for me that evening, with green beans, because she knew it was one of my favorite dishes. Suzy was altogether incredibly sympathetic about everything that concerned Babs; she even persuaded me to call the hospital again and ask how she was. From my diary I see that I waited with longing and anguish for Ruth's voice, but more anguish than longing. She didn't answer. A nurse told me that she had gone home, and connected me with the doctor on night duty. He told me Babs's condition was unchanged, perhaps a shade better, that she slept constantly but this was usual with meningoencephalitis, that they had my telephone number and would call me immediately if there was any change. Bracken was waiting in Le Monde for my call, and I passed the news on to him. Then Suzy and I got drunk and went to bed, and while this was going on I thought constantly of Ruth, which made things so difficult for me that I had to find other ways to satisfy Suzy. And at the end, under the same date: "Couldn't sleep. Got up and sat in the living room in the dark. Breakfast with Suzy at 6:00 A.M. She was friendly but sad. When I asked her what was wrong she said, 'You know what's wrong. It's depressing. I don't have any luck with the men I love. I wish the other woman all the luck in the world. . . .' "

8

From the diary:

Sunday, November 28, 1971. At the hospital at 8:00 A.M. Dr. Sigrand very friendly, Ruth cool when compared with yesterday. (Or am I imagining things?) Babs had a good night, relatively speaking. Still 104.3. Delirious, restless, twitching. The doctor says everything as expected. They're satisfied. Stayed in the clinic all day. In the afternoon all alone with Babs. Whenever I go out in the corridor I see a lot of visiting parents, rich and poor. The misery in their faces is frightening. Off to Sylvia. Tell her that Babs continues to improve. She was calm and seemed satisfied. She believes what I tell her. Very tired. Early to bed and slept well.

Monday, November 29, 1971. To the hospital at 8:00. Ruth much friendlier today. (All in my head. I'm crazy. I'm in love. Ruth is *always* friendly.) Babs unchanged. At the hospital all day. In the afternoon Babs regained consciousness for a while. Saw me but didn't recognize me. Tried to hit me again and screamed hysterically. Ruth told me to leave the room. To Sylvia. Tell her Babs is much better. She tells me they're going to remove the bandages in two days, take out the stitches in three. To Suzy's place. Phoned Rod. Won more than 65,000 francs in Auteuil. Told Rod to give Lucien 10,000 francs, and to hang on to the rest. Always tell Rod the truth about Babs. Suzy's little count called at midnight from Acapulco. He's staying another three weeks and adores her. Coitus. Slept well.

Tuesday, November 30, 1971. In the hospital all day. Ruth took me with her on her rounds. I got to wear a white coat. Some of the children look so horrible, I have to turn away. Water on the brain, heads twice as big as their bodies. Flee to Babs's room. She's sleeping. Fever down, below 104. Ruth comes. Babs awake for an hour but is completely disoriented. Something very wrong with her left arm and left leg. Moves them with much greater difficulty than the right extremities. Ruth says this is a part of the natural course of the illness. "You don't believe me, Herr Norton?" "No." And then, quickly, "Yes, I do. I believe you." To Sylvia. Babs continues to improve. Sylvia happy. Excited because they're taking the bandages off tomorrow and she'll see what she looks like. Suzy has bought a doll for Babs. I'm to take it to the hospital for her. Call Rod every day. He calls Joe Gintzburger every night. I told him to tell Joe Babs is improving all the time. Rod says Joe doesn't believe him.

Wednesday, December 1, 1971. I left Babs's doll in the Métro. On purpose. Then was conscience-stricken. Babs: fever dropping. Breathing normal. Not always conscious. Still restless. Sudden outbursts of temper. New medication. Babs doesn't know me. Two attacks today. Ruth calls them "localized" cramps, Sigrand "generalized." To Sylvia. Terribly depressed because she has seen herself in the mirror without the bandages. Face is swollen and bruised. Probably expected to be a raving beauty. Looks like a boxer in the tenth round. Two hours spent consoling her. "That will be gone in a few days." She doesn't believe me. Weeps. Doesn't ask about Babs. Is totally absorbed in her own misery. In the evening, give Suzy a kiss and tell her Babs loved the doll. Suzy weeps. Gets drunk. Falls asleep in front of the TV. Undress her and put her to bed. Sleep badly.

Thursday, December 2, 1971. At the hospital at 8:00 A.M. as usual. Travel only by Métro and bus. Babs 103.4! Orientation improved. But a new startling symptom: she is cross-eyed! Ruth: eye muscles paralyzed. Will pass. And what about the left arm and leg? Babs can barely move them. All passing symptoms, says Ruth. Am *very* disturbed. Ruth says, "Every dark night has a light ending." To how many people has she said that? Off to Sylvia, who is still totally absorbed with herself. Delamare has ruined her! She is going to sue! He's a criminal! She'll never be able to show herself in public again! Hysterics, tears, etc. Babs—the usual lies. I get the feeling she isn't even listening. Lost my dark glasses. Exhausted by the time I get to Suzy. Early to bed. Seven forty-five, the phone rings. Suzy takes the call. It's for me. Dr. Delamare. Beside himself. Has just found out that Sylvia is missing. All efforts to find her have failed. The doctor in a state of panic. What to do? I tell him I'll call him back in five minutes. Am on the point of calling Bracken when the phone rings. Ruth says . . .

9

"Sylvia Moran is here."

"What do you mean—here?"

"Here in the Hôpital Sainte-Bernadette. We're in trouble, Herr Norton."

"You're telling me!"

"What is it?" asked Suzy. She had on a short nightgown, no panties.

"Quiet!" I said.

"I beg your pardon?" said Ruth.

"Nothing. Where are you now, Frau Doktor?"

"In the hospital. I came here at once. So did Dr. Sigrand. The night watchman at the gate said a woman, a sister, told him the hospital had called her to come at once to a sick child. Frau Moran gave a false name, for herself and for the child."

"Sounds like her."

"The nightwatchman said he would have to call the doctor first and went back into his booth. He couldn't reach the doctor right away. One of the nurses told him to have the woman wait. The man went back out to tell the sister . . ."

"How did she manage to appear as a sister?"

"I'm coming to that. She was wearing dark glasses."

"Mine! I lost them. Apparently in her room."

"Probably. But there's no time now for explanations. The man of course had no idea who the woman was, and when he got back to the gate, she was gone."

"Where to?"

"To the ear, nose and throat clinic. She must have known where Babs was. At that hour things are very quiet here, so she didn't meet anybody. You must have told her how to find Babs. Did you?"

I had to clear my throat twice before I could say, "Yes. Unfortunately I did."

"Frau Moran managed to get into Babs's room. A nurse heard screams and went to see what was wrong. She found Babs thrashing around and screaming, trying to hit her mother. Frau Moran collapsed when she saw Babs's condition, naturally."

"Naturally."

"She was babbling in three languages. The noise woke the whole floor. Frau Moran behaved like a madwoman, and Babs had another spastic attack. It took three doctors and four nurses to control Frau Moran. One of the doctors gave her a shot to calm her. By the time I got there they'd put her in a private room. The drug has had its effect, but not entirely. Babs, though, has calmed down. She's asleep again. Frau Moran is not."

"But she was perfectly calm this evening when I was there! She believed everything I told her—that Babs was better and improving . . ."

"She didn't believe a word you said, Herr Norton. She is a great actress, and she knew you were lying."

Suzy had lit a cigarette and she was looking at me. "Bad news?"

I nodded.

"How did she get out of the clinic?" I asked.

"Very cleverly. She dressed, slipped out of her room and went to the nurse's station. There she apparently saw the nurse's cape. Her name is Hélène, isn't it?"

"Yes."

"She wasn't at her desk. Frau Moran took her cape and her cap. At the gate she turned her face away and imitated Sister Hélène's voice when she said goodnight. It was coincidentally Sister Hélène's time to leave anyway, so the man at the gate didn't bother to look up, just nodded and switched open the gate. We've found all this out in the meantime. After that she walked here in the rain."

"Goddammit!"

"Don't swear, Herr Norton. Try to imagine yourself in her place."

"All right, all right." I gave Suzy a sign that I had to have a drink. A noose was tightening around my neck.

"Tell me what to do, Herr Norton." Ruth Reinhardt spoke.

"I'm asking *you*."

"No. This is *your* problem. Frau Moran can't stay here. She has to go back to Dr. Delamare's clinic, the quicker the better. In both your interests, and in a way that attracts no attention."

"How can we manage that?"

"I don't know. Especially considering her condition. I'm sorry, but here you're going to have to take over. And you don't have much time. She can't stay here much longer or there'll be talk. I'm going to hang up now. I have to go to Babs. Dr. Sigrand is with Frau Moran. Call me as soon as you've decided what to do, but call me soon. Frau Moran's future is at stake, *and* yours." Click. She had hung up. Suzy came with a tall glass of Calvados. I drank it down fast.

"I know what's happened," said Suzy, stroking my hair. "Your whore's at the hospital and you have to get her back to Delamare's clinic."

I nodded. I couldn't speak for rage. I felt sick with fury. Mother love! That was all I needed. But I had to get Sylvia back to Delamare as quickly as possible or we could write off our future. Ruth was right.

186

10

I gave the whole matter some thought and called Lucien Bayard at Le Monde.

"Night clerk. Good evening." As soon as I heard Lucien's voice I felt better. "Oh, Monsieur Kaven!"

"Can you get away from your desk for a minute?"

"Certainly. Why?"

"You've got two public telephones there, besides the elevators. I'll give you a number. Call me back." I didn't need some creep at the switchboard to listen in. I was supposed to be in Madrid. Two minutes later he called. "Something terrible has happened, Monsieur Lucien. Madame Moran has gone to the Hôpital Sainte-Bernadette because she was determined to see her daughter. She couldn't stand it any longer."

"Merde!"

"Yes . . . *merde!* I've got to get her back to Delamare's clinic right away, but in a way nobody notices." Rod had told him about Sylvia's face lift. "You can do anything, Monsieur Lucien. Please help us! What can we do?"

He thought for a moment, then he said, "A car from the hotel won't do. Too dangerous. I can only think of one thing: the laundry service."

"The laundry service?"

"We use a lot of linen, Monsieur Kaven. Every hotel has a laundry service. So does every hospital. Nobody'll notice if you drive up with a laundry van. Our service is the Imperiale. So is the hospital's. The Imperiale has an old driver; he has a bunk in the garage where they keep the vans, poor devil."

"Why poor devil?"

"Borrows money from me. Plays the horses and loses. Never pays me back. I'll call him right away. He'll do anything for me. Call Monsieur Bracken. He can go there in a taxi, pick up a van . . ."

"What if it doesn't work?"

"It will. He'll get one. Don't worry. The poor old fellow will do anything for me. I keep on lending him money. Oh

187

yes—have him give you overalls so that you won't attract attention. Monsieur Bracken can drive. You meet him somewhere, and that's how you get to the hospital. Nobody will ask questions. You can go wherever you like in your overalls, and that's how you'll get Madame Moran out of the hospital."

"Monsieur Lucien, I shall never forget what you've done for us tonight."

"Don't mention it, Monsieur Kaven. I'm happy to help you whenever I can. Oh—monsieur?"

"What?"

"Next Sunday there's a very interesting race in Chantilly. There are two horses—sensational, both of them. You really should . . ."

Of course I really did. And I told Lucien again that he should do what he thought best, and that always made him feel important. Then I called Bracken and told him what had happened, and he swore like ten troopers, but I cut him short and said he should go down to the lobby and see Lucien and get the laundry service's address. He was to pick me up in front of a certain bookstore on the Avenue de la Grande Armée. Then I hung up and called the hospital. I told Ruth what we were going to do, and she agreed that it was a good plan. I dressed in a hurry, and Suzy called a taxi. After I'd kissed her goodbye she made the sign of the cross on my forehead, I swear she did, your honor.

Everything went off all right. Bracken came driving up the Avenue de la Grande Armée and stopped in front of the bookstore, and I got in. He had on his yellow overalls. I put on mine over my suit and left my hat and coat in the van. The words *Blanchisserie Imperiale* were written on the breast pocket, in red, just as they were on the sides of the van.

We drove to the hospital, went up the service elevator, and walked fast down the corridor of the administration section. Nobody paid any attention to us. No television sets were on. The business with the hostages had been brought to a conclusion without bloodshed after over a hundred hours of bargaining. The terrorists had been given exactly what they had asked for.

We reached Ruth's office. She was at her desk, looking upset. But all she said was, "That was fast."

I asked, "Where is Sylvia?"

"I'll take you to her."

11

The Beauty. There she lay on a narrow bed in a small room, an athlete of a doctor at her bedside. Ruth and Dr. Sigrand were taking no chances. She looked at Bracken and me as we walked in.

There was nothing in the room except the bed and a chair, and the burly doctor was sitting in that. He was watching Sylvia, that was what he had been assigned to do, nothing else interested him. A good doctor. Ruth whispered that she was going to Babs, and withdrew. Which left Rod and me facing Sylvia.

She stared at us. She was weeping. Her face was still swollen and bruised below the eyes and elsewhere. Green, black and yellow patches. You can't imagine what she looked like, your honor. But it wasn't simply a face shortly after a face lift. Something devastating had happened to the woman who went with the face, and that also leaves its mark. It was the first time I had ever felt sorry for Sylvia Moran.

"For God's sake, have you gone crazy? You—" Bracken started to say, but I interrupted him. "Shut up!" I told him, and I walked up to Sylvia's bed. The doctor nodded in my direction, then he looked at Sylvia again. His job.

"My poor Silky," I said, and said it for the first time with honest tenderness.

"Bastard!" she said. "You filthy bastard!" The tears kept pouring down her shattered face, and she spoke slowly, as if groping for every word.

"What's wrong with her?" I asked the doctor.

Without looking up he said, "Neuroleptica. Heaviest dose. She should be fast asleep. I don't understand it." Because you don't know how much alcohol Sylvia can consume, I thought. The light in the room came from a bright wall lamp. I could see that Sylvia's stockings had sagged and were torn and wet. Like her shoes. She had put on satin shoes. They were so dirty and wet that the soles had come loose.

She had on a black silk Dior dress, also dirty and torn.

189

Sister Hélène's cape hung over the back of the bed, soaked through, a puddle of water beneath it. Sister Hélène's cap, a complicated starched white affair, was a wet rag. Somebody had draped it across the cape. And on the blanket, beside Sylvia, I saw my dark glasses, under them a scarf. Sylvia had probably used it to hide her face. A scarf by Hermès—dirty, wet, crushed. So that was how Sylvia had been dressed as she had run here from the Rue Cavé, through the night, in the rain.

"Bastard!" she said again, and I didn't try to stop her. "Liar! 'Babs is better!' I knew you were lying. That's why I came here."

What was there to say? Nothing. I said nothing.

"Babs. My poor Babs. And it's my fault. God is punishing me."

I looked at Bracken. He nodded and left the room.

"But why does he punish Babs? My Babs? The only thing I have in the world? Why? Why does she have to suffer? She didn't recognize me. She screamed. She tried to hit me. I want to die." She spoke slowly, in a hoarse voice. It sounded just as tortured as her face. "I want to die right now. Why don't they give me something? I can't go on living with Babs so sick. She'll die soon, won't she?"

"No."

"Yes she will. I know she will. And so do you, you bastard, you fucking lying bastard!"

"I wanted to spare you the anxiety . . ."

"Spare me the anxiety? Is this the way you spare me anxiety? You'll die soon too. I hope it takes a long time and that you suffer horribly."

"Silky!"

"Never call me Silky again, do you hear? Never!" And she spat, weakly. It didn't hit me, but it hit the doctor. He wiped his face with a handkerchief.

"I'm sorry, monsieur," said Sylvia, with her bruised, swollen face and the scars still visible where the stitches had been removed; Sylvia with her beautiful hair combed back and done up in a knot, greasy, its sheen gone; Sylvia, with red inflamed eyes, weeping. And I felt sorry for her, your honor, truly sorry.

The door opened and Ruth came in with Bracken. Sylvia looked furious when she saw Ruth. "You!" she said. "You get out of here!"

"Right away, Frau Moran," said Ruth, and walked up to her.

"I hate you!" said Sylvia.

"Yes, Frau Moran," said Ruth. I saw Dr. Sigrand enter the room, but Sylvia didn't see him. She was glaring at Ruth.

"You have no heart!"

"No, Frau Moran."

"You aren't a woman!"

"No, Frau Moran."

"You're inhuman, do you hear? Inhuman!"

"I know, Frau Moran," said Ruth. And then, suddenly—at last!—the injection worked. Sylvia's head rolled over sideways, her lips parted, her body sagged. She had lost consciousness.

"How is Babs?" I asked.

"Asleep," said Dr. Sigrand, as he lifted one of Sylvia's lids. "So is Madame Moran. She'll probably sleep for several hours now."

He walked over to the door, opened it and nodded. Two orderlies came in with a stretcher. They laid Sylvia on the stretcher, covered her, strapped her in. One man took Sister Hélène's cape and cap; I put on my dark glasses.

The orderlies left the room with the stretcher, Sylvia lying motionless on it. Ruth and Dr. Sigrand followed, the burly doctor bowed, gestured with his hand—after you, sir—and we all marched down the passage to the service elevator. I noticed that quite a few nurses, orderlies and doctors appeared in doorways and saw to it that we didn't meet anybody. Only Sylvia's head was visible, and what a head! She could have been the Frankenstein monster's grandmother.

Then into the elevator. With a little luck we'd have her in the van in a few minutes and could drive her back to Dr. Delamare's clinic and everything would be all right again. The elevator stopped. Again nurses, orderlies, doctors, seeing to it that we met no one. Ruth and Dr. Sigrand had organized it all brilliantly. Out into the courtyard, into the dark and rain. Bracken ran on ahead. I saw him open the back door of the van. Now in with the stretcher and . . . then it happened. Flash—flash—another and another. Seven in all!

Oh yes, we'd been smart as hell, but not smart enough. All the way here I'd watched to see if anyone was following us, but not watched enough. One of the reporters must have followed us. I couldn't see anyone, I could see only where the flashes came from. I took off my glasses and ran toward that spot, fast as I could, flew into him and fell. It hurt. I got up and grabbed him by his coat lapels. I tore the camera out of his hands and threw it on the ground and trampled on it. The fellow went for me. I kicked him in the stomach, and it hurled him back against a wall. He came at me again, punched me in the eye, my sore eye. It hurt terribly. I raised my knee and hit him full force in the genitals. He screamed and tottered back. This time I went after him, fell on him and began to pummel his face. He hit back as hard as he could. I heard the van start and hoped Rod would have the sense to get the hell out with Sylvia.

It was a long battle. Then suddenly Dr. Sigrand was at my side, and he could fight, your honor. Unfortunately he didn't tackle the photographer, but me. "Stop!" he yelled at me. "You're to stop!"

But I couldn't stop. I shoved Sigrand aside and went on beating up the photographer. Headlights, screeching tires, as the van reversed and turned. It headed for the exit and the exit was beside me and everything was suddenly brilliantly lit. And by the light I could see whom I'd been beating to pulp I knew the photographer lying at my feet. We'd fought before. It was the photographer who had burst into Suite 419 in Le Monde a few days before—the little thin one, Harelip. The tires screeched again as Rod made the turn through the exit, the motor roared, and Bracken took off. I saw Dr. Sigrand and the orderlies help Harelip up and take him away, wailing. They all went with him, Ruth too. Suddenly I was alone. I looked around me, but because it was so dark, I couldn't find the camera. I crawled on all fours over the dirty, wet yard looking for it. Found it finally. It wasn't smashed, in spite of the way I'd treated it. I took the film out and stuck it in my pocket. I also found my dark glasses and put them on.

12

Half an hour later I was back in the hospital. Now Harelip was lying on the bed Sylvia had been lying on. A doctor in emergency had examined him and taken X-rays. Ruth had said something was wrong with his jaw, I don't know what and didn't give a damn anyway; his face was covered with bandages and one arm was in a sling. He was Italian and worked in the Paris office of a big photo agency. They'd found all sorts of identification papers on him, also his passport. Harelip's name was Angelo Notti; he was thirty-one years old and single. At my request they left me alone with him. In execrable French he told me he was going to report me to the police and to his agency. He didn't have any pictures but he could tell a pretty story about a woman called Sylvia Moran whom they'd just carried out on a stretcher. He had recognized her. Didn't need any pictures. The story was enough.

I let him talk because I saw how it hurt him to talk. And he had a lot more to say. He'd been after me ever since I'd beaten him up in Le Monde, but I'd always managed to elude him. But today he'd been lucky. He'd followed Bracken, and when the latter had driven off in the laundry van, he had followed it in his little Fiat. And now he had me cornered. What was Sylvia Moran doing in the Hôpital Sainte-Bernadette? What was wrong with her? What was wrong with Babs? Where was she? Where had they taken Sylvia? All he could take to the police was questions, but they'd find the answers to them. And of course he'd sell the questions to the papers, the press agencies, to ORTF, to the American papers . . . He went on and on like this for ten minutes at least, until he had to stop because it hurt him so much to speak.

Now it was my turn. I tried money first, because the man had to be silenced. Under no circumstances could he be permitted to talk. But he didn't want money. I offered more. He turned me down again. I offered still more. Nothing doing. He hated me too much. If I had offered him $10 million, he would have preferred $100,000 from some miserable little agency. A man of character, Angelo Notti. In the end both of us were silent.

Ruth came in. She examined Notti briefly and gave him an injection. Then she gave me a sign to leave the room with her. She closed the door. "Herr Bracken called. Frau Moran is back in Dr. Delamare's clinic. He told me he intended to stay there until you called."

I nodded.

"What are you going to do about this Italian?"

"I have no idea."

"A bad thing."

"Very bad. How is Babs?"

"All right. She's asleep. I just left her." She took a deep breath. "Is there anything I can do to help you, Herr Norton? But I guess there isn't."

I shook my head. Then I leaned against the wall and closed my eyes. "What's the matter?" she asked. "Do you feel ill?"

"No," I said. "But I've got to make a phone call right away. May I call from your office?"

"Of course."

"Somebody's got to watch the Italian so he doesn't get away."

"There's a doctor on his way, the one who was watching Frau Moran. Have you thought of a plan, Herr Norton?"

"I don't know," I said. "Perhaps. I hope so."

13

"Signore Marone?"

"Yes, dammit. Who is it?"

"Kaven. Philip Kaven." I was sitting on Ruth's desk, Ruth beside me. She never took her eyes off me.

"Kaven?"

"Yes, Kaven."

"Are you in Rome?"

Now I was speaking Italian. "No. I'm in Paris. At the Hôpital Sainte-Bernadette."

"You're drunk, yes?"

"No, Carlo."

"Phil! What are you doing in a hospital?" He sounded coarse and aggressive. He had never been able to shake off all the traces of his days as a pimp. I told him what I was doing in the Hôpital Sainte-Bernadette; I told him everything, your honor. I could see Ruth watching me, horrified. I shook my head, and my next words calmed her. "So now you know what's up, Carlo. And you also know what will happen if you pass on a single word of any of this to anyone, don't you?"

"Yes," said Marone.

"Then say it."

"I know that if I tell anyone any of this I'll never get another picture from Seven Stars or Sylvia."

"Right."

"And they're the films I live on. If I lose them, I'm finished."

"Right. And what would you do then?"

He said nothing, and I could hear him breathing.

"Then you'd go back to what you did before, Carlo," I said. "Then you wouldn't be a film distributor any more. Your castle, your money, your art treasures—Seven Stars would take all of it away from you, because you're up to your ears in their debt. Am I right? Then you can look for little girls again and make drug addicts of them and tie them to a bed and beat them half to death until they're ready to hustle for you, just as you used to do."

Ruth's expression never changed. Her brown eyes showed nothing but interest.

"And when you've established yourself as a pimp again, we'll close in on you and you'll end up in a little cell where you'll stay for a long time, Carlo. I can promise you that. A very long time."

"Stop it, Phil! What do you want me to do?"

Men like us understand each other right away. "You know what you have to do," I said.

"I'm to see to it that this photo agency persuades this man Notti to shut up," said Marone.

"Right. You know the top banana there." This wasn't a question, it was a statement of fact. Marone knew practically everybody in Rome who was important or dangerous or useful. And he also knew all about the vices, the secret sex orgies with children, the tax evasions, illegal foreign currency deals, the smallest and biggest crimes.

"Sure I know him," said Marone. "Pietro Cossa."

"And what's his specialty?"

"Sadism. He's involved in the case of a girl whose body was found on the beach in Ostia three years ago. They never found out who did it. I'll call Cossa right away. He eats out of my hand."

So there you are. "Good," I said. "I've looked up the schedule. There's a BEA arriving in Rome around two or two-thirty A.M. I'll have Notti with me. This has got to be settled right away."

"*Madonna mia!* At three in the morning? Cossa's going to love it!"

"He'd better," I said. "Send us a car to the airport. And see to it that Cossa's there."

"How did you happen to get into this mess in Paris, anyway?"

"Coincidence. I'm only passing through."

"It's going to cost you plenty."

"Naturally."

"Cossa's going to ask a lot. I can blackmail him up to a point, but there are certain rules."

"But of course it's going to cost us something. I have no intention of blackmailing anybody."

"Of course you haven't, Phil," said Marone.

"So what's Cossa going to get? Minimum? I'm not paying more than the minimum."

"Well now," said Marone, "it isn't all that simple. If you're going to be small about it, Cossa will refuse to play. And we've got a scandal on our hands and I'm finished and you're finished . . ."

"Don't forget Cossa!"

"He isn't necessarily finished," said Marone. "Italy is a wonderful country."

In that respect he was right.

So he told me what it would cost to buy Cossa's cooperation in this wonderful country of Italy, and it was a small fortune. With the present exchange approximately 100,000 marks. But actually I'd counted on 200,000. I asked Ruth, "Is there a jack in Notti's room? Can we put a phone in there?"

"Why?"

"His boss will tell him that he's to come to Rome, or we'll never get him out of here."

"Oh, I see," said Ruth in her calm voice. "Yes, we can put a phone in his room. Whoever's calling should ask for extension 617."

"Carlo?"

"Yes?"

"Call Cossa. He's to call here in ten minutes. The number is . . ." I gave Marone the number and had him repeat it and said, "Cossa's to ask for extension 617."

"Six-seventeen. Right away."

"Okay."

"Not so fast," said Marone. "You've got to bring the money with you. You realize that."

"Of course," I said, and wondered how Marone and Cossa would divide the money between them.

"You don't have that much cash on you."

"Of course not."

"Wouldn't be safe anyway to travel with that much cash. Cossa accepts checks. He trusts me so he'll trust you. Of course if you stop payment, or if the check bounces, Cossa will know what to do. And *not* a bank check. The whole thing has nothing to do with me. If you don't do the right thing by Cossa, I'm innocent!"

"Look who's talking about not doing the right thing," I said, and noticed that now *I* was toying with Ruth's little lamb. It must have been lying on the desk. "I'll bring along a check, and Angelo." I think all I had on me was a hundred francs.

"Very good," said Marone. "So Cossa will call Notti in ten minutes and tell him to come here at once. I'm looking forward to seeing you again, my good friend."

I hung up. Ruth was still looking at me. "You despise me, don't you?" I said.

"Despise you? Why? You're doing what you have to do, Herr Norton. You don't have any choice. I hope it turns out all right."

"So do I."

"But where will you get so much money so quickly?"

"I have to make another call."

I called Bracken at Dr. Delamare's clinic and told him what I needed. He was in Sylvia's room. She was still asleep.

"Then wake her up. Her checkbook's in the wall safe with her jewelry. Tell her to write a check, and tell her what for."

"How much?"

I told him. He whistled softly. "She's going to be mad."

After that I didn't hear anything for three minutes except the humming in the wire. I could imagine what Rod was going through. I read the words of Buddha that were framed on Ruth's desk: "Overcome anger with warmth." Very appropriate.

"I hope Mr. Bracken gets his check," said Ruth.

"I do too," I said.

"Phil!" Bracken on the wire again.

"Yes?"

"Man, that was something! If I don't get hold of some whiskey right away, I'll go nuts. Anyway, I woke Sylvia, explained everything to her, told her we needed a check, and when she found out how much she went berserk."

"Can she hear you?"

"She's dead to the world again."

"Have you got the check?"

"Yes."

"Was she able to fill it out correctly?"

"No."

I dropped the lamb. "No?"

"All she could manage was her signature and the figure. You'll have to fill out the rest. But she was still perfectly capable of seeing to it that I put the checkbook back in the safe and locked it."

"And hung the key around her neck again."

"No. She rang and gave the key to the doctor on duty. No woman's ever loved you like that! Congratulations! Or ever trusted you that much."

"Drive the van to another street, take off your overalls and come to me here at the hospital as fast as you can. Take a taxi. Wait in front of the hospital. And bring my hat and coat."

"Yes, Phil."

"Just a minute—one more thing."

"What? For crying out loud . . ."

"Sylvia's jet's in Madrid, isn't it?"

"Sure."

"Call the airport. Tell them to take off at once. For Rome. Leonardo da Vinci airport, as usual. Runway 45. Away from the main runways. And they're to make it as fast as possible. I'll come back to Paris on the Super-One-Eleven. That'll look better."

"Right," said Bracken. "Anything can happen. You never know. I'll call Madrid right away. But first Cossa in Rome. *Ciao,* lover!"

I hung up and picked up the lamb again. "We'd better get the phone into Notti's room," said Ruth, as if she were an accomplice. "The call could come any minute."

"You're right." We got up simultaneously, in the course of which we came so close to each other our faces almost touched. I was overwhelmed with the desire to kiss her, but of course I didn't dare. Instead I stepped back.

"You said something to that man, the Italian, that I can't forget," said Ruth.

"What?"

"You said, 'I'm only passing through.' "

"Yes. And?"

"With that sentence you described your entire life."

14

Pietro Cossa, head of the most prestigious photo agency in Italy, called up just two minutes after Ruth and I had put the phone into Notti's room. The burly doctor was still on duty. When the phone rang and I told Notti that Signore Cossa wanted to talk to him, he looked at me like a cow in a thunderstorm and I had to shove the receiver into his hand and practically lift it to his ear. Cossa didn't let him speak; I could hear him yelling in a way that made it difficult for Notti to contribute even an occasional *"Prego"* to the conversation. Fifteen minutes later Notti was finished. When he put down the receiver he was so exhausted he couldn't even look at me with hatred any more.

"Got it?" I asked.

He nodded and licked his wounded lip.

"I'm flying with you," I said softly. "Don't worry about it. I'm not going to create a scandal. I'm perfectly calm and peaceful."

He said, "The bastard!"—meaning his boss. He evidently had to hate somebody constantly.

"Well then, let's go."

"But not like that!" said Ruth. "We've got to make him look human first or the police will stop you." To Notti she said, "Come with me."

"Yes, ma'am. Right away, ma'am. Thank you, ma'am," he stammered as he got out of bed, put on his shoes and looked for his jacket. The burly doctor helped him as if he were a child.

"Forgive me!" I whispered to Ruth.

"For what?"

"Everything you're doing for me is illegal."

"I know," she said, and looked at me calmly, seriously.

"If you ever have any trouble about all this with the police, I'll take all the responsibility. I'll admit everything. The whole thing."

"Don't be ridiculous!"

"But I can't bear the thought that you might get into trouble on account of me."

"I won't get into trouble, but I can't bear the thought that you think I'm doing this for you."

"Then—"

She said nothing, just looked at me.

"May I go and see her once more?" I asked softly.

"Go and see her," said Ruth. "You know your way around by now and you have a little time. Then meet us in Emergency."

15

"Get well. Get wholly well. So much depends on it. I shall love you truly and play with you and do everything you want me to do. Just get well. So many people will be in terrible trouble if you don't. So try. Please, please try. I know things are hard for you now, harder than for any of us, but if you try, you have a much better chance of getting well. And you can ask for anything you like—I'll give it to you. You know, it's not true that I hated you. I mean *you*. I hated all children. And you were such a nuisance sometimes. Then there was the act I had to put on because of you. But I swear I'm not putting on an act now. I love you truly, just as you loved me, only get well, please."

I thought all this, your honor, as I stood beside her bed and she lay there on her side, so lost, so small, with only the blue lamp lit. A nurse was lying on the couch beside the window, fully dressed. She had covered herself with a light blanket and had been reading by a small lamp clamped on the windowsill. I can recall what she was reading: *L'Espoir* by André Malraux.

I looked at Babs again and went on begging her to get well, but I might just as well have been addressing myself to a marble statue. I said goodnight to the nurse; she nodded and went on reading Malraux's *Man's Hope,* and I left the room. It was 9:30.

16

That was some night, your honor! Ruth and Dr. Sigrand and the burly doctor had fixed Harelip up so that he could show himself, at least at night. There were adhesive strips all over his face; they had cleaned his hat, coat and shoes. Dr. Sigrand—yes, Dr. Sigrand!—had given him one of his shirts and ties because he'd bled all over his own. Of course the shirt was much too large for Harelip, and the tie hung down to his stomach. I had called Suzy and told her briefly what had happened, and that I had to fly to Rome. Suzy had wept and I said, "I'll be back tomorrow, *mon petit chou.*"

"So much can happen by tomorrow," she said. "I won't be able to sleep, I know. Have you got everything? Your passport? Money? Are you dressed warm enough? I'll come to the airport and bring you all the cash I have in the house . . ."

"No, *mon petit chou,* I have everything."

And I really did have everything. What I still needed was waiting for me at the entrance to the hospital. Bracken was bringing it. While they were powdering Notti's face a little over the worst bruises, Ruth showed me the way to the incinerator in the cellar and I burned Notti's films and threw his camera after them. Then I went upstairs again and outside, where a taxi was waiting. I got in, nodded to Bracken, took off my overalls and put on my hat and coat. I had my passport with me, and Bracken gave me the half-filled-out check. Then he took my overalls and got out and whispered, so the driver couldn't hear, that he was going to drive to Le Monde in another taxi, and that he'd stay awake all night in case I needed to call. He'd reserved two first-class tickets on the BEA flight to Rome, leaving Orly at midnight, in my name and Notti's; wasn't possible any other way—they'd look at our passports.

17

It took us five minutes to drive through the park to Marone's castle, then at last the car drew up in front of the building with its white marble facade, studded with the wildest ornamentation. Another five minutes carried us through salons and libraries and rooms with pictures on the walls, like a gallery, until we reached Marone's office—white marble, dark-red upholstery, the finest woodwork, gilded. Enormous mirrors. A Greek statue, a naked man—the Discobolus. All antique furniture, naturally. Marone had certainly made a killing with Sylvia Moran's pictures.

I had to give Notti a none too gentle shove to get him into the room, because he stopped dead, as if turned to stone, and stared at a Gobelin that covered an entire wall and was certainly at least three hundred years old. Then he staggered on, straight into the arms of a man who had just risen out of a deep chair. This man took hold of Notti by Dr. Sigrand's tie and began to shake him so hard that he was thrown from side to side, and pounded him in the stomach, whereupon I realized that the gentleman had to be Pietro Cossa, head of the famous photo agency. Marone, meanwhile, was sitting in a Renaissance chair, smoking, his eyes half closed as he watched Cossa beating up Notti, his stomach and below it, everywhere except his face. All the time he was beating up his photographer, Cossa was yelling at him. I can understand Italian, but a lot of what Cossa was yelling was beyond me; however, I'm sure Marone understood.

I heard somebody gasp and turned around and saw a girl lying on a bed hung with red and gold. She had blond hair,

202

enormous breasts, and long legs, and she was wriggling her beautiful body lasciviously. She had nothing on but a bra and panties. "Oh my God!" she breathed. "This is dreadful!" But she was quite evidently enjoying it. And she was high, your honor, sky high. She kept sniffing. Her nose seemed to be dry. Cocaine, I decided. I had evidently interrupted one of Marone's happy hours. Too bad!

Notti tried miserably to emit a few words in his defense but couldn't, because Cossa never stopped beating him. Notti was howling, the blonde was screaming. Finally Pietro Cossa, sex murderer, millionaire and head of a gigantic photo agency, dragged Notti into another room. The doors were white with gold-leaf inlay. The door, which was at least two and a half meters high, closed. "Get out!" Marone told the blonde.

She laughed, a silly laugh, got up, her behind undulating like a stripper's, and walked on very high heels to a small door in the wall hanging. She turned and in terrible Germanic Italian said, "I'll go lie down, Carlo. Come soon, please."

"I'll come soon," said Marone from his desk. "And if I don't, start without me, Christiana," which she evidently found terribly funny. "And close the door," said Marone. Christiana withdrew.

"The bad thing about Cossa is that he always needs an audience when he tortures anybody. *Dégoutant,* isn't it?" said Marone.

"The poor devil," I said.

"Who?"

"Harelip. Notti. The photographer."

Marone shook his head. "He's not poor."

"He isn't?"

"Not at all. He and Cossa are an old couple. You have no idea how many beatings Notti has already enjoyed with his old sweetheart. And how he loves it. And he too likes an audience."

"So this guy Notti is . . ."

"A masochist." Marone sounded bored. Then he said something I didn't get. "What?"

"The check," said Marone.

"I've got to fill it out first."

"What do you mean—fill it out? Now listen here, Phil, if you're going to . . ."

"I'm not 'going to' anything," I said, and explained. I sat

down at a marble table and made out the check, and I was very careful to get everything right, because Sylvia had signed only this one check. When I was done I handed the check to Marone, who looked at it for at least two minutes, and told me once more what I could expect if the check was no good. I told him what would happen to him in that case, and he laughed and asked me if I wanted a whiskey.

"Yes."

We sat down with our drinks and could hear the big fat sadist raging next door. "Won't last much longer," said Marone. "No audience. This is just the epilogue." He looked at the check sadly.

"Don't cry," I said, "you'll get half."

"No. I have to give Cossa the whole thing."

"Why? You know about the death of the girl. You've got him over a barrel, haven't you?"

"I'm telling you—I've got to give Cossa the whole thing."

He was so beautiful, I could barely stand the sight of him. You know how beautiful Romans can be, your honor: noble features, a Caesarean nose, glowing eyes. A few girls had told me he was impotent. I'd asked them why they took him on if he was impotent, because Marone was notoriously stingy. And to my astonishment every one of them had said, "Because he looks so gorgeous!" And now he was saying, and his eyes were sheer velvet, "I'll do anything for you, Phil, under one condition. There's got to be something in it for me too."

"You still distribute Seven Stars."

"Let's not make it sound like blackmail. I'd have gone on getting the Moran pictures anyway if this unfortunate incident hadn't happened."

"So what's your condition?"

"How did Sylvia's last picture turn out?"

"Fantastic!"

"Then I'll only play along if you can arrange to have the world premiere here in Rome." Marone was chewing on his cigar, and next door Pietro Cossa was still bellowing at his lover.

"Hm."

You see, your honor, Rome isn't exactly a city in which one likes to premiere a super picture. It's too provincial. In a way all Europe is too provincial. Until now Sylvia's pictures had always premiered in New York.

"I can promise you the best house—the Festival Motion

Picture House next to the Colosseum, or the Teatro Sistina. I swear I'll get the best, the richest, the most famous people to come. Rome will never have seen anything like it. People will be talking about the premiere of *So Little Time* ten years from now!"

"Hm."

"I'll fly in the top reviewers from wherever you say! Or Bracken, if you don't know them well enough." (I swallowed that one.) "I promise you I'll get somebody from the Vatican, and the government, every last one of them, and a few prominent Russians. Aristocracy, publishers, industrialists, bankers . . . you name them, I'll get them!"

"Why are you so crazy to get this picture, Carlo?"

"Alfredo Bianchi."

"What about Bianchi?"

"Well, he's Sylvia's co-star in *So Little Time,* isn't he?"

"So?"

"Where are we now? Beginning of December. And when will the picture be ready, with copies and advertising?"

"Not before April."

"Then we've got it made," said Marone.

"What have we got made?"

"Bianchi is in the hospital, isn't he?"

"Yes. Here in Rome."

"This time he's not going to make it," said Marone. "I have my connections, Phil, and I'm telling you—Bianchi doesn't have three months more to live. He'll die just in time."

"And if he doesn't? It's often looked as if he didn't have another month to go, but he made it all right."

"This time he will. You can have this house if Alfredo's still alive by April. I have my information from the secretary of the chief of staff. Personally. He can't make it through April. At best. Chin-chin!"

"Chin-chin!" I said, but I didn't feel good about it.

"Phil! The most popular actor in Italy! Popular all over the world! A Roman. Dies in Rome. And when he does, we premiere his last film with Sylvia! That'll net you three times as much in Italy alone! And in France! Ask Joe. Want to call him and ask?"

I shook my head. If Alfredo really had only a few more months to live, and the movie premiered right after his death, then it would have to premiere in Rome. I found the whole scheme somehow repulsive. But business is business, I thought, and I said, "Okay. But you'll have to fly to Hollywood and talk to Joe. If you stand to make so much more this way, you'll have to let Joe in on it."

"Listen, Phil—"

"No two ways about it. Otherwise you'll get nothing out of Joe," I said, and decided to call Joe as soon as I got back to Paris. "If you can meet Joe's demands, then you can be sure that Sylvia will agree to premiere in Rome. I'll persuade her, so will Bracken. And Joe. She'll come to Rome. If you'll respect Joe's demands. You'll still make plenty. All this, of course, only if Alfredo dies on time."

"He'll die on time," said Marone. "Give me your glass." He filled our glasses again and we toasted each other. Just then the door opened and Angelo Notti came in, head lowered, feet dragging, behind him his fat boss. "Go ahead, speak up!" said Cossa.

Notti didn't look at me. His tears dripped onto the carpet as he sobbed, "I beg you to forgive me, Monsieur Kaven. What I did was malicious and vile. And I'm very sorry. Please forgive me. I have received my punishment." The eyes of his boss were sparkling.

"So what is your punishment, Notti?" asked Marone.

Notti was silent. "Tell him!" yelled Cossa.

"I've been fired from the Paris office," said Notti. Now he was sobbing. "I'm leaving today, by plane. I'll be working in another office, far away."

"Where?" I asked.

"In the Near East," sobbed Notti. "Tel Aviv."

Cossa looked at me triumphantly. "Signor Kaven hasn't forgiven you yet."

"Please forgive me, Monsieur Kaven."

"It's okay," I said. "I forgive you."

"Thank him!" shouted Cossa.

"Thank you, Monsieur Kaven, thank you."

"And now get out!" yelled Cossa. "Have the butler call a taxi. You're to be at my office at ten."

Notti withdrew, walking backward, bowing all the way. I said, "Thank you, Signor Cossa."

"Don't mention it. Where's the check? Ah, there it is. Fine, fine. And now, what next?"

"Phil's flying straight back to Paris."

Marone had his chauffeur drive me to the airport in his Bentley after we had agreed that he would call Joe and fly to

Hollywood as soon as Joe could fit him in. The flight back to Paris in Sylvia's Super-One-Eleven, which was waiting for me on Runway 45, was pleasant and calm. I slept for two hours. We arrived in Orly late in the morning, and I was wearing my dark glasses again as I went through the barrier. I got the feeling that the customs officers were looking at me strangely. When I passed a newspaper stand I realized why. The most scurrilous paper in Paris, and therefore the most widely read, lay there, piled high. I read the headline: "Philip Kaven beats up Italian reporter in the Hôpital Sainte-Bernadette." And below it: "What was Sylvia Moran's steady companion doing in the hospital?"

18

"Rod!"

"Phil! Where are you?"

"Orly. Just arrived. I'm in a booth."

"No reporters around?"

"I haven't seen any."

"Have you seen the paper?"

"That's why I'm calling. How did they find out?"

"No idea. Maybe the guy who drove you and Notti to Orly. We've been in touch by phone for hours."

"Who's we?"

"The doctors at Sainte-Bernadette. The nurses and orderlies. Delamare and I. They've shut her up for the time being."

"And what does that mean?"

"When she got to the clinic she began to rave again. Sister Hélène called Delamare, and he put her under."

"And what do you mean by that?"

"Well, he knew what Sylvia had done, and to prevent her from doing it again he gave her a few shots. She won't be with us for the next three days at least. A little sleep cure. They'll keep giving her the stuff. We don't have to worry about her—for the moment."

"Great!"

"Then I spoke to your friend, the night clerk at Le Monde. He called the laundry people . . . and so on."

"And what?"

"And nothing. Nobody knows how the paper found out. Joe says it's a catastrophe."

"You've spoken to him too?"

"Are you crazy? I spoke to him before anybody else. He took the first plane. He's on his way here."

"And what did he say?"

"That the fat's in the fire. From here on you'll have every reporter in Paris on your neck. We've got to get that rag to print a retraction. I'm working on it."

"What are you going to do about it?"

"It's done. You take a taxi and drive into the city. Maître Lejeune is expecting you at noon. At Fouquet's. Do you know where it is?"

"Who is Maître Lejeune?"

"Joe's lawyer in Paris. Has a date with the publisher of that rag. At two P.M. You've got to be there. In tomorrow's edition we'll have our retraction. A beaut!"

"How do we get the retraction?"

"Don't worry about it! Joe says you've got to take over from there. And that's not going to be simple. But it's got to happen, no two ways about it."

"What?"

"We've got to get Babs out of the hospital fast."

"But we can't take her out. First of all, she can't be moved yet, and then—you said so yourself—there'll be reporters all over the place."

"I'll take care of the reporters. And this guy Lejeune—you'll recognize him right away. Joe says he's the fattest man in Paris. As for Babs—she *can* be moved. I've spoken to Dr. Sigrand. Under certain conditions and with the greatest caution. We've got to get her out of Paris today, and you go with her."

"Where to?"

"To Nürnberg. To Dr. Reinhardt's clinic. She's getting everything ready."

"What?"

"Babs is going to Reinhardt's clinic, idiot! She's flying with her. And you'll go with them!"

19

Maître LeJeune was eating mussels when I got to Fouquet's. One couldn't really say he was eating them. Never in my life have I seen anyone with such disgusting eating habits as Lejeune, whom Joe trusted blindly. He was sitting on a red velvet bench under a mirror. An ice bucket with a bottle of white wine and two plates stood on a table in front of him. There must have been a lot of mussels once on the one plate because the other was piled high with shells. He was eating the few that were left with his fat, rosy fingers.

I stood in the doorway and watched him for a while, because I'd never seen anyone eat quite like that. He had ordered baked mussels, prepared with parsley, garlic and oil. He had the face of an aging pig in ecstasy. He popped one mussel after the other into his rosy little mouth. After swallowing it, he licked the shell inside and—word of honor—*outside* with his rosy tongue. And after every mussel he drank. His hands were fat, his cheeks hung down over his collar, almost to the lapels of his jacket. His neck was practically nonexistent; his pig head was perched directly on his shoulders. He was completely bald. His stomach was so big that he had had to move the table to sit behind it, and his arms were so short it was difficult for him to reach the mussels and wine.

A waiter came up to me. I told him I had an appointment with Maître Lejeune. A minute later I was standing in front of him; five minutes later I knew that not only was he an extraordinary glutton but he was also extraordinarily astute. He gave me only the briefest glance out of his tiny little pig's eyes as I walked up to his table. "There you are, Monsieur Kaven," he said, in a high-pitched boyish voice.

"How did you know that I—"

"No stupid questions, please." He was working on his last mussel. "Sit down. Sorry there's no room beside me. On the plane they always have to remove an arm rest for me. I take up two seats. Pay for two. Something to do with my glands."

He sighed. Two waiters brought another serving of mussels, two plates and clean cutlery. The tablecloth looked like a greasy map. He ordered a bottle of Blanc de Blanc and I sat down.

"First of all, bring my friend a dozen oysters. Imperial, not the Spanish ones—they're too rich."

"I don't think I want oysters," I said.

"Of course you want oysters!" When he spoke the smell of garlic nearly asphyxiated me. "So," to the waiter, "twelve Imperial, Charles, to start off with."

"Yes, Monsieur le Maître."

"And a glass. Do you drink Blanc de Blanc?"

"It gives me a headache."

"Then bring us white wine 162." He waved the waiter away and fell like a wolf on the second order of mussels. "After we've eaten, we'll go over to that little newspaper." He licked a shell. "Delicious!" he said. "It's the only way I like them—baked." He burped. Then he said, "Terrible, what's happened to that poor child. Really hit me. Lost my appetite."

The waiter brought the wine, waited while I tasted it. Number 162 was excellent. I nodded. Waiter Charles filled my glass and withdrew.

"Got a lot to attend to today," said Lejeune. "I mean you."

"Yes," I said. "You too."

"Me? Oh, I see. You mean the business with the paper. Ridiculous. I'll swallow that like one of these mussels." He burped again. "Let me tell you how we'll go about it while we wait for your oysters and my Cordon Bleu."

I listened and he explained. Quite a character, this Maître Lejeune. To this day I don't know his first name.

20

And he actually did down the affair with the paper like a mussel, and wiped up the floor with the suave publisher. He didn't let the man—who publishes two serious papers as well as two of the leading illustrated magazines in France and owns a publishing house—say much. "You know, monsieur, that I can sue you for ten million francs," he said, as a greeting. He was still shaking hands with the publisher, who now took a hasty step back. The smell of garlic filled the room, a big room, elegantly furnished.

"We have witnesses and proof of what we printed," said the publisher, who had retired behind his desk. "I only received you, maître, to oblige you. You'll have to take the matter up with our legal department. What we printed is fact. You're not going to intimidate me, maître, with your usual methods."

The fattest man I had ever seen, with the singsong voice of a eunuch, took a file out of his attaché case and laid it on the publisher's desk. "This is Monsieur Kaven's complaint against you for libel. Our first demand is that you print in your . . . hrrmm . . . paper, set in the same size and the same place, the fact that your scandalous report was false, and that you print the truth and—"

"Look here, maître, even my patience can be exhausted. I must ask you to—"

"Furthermore, my client, Monsieur Kaven, intends to sue you for the sum of ten million francs, for libel and damage to his reputation. Here is my power of attorney. We intend to submit the complaint today if we can't come to an agreement regarding the retraction." He burped. "But you know me as a man who works fast and leaves nothing to chance."

The publisher said, "Monsieur Kaven. Do you intend to declare that you did not beat up a photographer in the courtyard of the Hôpital Sainte-Bernadette?"

"Monsieur Kaven is German, as you know, monsieur," Lawyer Lejeune said quickly (we had agreed in the restaurant that I wasn't to say a word). "And he finds speaking French difficult. That is why I will now read to you a prepared statement explaining the events." He took a paper out of his file and read fast: " 'I, Philip Kaven, declare that on the evening of December 2, 1971, I went to the ear, nose and throat clinic in the Hôpital Sainte-Bernadette to visit Mademoiselle Clarissa Geiringer, our governess. Mademoiselle Geiringer had been a patient in the clinic since November 28, 1971, after suffering some alarming symptoms in her nose and throat.' " He burped, then went on. " 'As I left the hospital'—this is still Monsieur Kaven's statement—'a man came up to me, used some abusive language and knocked me down. I defended myself as best I could, whereupon the unknown man fled. According to the report in today's edition of' "—and Lejeune gave the name of the paper in his singsong

211

voice, which now had a pronounced malicious ring to it—" 'the man who molested me was a reporter and was acting on behalf of his publisher, who had chosen me as the victim of his scurrilous and unscrupulous gossip column, an action evidently prepared well in advance.' " Lejeune burped again. " 'Mademoiselle Geiringer is a patient in the aforementioned hospital, third floor, private room Number 36. She is ready and willing to corroborate this statement. I therefore wish to file suit—' "

"Stop!" cried the publisher, and to me. "So you admit you were at the hospital and struck this reporter, Monsieur Kaven."

"You are to address your questions to me, not to Monsieur Kaven," said Lejeune. "Yes, Monsieur Kaven admits to having done so. With pleasure. He also intends to sue the reporter for his assault. He has no idea what the man's name is. It is very strange that the man seems to have disappeared from the face of the earth since the incident."

"How do you know that?"

"Before we came here we called on all newspaper editorial offices and asked the reporters, especially the photographers."

"There is such a thing as professional discretion, maître."

"In this case the court will rule out professional discretion in order to get at the truth. After all, it is a case of bodily injury. We will prove that you, not the editor-in-chief, are responsible for the libel."

"That isn't true!"

"Because you are the man in charge of all editorial conferences that decide what is to appear next day in this miserable paper, to which you seem attached because it brings in more money than any of the others. You are the man who gives the orders." Once again a burp. "We will prove that it was you who gave the order to follow Monsieur Kaven when you found out that he had been at the Hôpital Sainte-Bernadette twice, and decided that something sensational was going on. In the interest of the reputation of the French press—"

"That's enough!" said the publisher, pressing a button on his desk.

"—it is essential that your scurrilous paper be brought to account," Lejeune went on, imperturbably and reeking of garlic. "And that is why my client will approach the French Press Bureau with the request that your paper be appropriately censured." Lejeune examined his fingernails. "With your budget and the loss of advertising revenue that will

212

occur in this case, I imagine it may well spell the end of further publication, monsieur."

A very pretty secretary came in. "Please call the Hôpital Sainte-Bernadette, Mademoiselle Henriette," said the publisher, "and ask for the ear, nose and throat clinic, Room—"

"Number 36," said Lejeune helpfully.

"When you have the connection, put me through."

"Yes, monsieur," said the secretary, and withdrew. And I thought again what an astute man Lejeune was. I'd thought so for the first time at lunch, when he'd explained his plan to me. To the question of how he was going to persuade Clarissa to proceed to the Hôpital Sainte-Bernadette, he had told me, "Monsieur Bracken called in the night and asked me what could be done. The paper was out on the street at one A.M. I went over at once. One look at Mademoiselle Clarissa and I knew that she is in love with you. *Voilà,* monsieur. My compliments."

I had asked, "But at the hospital . . . that couldn't have been so simple. They must have had to falsify reports, the doctors and staff must have had to cooperate, and the administration."

And he told me, "I only spoke to one person, Monsieur Kaven, and she arranged everything. This doctor . . . I'm sure you know whom I mean . . . also loves—no, not you, but *children.* She loves a certain sick child. By the way, her condition is worse."

So Babs was worse, I thought, and I had to fly to Nürnberg with her today. With Ruth. And Joe is on his way to Paris with his bloodhounds. In a day or two Sylvia will wake up . . .

The telephone on the publisher's desk rang. He picked up the receiver, gave his name and addressed Clarissa by hers. He didn't get any further than that. I couldn't make out exactly what she was saying, but I recognized her voice and gathered that she was giving the man a piece of her mind, and heart and soul. She got our publisher to the point where all he could do was stammer, "I'm sorry . . . terribly sorry . . . no, no . . . they were *not* reporters from my paper. I don't know . . . I really don't know . . . my word of honor, mademoiselle. I can't influence reporters from other papers, you must understand that, mademoiselle . . . but my reporters . . . not one of them will be there five minutes from now, I promise you!" He hung up and looked at Lejeune bitterly. "You . . . you . . ."

"Yes, monsieur?" the old eunuch said amiably.

The publisher jumped up suddenly and rushed out of the room. "You see," said Lejeune, yawning, "it worked."

"So I see. But how do we get rid of the other reporters? Every Paris newspaper has its men out there now."

"One thing at a time, dear Herr Kaven," said Lejeune.

I said, "I'm sorry. You know what you're doing, and I thank you."

"You don't have to thank me, Herr Kaven. Monsieur Gintzburger will get my bill."

The door opened. The publisher came back with two gentlemen. He introduced one as the editor-in-chief, the other as the house legal adviser. We sat down at a conference table. During the next half hour I didn't speak a word, and in that half hour the whole thing was settled. The retraction was to appear in the paper next day, on the front page. The original report was to be reprinted, and Lejeune handed over the retraction, with instructions as to type size and design, ready to go. He also handed over something else, and publisher, legal adviser and editor-in-chief had to sign it, namely a statement to the effect that if his client was not in possession of said front-page proof by 5:00 P.M. today, and had pronounced himself satisfied with the content, Lejeune would proceed to sue on my behalf. He threw in the fact that there was a prosecutor, a good friend of his, who was responsible for all such cases against the press.

If Lejeune hadn't been so brutally forceful and insidious and hadn't left his opponents no time to think things over, the whole thing would probably have collapsed, because during any further questioning, somebody at the hospital would surely have given the show away. I held my breath until the three had signed. The publisher and his two employees escorted us to the elevator, where the publisher shook my hand and apologized. I forgave him. So did Lejeune, not that he'd been asked. The rest of us went down in the elevator together. At the fifth floor the editor-in-chief begged us to forgive him. We did, and he got out on the fourth floor. The legal adviser accompanied us down to the lobby. He was an elderly, dignified gentleman. At the revolving door of the entrance he said, "You blackmailed us. You lied and deceived us. All of us know that." He looked at me. "I despise you," he said. He looked at Lejeune, "And I find your behavior revolting."

"Tant pis!" Lejeune sounded blithe.

21

"Originally," said Ruth, "I studied history of art. I was also very interested in aesthetics and history of literature. Then these subjects didn't satisfy me any more and I studied philosophy."

This conversation took place on December 3, 1971, at about 8:00 in the evening, and we were sitting in the little salon of Sylvia's Super-One-Eleven, Babs in a bed between us, fast asleep, because of the heavy sedation that had been given her for the trip. Sylvia's jet was flying smoothly through the starry night. There was a full moon. The shades were drawn over the windows of the little salon, but you could see the stars and the moon through the windows up front.

We had left Orly Airport a quarter of an hour before. The four-man crew was in the cockpit. I knew I could trust them; they had been in Sylvia's employ for years. There wasn't a chance that any one of them would betray us. Babs lay so still, one might have thought she was dead. You could hear the muffled sound of the engines. The only light came from a small shaded lamp.

"It was all rather crazy," Ruth went on, and I knew she was talking to calm and encourage me, and I was happy that she kept talking through this strange night, high above the lights skimming by below us, with a child between us, wavering between life and death. "I wanted to write my thesis on aesthetics, but the longer I studied the more it came clear to me that the question—for instance of how we experience beauty—is in the last analysis a psychological question. So I stopped then and there and started all over again, studying medicine. A slightly chaotic career, wouldn't you say?"

She leaned over Babs, took her blood pressure and examined her as she lay there in an awkward position on the bed on which I had slept so often with Sylvia. The captain came in and watched her silently, then he said, "How is she?"

"Not worse."

215

"We'll be in Nürnberg in forty minutes," he said. "There'll be an ambulance at the airport. It'll pull up to the plane."

"Thank you, Mr. Callaghan," said Ruth. The captain bowed and went back to the cockpit. Callaghan was Canadian.

"He's very fond of Babs," I said, "and he told me a while ago how much he admires you, a woman with such a wonderful profession, the most humane of all professions."

"He shouldn't think like that," she said. "No one should see the medical profession in those terms, but above all no doctor should. Any doctor who does, and who takes care of sick children, as I do, for instance, and who thinks he is an ambassador sent down to earth by God with the mission to do something colossal for humanity, will soon be disappointed. A doctor is not a philanthropist, and his work has nothing to do with charity." Ruth stroked Babs's damp hair off her forehead.

"But you are here for these children," I said. "You are sacrificing your life for them."

"That, Herr Norton, is just not so, if you don't mind my saying so." She didn't look at me as she spoke. She took the little lamb out of the pocket of her suit and began toying with it. "For instance, these children are here for me just as much as I am here for them."

"I don't understand."

"When we get to the hospital where I work, you will get to know a lot of children with all sorts of illnesses. I think then you'll understand what I mean when I tell you about a conversation I had with one of those children, a boy called Tim. He is paralyzed from the waist down, extremely intelligent but incurably ill. He is seventeen years old. He said to me, 'You know, I don't think you're here just to talk to me and listen to me and nurse me.' Of course he didn't say it just like that, not in so many words, but that was what he meant."

The plane rose suddenly, and both of us leaned forward to prevent Babs from slipping. " 'What do you think, Tim?' I asked, and he said, 'I get the feeling that you're not only trying to find out what's wrong with me, but that you're also trying to find out what's wrong with yourself.' " The plane leveled off, and we sat back again. Babs sighed.

Ruth looked at me. "Tim is right, Herr Norton. I . . ." She hesitated for a moment, then went on. "However ill they are, children come much closer to one's true feelings than adults. They are also much more honest among themselves—that is, if their thinking capacities haven't been destroyed. Even then they sometimes want to understand what's wrong with *you*. For me it has been a unique experience to work with these children. You see . . ." Strange, I thought, that such a strong, forthright woman should suddenly have difficulty in finding the right words. "You see . . . sometimes it's . . . it's difficult to understand one's own feelings and . . . and what drives us to do certain things. But in my hospital I am forced . . . I have to come to grips . . . to answer to myself for every mistake I make. And I make mistakes, Herr Norton, plenty of mistakes—daily."

22

At just about this time (I found out about the following later, from Rod) two radio scout cars stopped in front of Aeropuerto Barajas in Madrid. They had been summoned by the manager of the airport restaurant. Some drunks had started a fight. They happened to be reporters. The four officers took one look at the fracas and called for reinforcements. The whole thing erupted into a riot with approximately seventy roughnecks participating. Quite a few were arrested, hauled into court. The Madrid papers demanded that the culprits be punished, and eleven Spanish reporters and photographers actually were fired, among them two employees of the state news agency EFI. Twenty-one foreign correspondents from various countries, newspapers and agencies were also dismissed. They were forbidden to work in Spain or to enter the country for a period of five years.

In Suite 315 of the Castellana Hilton, Rod and obese Lejeune were watching television. Both gentlemen were drunk. A bottle of whiskey, two bottles of soda and a silver ice bucket stood on a table between their chairs. They were enjoying the broadcast of the events at Barajas.

"Well, how did I do?" asked Maître Lejeune. Both men had taken off their jackets and opened their shirts. Lejeune was devouring a cold chicken.

"Splendidly, maître! Splendidly!" said Rod.

217

"You might mention it to Joe when you get the chance."

"That's the first thing I'll do when he gets to Paris. But to tell you the truth, I can't figure out how you did it."

"Why not?"

"Well, I've had plenty of experience with journalists," said Rod, "but that was almost a riot at Barajas. I mean—none of them would exactly have dropped dead with surprise when they found out we'd tricked them. They could have been mad at us. But to go berserk like that, so that the police had to be called in, and risk arrest and deportation . . ." He shook his head.

Lejeune was gnawing on a bone. "Had to prod them a bit," he said.

"How?"

"With the help of some friends who stood in as reporters. Always useful to have friends." He burped. "It simply had to happen now," he went on, nodding solemnly. "Because we're in a hell of a spot, Monsieur Bracken. Those reporters and news agencies had to be given a thorough beating—with deportation and loss of their licenses—to keep them off our necks for a while. We had to fuck them up royally, and I think we succeeded."

"But a few reporters followed the ambulance to the Salméron clinic," said Bracken.

"And what a good thing that was. I called Salméron before we left. When the ambulance drove up he was there to meet Clarissa and talk turkey to the reporters. Salméron is my friend. I did him a favor once when one of his French patients departed this life on the operating table. Now he has returned the favor. She'll spend a little time with my friend Salméron, good old Clarissa. After all, I got her into the Sainte-Bernadette, didn't I?"

"Is the director a friend of yours there too?"

"No," said Lejeune. "At Sainte-Bernadette I spoke to Dr. Sigrand. He told me he could take in any patient he liked. This woman, Dr. Ruth Reinhardt, took care of everything else. She also said she would take the responsibility for any possible problems later. Gave it to me in writing, because she's a young woman filled with love."

"For Kaven?"

"Heavens no!"

"For Babs?"

"For all children," said Lejeune. "A remarkable woman, Monsieur Bracken."

218

"And you are a remarkable man, maître," said Bracken, impressed.

"I know," said the fat lawyer. *"Santé,* my friend."

To backtrack for a moment: After Lejeune and I had left the office of the aforementioned newspaper publisher, we had driven straight to meet Bracken and Lejeune at Le Monde. They had discussed what was to happen next with me and Dr. Wolken. Lejeune made several phone calls. At 4:00 P.M. he and Bracken left us, the latter with a suitcase. I called Suzy at her beauty salon. She was terribly excited, because she had seen the headlines too. "And what happens next, *mon petit chou?"* she asked.

"You must please go straight home and pack all Babs's things in both suitcases and also a suitcase with things for me."

"You're leaving me!" she cried.

"Sh! Pull yourself together."

"Forgive me, but when you go away it's so terrible . . ."

"I'm only going away for a little while. Wait—can anyone hear you?"

"No."

"Good. Now listen. We have to get Babs out of Paris because of the reporters. I've got to go with her. Right away."

"Where to?"

"To Germany. We're taking her to a clinic in Nürnberg. Dr. Ruth Reinhardt is flying with us." That's how easily stupid things happen, your honor. It simply slipped out.

"Who is she?"

"The doctor who's been looking after Babs."

"How come she's going with you to Germany?"

"Because she's German and works in Nürnberg."

"I thought she worked in Sainte-Bernadette."

"She does, but . . ."

"I get it. You're sleeping with her, right? You've been sleeping with her all along! That's why you said you can't stay with me. What's she like?"

"Suzy, please!"

"Sure. You're sleeping with her."

"I am not!"

"Oh yes you are!"

"No!"

"I'll find out all about her. I'll call the hospital!" And I was in trouble.

At last, after innumerable declarations of love and swearing by everything under the sun, I managed to calm her down and she promised not to call the hospital. "Don't be an idiot!" I said finally. "Practically all my things are remaining with you. I'll be back tomorrow."

"I don't believe you! You'll never come back!"

"I swear I'll be back. The guys from Hollywood are arriving tomorrow. I've *got* to be in Paris to meet them."

Suzy's voice was choked as she said, "You shit in your pants for those Hollywood goons, but I don't mean a thing to you. If the guys from Hollywood are coming to Paris, I know you'll be back."

. "*Chérie,* I love you!"

"And I love you, or why do you think I get so upset? So, where's your stuff to go?"

I told Suzy where to send the things.

23

It was still light when Bracken and Lejeune drove up to the Hôpital Sainte-Bernadette in a taxi. *"Merde alors!"* said the driver. "What's going on here?"

According to Bracken, it really was a sight to behold. Cars were double-parked on both sides of the street. Men in leather jackets, fur-lined coats or thick sweaters were lolling in their cars or outside leaning against them. A lot of them with cameras. "Reporters, eh?" said the driver.

"Looks like it," said Lejeune.

"What do they want?"

"No idea."

"Oh yes!" The driver was a little slow on the uptake. "There was that fight last night with that guy of Sylvia Moran's and a reporter. I read about it."

"You did?"

"Yeah. Didn't you?"

"No," said Lejeune. "Drive through the first entrance, please, and stop in front of the ear, nose and throat clinic."

"Sorry," said the driver. "It can't be done. I can't go any farther. The entrance is over there."

Bracken paid, and he and Lejeune got out. Both of them were immediately buffeted around, photographed, yelled at. They wanted to know what Bracken was doing there, what famous Maître Lejeune was doing there, and where was I? Bracken said nothing. He walked behind Lejeune, who was ramming his way through the reporters. Two policemen were standing in front of the entrance. They tried to make a lane for Bracken and Lejeune to pass through with little success, but at last both of them were in the clinic. A young doctor came up to them. "Monsieur Bracken? Maître Lejeune?"

"Yes," the fat lawyer piped up. "You are Dr. Rivière? We just talked on the phone. I recognize your voice. Everything ready?"

"Everything's ready," said the young doctor, and led his visitors into a room to the right of the entrance. Dr. Sigrand and Ruth were there, and on the floor was a stretcher with Clarissa strapped to it, covered with a blanket, only her face showing. She nodded, looking pale and determined. "Now this has to go fast," said Dr. Sigrand, "or we're in trouble."

"We're ready if you are," said Lejeune.

Sigrand used the phone, then said, "The ambulance will be at the entrance in a minute. The orderlies will be here right away."

"Thank you, Monsieur le Docteur," said Bracken, then he knelt down beside the stretcher. "And thank you, Clarissa. I'm sorry, but for a while you're not going to be able to see anything." He turned to Sigrand. "Will she get enough air?"

Sigrand showed Bracken several small slits in the blanket through which Clarissa would be able to breathe. Then he covered Clarissa's face with it. Two orderlies came in, silently lifted the stretcher, and carried it toward the entrance. Bracken and Lejeune followed; the latter bowed to Ruth and Sigrand. "My profound thanks."

And then all hell broke loose. An amubulance was standing at the entrance to the clinic. Five police officers were there, plus the two mentioned earlier. As the reporters surged forward the police officers were jostled, beaten, kicked. One especially smart guy tried to get at the blanket covering Clarissa's face. Bracken kicked him where it hurt most. The reporter sat down on the pavement. A lot of reporters were already starting their cars while the photographers were still taking pictures of the orderlies getting the stretcher into the ambulance. Lejeune and Bracken got in last. The siren howled, the blue light revolved, the driver started the ambulance and drove off. Out of the back window Bracken could see the reporters jumping into their cars and starting to follow. In a moment a convoy of their cars had formed behind them. *"Violà!"* said Lejeune, taking a chocolate bar out of his pocket. "With nuts!"

24

The ambulance drove to Le Bourget, the smaller of Paris's two airports, where three chartered planes waited. The stretcher was put on one of them, as conspicuously as possible. The horde of reporters had meanwhile assembled; Lejeune had given orders that the stretcher shouldn't be put on the plane until they were present. By now it was dark. The plane remained brilliantly lit for fifteen minutes with flood lights.

Lejeune had really prepared everything extraordinarily well. The crew of the charter plane arrived only after the stretcher was on board, a crew of three. They readily told every reporter who asked them that Monsieur Bracken had chartered their plane for a flight to Madrid. Most of the reporters tore off to phone booths to report this to their colleagues in Madrid, while others found out—oh, wonder of wonders!—that one of the other charter planes could be rented. Lejeune had prepared the crew of the second plane for the onslaught that now followed. So in the end, two planes departed—Clarissa, Lejeune and Bracken in the first one, the other full of reporters. Bracken told me that they had had as good a time as possible on their flight, under the circumstances. They had removed one of the armrests for Lejeune so he could sit down, unstrapped Clarissa, and played the game all the French were crazy about—421. They drank a little too. Over the Pyrenees, the pilot was able to ascertain that the second plane had passed them and would be arriving in Barajas ahead of them. "Fly a little slower," Lejeune said, "so that the good fellows have plenty of time to prepare for our arrival."

And they were prepared, your honor! The reporters on the

other plane had been joined by a lot of reporters from Madrid. As soon as the plane carrying our three had taxied to a halt, it was surrounded. The door opened and two crew members carried the stretcher down the gangway, while an ambulance came driving up to the plane across the airfield. And the whole performance was repeated—reporters, photographers, the works. Lejeune walked beside the stretcher, and was very clumsy about it. He stumbled, in the course of which the blanket covering Clarissa's face was brushed aside. This was followed by a positive fireworks display of flashes—and by complete silence. Every man present had seen that neither Sylvia Moran nor Babs was lying on the stretcher.

Some of the reporters knew her face, some didn't, but every one of them knew that the person was neither Sylvia nor Babs. Lejeune broke the silence. "For your information, gentlemen, the lady's name is Clarissa Geiringer and she has been Babs Moran's governess for years. A few days ago she entered the Hôpital Sainte-Bernadette in Paris with alarming symptoms in the ear, nose and throat area." While they lifted Clarissa into the Spanish ambulance, Lejeune went on in his singsong voice. "The doctors diagnosed her condition as a seepage of the cerebral spinal fluid due to an injury of the membrane between nose and brain. In such cases there is always the danger of an infection of the brain. The Paris doctors wanted to operate. Anxious to avoid any risk, Monsieur Kaven—you know, I am sure, that Madame Moran is on vacation, but perhaps you don't know that since Mademoiselle Clarissa's illness, our dear little Babs has joined her mother—Monsieur Kaven therefore asked the doctors at Sainte-Bernadette to recommend the best surgeon for this delicate operation, and was told this would be Dr. Arias Salméron. His clinic here in Madrid is world-famous. We are taking Mademoiselle Geiringer to Dr. Salméron. Thank you, gentlemen."

"What do you mean—we? What are *you* doing here?" yelled one of the reporters. "Why isn't Mr. Kaven with her, or a doctor?"

"Mr. Kaven is a very good friend of mine. He doesn't know Madrid. There will be certain formalities to attend to."

"And why didn't you tell us all this in Paris?" cried another reporter.

"Because none of you asked me," said Lejeune, getting into the ambulance after Bracken. He closed the door and yelled in

Spanish to the driver, "And now let's go! Fast! Things are going to get hot here."

I have already reported what happened after that, your honor. Meanwhile, as the reporters were following Bracken's plane in the plane they had chartered, Babs was being prepared for our flight. She was put to sleep and, accompanied by Ruth, was driven in an ambulance from the Hôpital Sainte-Bernadette to Orly, where I was waiting for them at the gangway of Sylvia's Super-One-Eleven. Babs's and my luggage was already on the jet. Suzy had had it brought to the airport. I was handed a letter. Suzy had written: "Please come back! I'll do anything you like, but come back, *please!* Suzy."

25

Allow me to introduce myself—Nero. You have heard about me. I was emperor of Rome. But I much preferred racing chariots, acting and singing. I murdered my mother and forced my teacher, Seneca, to commit suicide. I set fire to Rome and burned Christians as living torches in my garden. Mine was a dissolute life, to its dreadful end in the year 68 A.D. If my story interests you, tell Dr. Reinhardt. There is a perfectly wild book about me in the hospital library.

The words were printed, big and red, on a piece of brown paper stuck on the wall of the entrance hall of the Sophienkrankenhaus for children in Nürnberg. The picture of a bronze bust of Nero had been cut out of some magazine and pasted on the paper. The words came out of the mouth of the head inside a comic-strip balloon. Very effective.

At the time—9:45 P.M.—only two people were present in the lobby: the man on duty in his booth, behind a sliding glass window, and a man of medium height in a dark-blue winter coat. Like me the man wore glasses and looked depressed.

We had arrived in Nürnberg on schedule; an ambulance from the Sophienkrankenhaus was waiting for us, and Babs was moved, with the utmost care, from the plane into the ambulance. She had barely been placed inside when she woke up in a state of utter confusion. She was frightened, and the pains had come back. Ruth and a young doctor from the hospital tried desperately to calm Babs, who was thrashing around, arms and legs flailing in the air. "It's a reaction from the flight," said Ruth.

The ambulance siren wailed, Babs screamed and screamed. "Faster!" Ruth told the driver. His foot went all the way down on the gas, and the ambulance shot forward, through red lights and across intersections. It turned into a side street practically on two wheels. At last we were there. As far as Ruth was concerned I had ceased to exist. All her attention was concentrated on Babs, who was being rolled into the clinic. I wanted to follow her, but a young doctor stopped me. "You can't come any further, Herr Norton."

"Who says so?"

"I say so. What we have to do to try to keep the child alive after all this exertion, we have to do alone. Please go out in the yard again and wait in the lobby. Dr. Reinhardt will come to you just as soon as she can. Please." So I did as he told me.

It was very cold in Nürnberg; the sky was clear. I walked out into the yard and around the clinic to the entrance, where I told the man in his booth that I was going to wait for Frau Doktor Reinhardt. He nodded absentmindedly. He was arranging stamps in an album.

I sat down, looked at the strange Nero poster and noticed a quiet man seated at the other end of the hall. I sat there for an hour and thought that in this hour, Babs would surely die.

"Norton!"

I looked up. The man in the booth had spoken. He was holding a telephone in his hand. "You're Herr Norton, aren't you?"

"Yes, why?"

"Telephone."

"Who is it?"

"Jesus, Mary and Joseph! How should I know? Central's asking if you're here. So . . . d'you want to talk or not?"

The quiet man at the other end of the lobby was looking at me seriously. I got up. When I reached the little window in the booth, the man handed me the receiver. He had a lot of pretty stamps laid out in front of him. I saw that it was a complete Monegasque set from the years 1969 and 1970. I supported myself on my elbows on the windowsill and said, "Hello?"

"What do you mean, 'Hello'? Since when is your name Hello?" Bracken.

"What's up?"

"Joe is in Paris. With his crew. At Le Monde. He wants to talk to us as of this minute."

"Joe can kiss—"

"Shut up! D'you think I'm enjoying this? I've got to fly back tonight too, with Lejeune."

"Where are you, anyway?"

"In Madrid. Everything's okay here. How are things there?"

"I'll come tomorrow. I've got to get some sleep."

"You'll fly tonight, brother. Tomorrow at eight A.M. we're due at Joe's. And I want to know what's going on at your end."

"Don't know. I've been waiting forever."

"Maybe things aren't going too well."

"Looks like it. I'm staying here."

"You'll be at Le Monde at eight A.M., even if the kid's dead! Joe's in a foul mood."

"Joe can kiss—"

"You're repeating yourself. Tomorrow at eight."

I said nothing. I handed the man the receiver, and he hung up, and I remained standing where I was, my head in my hands.

"Herr Norton."

I turned around. Ruth was standing there. She had on a white coat, and the dark circles of exhaustion ringed her eyes again. "Oh, Frau Doktor, how is she?"

"Not good." Ruth began to walk away from the booth. "The flight was too much for her."

"I have to go back, Frau Doktor," I said. "Tonight. I have to be in Paris tomorrow morning at eight. I just got a call."

Before she could reply I heard a child's voice beside me. "Who are you?"

I looked down. A boy of about ten was standing there. He had black hair and big black glowing eyes. He was wearing a robe over his pajamas, and slippers.

"Sammy! What are you doing here?" Ruth sounded startled. "Why aren't you asleep?"

The boy called Sammy paid no attention to her; he went right on staring at me and said, "I see you don't want to tell me who you are. I'll tell you who I am. I am Malechamawitz."

"You are . . ." I started to say but was interrupted by a nurse who came running up to us. "Sammy! I've been looking for you everywhere. You know you're not supposed to get up at night!"

"And you know it too, Sister Lenore," said Ruth, "and you also know that Sammy often gets up at night. He's on your floor. How did he manage to get away again?"

"How can I possibly look after thirty children and twenty of them restless? We're understaffed, Frau Doktor. Personnel has been begging for a second night shift."

"I know. Take Sammy back now. Go with Sister Lenore, Sammy. Goodnight." She stroked his head gently and smiled. *"Shalom."*

Sammy said, *"Shalom,"* and let Sister Lenore lead him away. He looked back at me and said, "I am Malechamawitz. You understand, yes?"

"I understand," I said helplessly. The little boy and the nurse withdrew.

"Is his name really Malechamawitz?" I asked.

"No."

"But . . ."

"He is very ill, Herr Norton. He insists that he is Malechamawitz. It is a Yiddish word."

"What does it mean?"

"It means Angel of Death," said Ruth, and went right on, "What do you mean—you have to leave? You can't leave. I've brought along all Babs's records, and your power of attorney, and the false papers. I'll see to it that nobody finds out who she really is—and you too—but you can't leave Babs alone here!"

"I have to."

"Who says so?"

"My bosses have arrived from Hollywood. There's going to be an important conference tomorrow. I have to be there."

"And the child stays here? And you stay in Paris?"

"Yes . . . no . . . yes . . . dear God in heaven, I don't know what's going to happen! How can I?" I shouted.

"You don't have to raise your voice, Herr Norton, not here."

"I'm sorry. I didn't mean to shout. I don't feel too well. I haven't slept for . . ."

"Neither have I, Herr Norton."

"Forgive me, please. It's nerves."

She nodded. "That's all right, Herr Norton. Everybody must do what they have to do. But you'll come back? Just as soon as you can?"

My smile, I could feel, was a grimace. "As soon as I can, of course. I . . ." I nearly choked over these words. "I love Babs, don't I? And I . . . I also want to ask you for that book."

"What book?" She looked at the wall where I was looking and saw the poster. "Oh, I see." She nodded. "Yes. You've got to come back for that too, Herr Norton. Perhaps mainly for that."

"What do you mean?"

"Do you remember what I told you during the flight, about the incurably sick boy we have here—Tim?" I had to lean against the wall or I would have dropped. "And do you remember what he told me? That I was here just as much for myself as for his and the other children's sake?"

I nodded.

"I want you to meet Tim. He can tell you more about yourself than any of us doctors. He can—"

"No," said a man's voice.

Ruth turned around. The man with the sad face had come up to us. Now he bowed. Good evening, Frau Doktor."

"Good evening, Herr Pfarrer." He was a minister. "What do you mean—no?"

"I mean," the minister said softly, "that our Tim can't explain anything any more to anybody."

"What . . . what's wrong with Tim?"

The minister nodded seriously. "Tim is dead, Frau Doktor. He died three hours ago."

26

"Phil," said Joe Gintzburger, his hands folded over his stomach, a small, frail-looking man, with a gentle, kindly voice, gentle kindly eyes, long lashes, white, bushy eyebrows; his thick hair was white too, and so was his meticulously groomed mustache. "My dear Phil. First I must thank you on behalf of myself and all of us for what you have done for us in this terrible situation."

It was 8:05 A.M. on December 4, 1971, a Saturday. I'd made it. It was still dark outside and the lights were on in Joe's suite. We were breakfasting at several small round tables. Most of those present were red-eyed and had no appetite, and this breakfast had something unreal about it. It was as if we were breakfasting in an overheated funeral parlor, and the luxurious surroundings made it seem more unreal.

Only two of those present ate heartily—Joe Gintzburger and Lejeune. They downed oatmeal, ham and eggs, brioches with butter and assorted jams. Lejeune gave the waiter a second order for ham and eggs, three every time, and ate like a pig. I drank quantities of black coffee. All the others, Rod Bracken too, were only half awake, but even in this condition they were demonstrating their eternal devotion and tremendous respect for Joe Gintzburger.

"The same applies to my good friend Maître Lejeune. He too has made great sacrifices and performed miracles."

"No, no!" the obese lawyer protested in the phoniest embarrassment. The two words of protest, spoken from a mouth full of bread and jam, managed to soil the tablecloth.

Beside Joe, Rod, Lejeune and myself, the following were present: the public relations manager of Seven Stars, three American lawyers whom Joe had brought along, a man who looked like a doctor, and the director of *The Chalk Circle*, a Spaniard, Julio da Cava. He had come to Paris from Madrid with Rod and Lejeune.

I drank coffee and listened to Joe, but what he was saying didn't really sink in. Ruth's voice was in my ears. "You've got to come back to Nürnberg, Herr Norton, as soon as you can. I know you will. Because there simply isn't anyone here who can help us help Babs. We can't do it alone. We need you now, Herr Norton, desperately!"

She had called a taxi and walked to the entrance of the hospital with me. When the taxi arrived, she had placed both hands on my shoulders, and her face was close to mine as she said, "You are more important to Babs now than any medication." And I too had done something strange: I had taken Ruth's hand and kissed it. It startled her, and she ran back into the hospital even before I got into the taxi that took me to the airport and Sylvia's jet.

"You see, my friends, all of us are doing and will do all we can so that, in spite of the tragedy that has stricken Babs, our Sylvia will be able to make this marvelous film about mother love ... *The Chalk Circle* ... our biggest production to date." That velvety voice, eyes raised heavenward. He hasn't read a line of Brecht in his life, I thought. "All of us at Seven Stars, from the biggest stars down to the last electrician, are one big happy family. And that's the only way we can produce truly great international films."

. "And how right you are!" fluted Maître Lejeune.

I looked at him. His bald head glistened in the light, and because of his huge stomach he again had had to sit far back from the table.

"Our thinking is universal," said Joe, "and our creative urge is revitalized constantly by the strength that flows from our humane attitude toward life."

"Bravo!" cried Maître Lejeune, getting ready to attack the cheese plate.

"But what would we be without our Sylvia?" Eyes raised heavenward again. "This wonderful, marvelous woman! The greatest film actress in the world! And why is she the greatest?"

He was about to answer his own question, but his public relations man got there ahead of him. "Because she is so humane and her emotions run deep and pure," he said.

"That's it!" said Joe. "I am telling you here and now, not even *Gone with the Wind* brought in a fraction of what Sylvia and her *Chalk Circle* will net us! Sylvia will shake every mother's heart on this earth to the core! Sylvia will show them what it really means to be a mother!" He looked at Lejeune. "Do you still have your mother, my good friend?"

"Yes, Monsieur Gintzburger," said Lejeune, and a piece of Camembert plopped on the tablecloth.

"Then cherish her, my friend."

"I do. I do." Another dollop of cheese.

"Yes, cherish your mothers," said Joe, his voice trembling with emotion. "For he who still has a mother is fortunate!" He blew his nose. "I don't have a mother any more. Motherhood—the most honorable institution in the world. And *that*, gentlemen, is why we are filming *The Chalk Circle.*"

I looked at da Cava. He looked miserable. Wait, I thought, you haven't heard anything yet!

"There are people who laugh at me for this conviction,"

said Joe, shaking his head sadly. "Look at the pictures these people make! What are they like?" He folded his hands. "Cynics! All of them! What do they do with a mother in their films? They knock her on the head, they throw her down the stairs!" His voice rose. "*That* is their idea of art, my friends! And when these miserable fools go broke, they're surprised! Isn't that so, gentlemen?" He looked at his lawyers. One said, "That's what it's like, Joe."

The Spanish director cleared his throat. Joe's smart PR man could see that things were about to go wrong. He said to da Cava, "Mr. Gintzburger is one of the great old American producers. Like Louis B. Mayer. I worked for Mayer. Just like Joe, exactly. You must read Thoreau, Mr. da Cava." The Spaniard nodded. "He said that most of us lead lives of quiet desperation. Well, at Seven Stars we believe that films should uplift the audience, not depress them."

"You're goddam right, Charlie! And with that we have arrived at the heart of the matter. Our wonderful Sylvia has been struck down by a terrible blow of fate. All of us know how much she loves Babs, and Babs is seriously, very seriously, ill."

He had finished his breakfast. Now he took an aluminum cigar case from his jacket, took a large cigar out of it, cut off the tip, and moistened it with his tongue. PR man Charlie jumped up to light it for him. Joe blew out a lot of blue smoke and leaned back in his chair. "We cannot expect Sylvia to make *The Chalk Circle* as long as she is bearing this dreadful burden." He puffed at his cigar. "We must see to it that Babs gets the best possible medical care, but—and this seems self-evident to me—we have to keep the two separated. No woman in the world could bear such a double burden—to play a difficult, serious role and to have a seriously ill child near her, at the same time."

"Not in a film with a twenty-five-million-dollar budget," said one of the lawyers, and now, one at a time, those present awoke and were ready to talk.

"That's it," said Joe. "Go on, Jim."

The lawyer went on. "Quite apart from the fact that it will be impossible to show Babs in public with her mother as we used to do."

Everybody nodded. Only I didn't. "Babs's condition may improve radically," I said, feeling as sick as a dog.

"Doc?" said Joe.

The man who looked like a doctor said, "No."

"No, what?"

"Mr. Kaven, surely you have seen and heard enough about this illness to realize that Babs cannot get well. Her condition will *not* improve." He snorted. "Or do you really think she will be able to appear in public again in the near future?"

I didn't answer. I was feeling worse all the time.

Doc went on. "Of course we are presuming that Babs will recover. What's the matter, Mr. Kaven? Is something wrong?"

"It's your tone, doctor," I said. "I don't like it."

"That's too bad," he said, and he continued. "If Babs survives, which all of us naturally hope will be the case, then, as a result of such a serious infection it is to be expected that considerable damage will remain evident for a long time, if not forever, making it quite simply impossible to show the child in public."

"For God's sake!" I shouted. "Will you please express yourself differently?"

"You can't shout at me, Mr. Kaven," said the doctor.

"Please pull yourself together, Phil," said Joe, licking his cigar. "And let Doc finish."

Doc finished. "She can't be shown in public any more, and I am not going to express it in any other way, Mr. Kaven. But even if we want to presume that there will be some improvement in her condition, one thing is certain—Babs will never again be the World's Greatest Little Sunshine Girl."

"And for the same reason her mother will no longer be the greatest film actress in the world!" I cried angrily. "Frankly, I don't think Sylvia will make another picture, least of all *The Chalk Circle!*"

"That," said Joe, pointing his cigar at me, "is our business. Leave it to us, Phil. Sylvia *will* continue to be the greatest film actress in the world. She *will* make *The Chalk Circle*. She has no choice, am I right, gentlemen?" He looked at his lawyers.

"How about your saying something for a change?" I asked Bracken.

He shook his head.

"Whoever survives such a case of meningoencephalitis," Doc went on, "has such a serious brain illness behind him that months, perhaps even years later, new diseases may be counted on to appear. Epilepsy, for instance, or a form of Parkinson's disease. Parkinson's becomes evident with symptoms such as muscular rigidity, a masklike facial expression, walking disability, salivation, tremors, and so on. All this can happen to Babs. She could have an epileptic seizure on Sunset Boulevard or during a press conference, and such things are not pretty to watch, especially—"

"Stop!" I shouted.

"You're not to shout!" he yelled.

"Children, children!" said Joe, still leaning back in his chair, puffing on his cigar. "Have you forgotten what I said about our being one big happy family?"

"Quite right," said one of the lawyers, "and with that we come to another point. The public must *never* find out what has happened to Babs, and that means that you, Mr. Kaven, and Miss Moran must continue to appear in public, now as never before, as the ideal lovers of the century."

"But without Babs," I said.

"But without Babs."

PR man Charlie said, "As you all know, there is an artist" —and he mentioned a famous singer—"who has a retarded child and doesn't mind admitting it. She is not admired or loved less because of it. In Miss Moran's case—and I have with me legal opinions attesting to the fact—this would not be the case, and all of you know why."

"Monte Carlo," whispered Bracken.

"So?" I said.

"So," said Joe, puffing on his cigar, "things are really quite simple, dear Phil. Sylvia is still . . . on vacation. We don't want to confront her with this dreadful turn of events now. The time for that will be when or if, God forbid, Babs's condition becomes critical or, what all of us hope, when it shows signs of improvement—after Sylvia has come back. Then we will discuss the situation with *her*. I am sure that when the time comes, Sylvia will be in full agreement with our decision. Today we have to address ourselves to you, Phil." Two of the lawyers were smiling; Bracken swore, but inaudibly. "We have to talk to you, because in the meantime and later on as well you will be the only one who can look after Babs's interests on the one hand, and on the other function as the man in whom Sylvia has found fulfillment. That Babs will no longer figure as a third member in your lives has many plausible explanations."

And then I experienced another facet of our clever, resourceful Maître Lejeune. He turned around, his face expressionless, and said, "Got it?"

"Yes," I said. "I got it. So that Sylvia may remain a star and you can make your millions, I am to lead two lives—prince consort and nursemaid."

"You could express yourself more delicately," said Lejeune, and I said, "You can kiss my ass."

I looked at all of them seated in Joe's salon. I couldn't see a trace of sympathy or compassion on any of their faces. And so my old character quickly reasserted itself. I crossed my legs and said, "Very well. It's your decision. I am the man who is to keep Babs out of the limelight, who is to go through God knows what that still lies ahead with her, and God knows where the two of us will end up. But if I am to continue in the role of Sylvia's constant companion, the great love of her life—then, gentlemen, I must have security, because not one of us can look into the future."

"And what do you mean by that?" asked one of the lawyers softly.

"I mean," I replied, just as softly, "that if I am to remain at your disposal in this shitty game you're playing, I demand an immediate payment of half a million dollars. In cash. In small denominations. I shall open an account in my name for the amount." What I had in mind actually was a safe, but I kept that to myself.

My demand was met with absolute silence. Everyone present, Bracken included, stared at me as if I were a pestilential insect. Then Joe Gintzburger said softly—suddenly all of us were speaking softly—"Get out!"

"What did you say?"

"I said, 'Get out!' And I mean right now," whispered Joe. "I don't want to lay eyes on you again! Ever! Get out, you blackmailing bastard!"

What could I do, your honor? I got up and walked out of Joe's suite.

27

"I am so happy, *mon petit chou,*" said Suzy. "I'd like to run to the nearest church and light candles and put a hundred francs in the alms box." She kissed me. Both of us were lying naked on her crazy bed, drinking Calvados.

Suzy was so ecstatic because I had called her and told her to meet me at her apartment. I had given it all a lot more thought and had decided to accept her offer to establish this little enterprise of hers, and to run it for her in style. She had screamed with joy.

She was already at her apartment when I arrived, and she almost suffocated me with her kisses. "I've got to have something to drink," I said. I was still enraged over the way Joe had thrown me out, and over the half million I hadn't been able to get out of him. Even more about the latter. And that was why I had called Suzy. One can earn quite a lot of money without resorting to blackmail. I was an absolute bastard at the time, your honor. I could only think my way through to: Call it quits, quits, quits! Who do they think I am? What are they trying to do to me?

So Suzy and I did it and she was stoned and I was cold sober. Then I went into the kitchen with her, both of us naked, and watched her cut up a cooked lobster with a large pair of shears. We sat in the kitchen, the feeble winter sunshine outside, and I was very hungry. Suzy was too. While we ate she talked on and on about what a wonderful life we would have now that I'd come to my senses at last. "I'll write to my count today and tell him it's all over between us, and tomorrow I'll have all my girls come here, but today we'll stay by ourselves, yes? And you'll see how much they'll love you right away, *mon petit chou*. And then we'll all sit down together and discuss everything in detail and . . . what's the matter? Not hungry any more?"

She had opened a bottle of champagne, and I emptied my glass, and I must have looked at her like a sleepwalker as I said, "I can't do it."

"Can't do what?" She put the lobster claw she'd been picking at back on her plate and looked at me, startled.

"The two of us. It won't do," I said.

"You're drunk, *mon petit chou.*"

"No."

"Then you're crazy!"

"I'm not crazy either."

"But you must be crazy, *mon petit chou,*" said Suzy. "We started off so happily together, then the brat got sick and your whore had to have a face lift . . ."

"It's the other way around," I said.

"*Merde!* And you come back to me and I make you a proposition and you say no because you've suddenly found a place in your heart for the brat who isn't even yours! And I try to understand and pull myself together and I tell you I understand and realize nothing can come of my plan. And then . . . my God, you *are* ready for the nut house! You go off and you come back and you say now you're ready to shit on it all, now we'll open our cathouse. And you come here and we're happier than we've ever been and at last everything's settled, and then you tell me *again* it can't be done! *Mon petit chou,* we can't go on like this! Whatever I may be, I'm a human being! And you can't treat a human being like that!"

"Yes," I said. "No," I said.

"What, yes? What, no?"

"No, you can't treat a human being like that, as you just said."

She poured her glass full and drank the champagne down in one go, then she clutched her head with both hands. "This is it," she said. "I'm sozzled! You're sitting there, *mon petit chou,* and I hear you saying things you've never said."

"I have said them, Suzy."

"But it's crazy!"

"Of course it's crazy."

"But that guy from Hollywood threw you out! Said you were a crook, a blackmailer. You don't have a damn thing and you're worth nothing. What are you going to do now, *nom de Dieu?*"

"I don't know," I said, and got up as if in a trance and walked into the bathroom and washed, and went into the living room and dressed slowly, putting on all the things I'd taken off so fast on arrival. Suzy ran after me or stood beside me, and the tears were rolling down her cheeks as she watched me silently, still naked, then her sobs convulsed her and she folded her hands and said, "The trouble is—you're a decent human being."

By that time I was in the living room, my shorts and socks on. "A decent human being—shit!" I said.

"A decent human being, no shit."

"Yes, yes," I said. "Where's my shirt?"

"Here. Wait. I'll help you. It's just like the last time. The child that isn't your child. Babs! Poor sick Babs! You can't get her out of your mind. Her mother, the bitch—you don't give a damn about her, but you care about the child. She's become the most important thing in your life!"

"No!"

"Yes!"

"No!"

"Stop saying no! Wait, I'll button your cuffs. You don't have a child of your own, so you made Babs your child. And now that she's sick and needs help, you have to go to her."

Your honor, I swear if Babs had died that very moment I wouldn't have given a damn! After what I had found out in Nürnberg, and even more after hearing what Joe Gintzburger expected me to do, there was no one on this earth I hated more than Babs! But there was another reason why I didn't stay with Suzy, why I was determined to leave her with no idea where to go, no idea what to live on, and that reason had come clear to me like lightning as I was eating Suzy's lobster. I couldn't disappoint Ruth. I was ready to do anything if only to be near her again, to hear her voice, to see her face, her figure, the way she walked . . .

As I put on my pants, Suzy said, "Yes, you've got to go to Babs. I wish I could stop you, but I can't. And I don't want to any more because I realize now what's wrong with you. You're too good for me." Oh my God! I thought, zipping up my trousers. "And that's the end of my plan," she went on. "Forget it! Forget it fast, please! I shall never betray you, or Babs, or that bitch, or anything else I happen to know, I swear I won't." She knelt down and helped me into my shoes while I knotted my tie. "I can swear to that easily," she said, "because I love you much too much to do you any harm."

"Suzy, *mon petit chou*, please . . ."

"Be quiet! I love you much too much, but never come here again. Do you hear me? Never!" I put on my jacket. "It's all over between us, has to be. As of right now and forever.

Because otherwise .... otherwise ... if anything like what happened today happened again, I swear, I'd make trouble. I know I would. I wouldn't be able to help it."

I walked into the foyer and put on my coat and said, "But we can remain friends, can't we?"

And she screamed suddenly, the tears still running down her face, "Get out! Fast! I told you I was a piece of shit, and if I have to look at you one minute longer, I'll behave like a piece of shit. Get out!"

I left her.

28

I still had 55,000 francs from my first winnings, thanks to Lucien Bayard, perhaps a little more if I'd won the second time, right, your honor? That was quite a lot of money. I took a taxi to Le Monde. I knew that Lucien had left an envelope for me, and now I needed it. It was practically all I had, because I couldn't count on Sylvia any more. When she came to they'd enjoy telling her that they'd fired me, and why. And there would be nothing Sylvia could do about it but throw me out too. Of course I could try to bring her around by doing everything a gigolo like myself was capable of, but I didn't want to do that because I knew I'd succeed. Of course I could have kept my mouth shut and run an attractive little cathouse with Suzy, but I didn't want to do that either. There was simply no solution. There were the diamond cufflinks in my safe at the hotel, and a platinum wristwatch and a few other things Sylvia had given me, and I knew I'd better get them before Sylvia took them away from me. And there was the Maserati Ghibli in the garage at the airport. I could probably realize quite a sum if I sold it. And there were a few fairly valuable items in the suitcases that had gone to Suzy's. Every franc counted, because now I was flat broke. I had no idea what was to become of me, and I couldn't seem to keep my mind on it because all I could think of was Ruth. I didn't know how I was going to get back to her and what would happen if I did. To say I was confused was an understatement. But above all I was afraid, terribly afraid of seeing Joe again and that godam fag Lejeune with his eunuch's voice, the glutton who had stabbed me in the back.

At the desk they nodded and smiled at me as in my carefree days, and so did the captain and bellboys, and I nodded and smiled back. Charles Fabre, the legendary bell captain, was on duty, and he gave me my key and the envelope with the money. I sat down in the lobby and tore it open. It contained 55,000 francs in 500-franc bills. I also found a sheet of fine paper in it, with a note from Lucien Bayard. I read:

Dear Monsieur Kaven,
  Many thanks for the 10,000 francs that Monsieur Bracken gave me in your name. I enclose the rest of your winnings: 55,000 francs. I regret more than I can say, monsieur, that we were not lucky in the races at Chantilly. King's Twist was disqualified and Le Parleur came in fourth. I can't tell you how embarrassed I am. I placed your money as you wished—all in all 4,500 francs. That they were my tips means of course that I was a loser too.

Good old Lucien! Before leaving the hotel I would call him up and speak to him, and I would repay what I owed him, no two ways about it. I went on reading.

  I very much want to have a talk with you, monsieur, on one of the next nights, if possible. On Sunday, December 12, three horses are racing at Vincennes, and I am absolutely sure they are winners. Please get in touch with me as soon as you can. I have been trying to contact you, but couldn't reach you.
    With my most sincere regards, Monsieur Kaven,
                    Very truly yours,
                    Lucien Bayard

I sat down at one of the desks in the lobby and wrote Lucien a letter, thanking him for what he had done for me. I described my situation only in very general terms, and I enclosed 10,000 francs. Lucien had placed 4,500 francs on the second series of races for me, 5,000 on the first. The extra 500 was a final gesture of friendship. I addressed the envelope, took it over to Charles Fabre, and asked him to give it to Lucien that evening.

239

"Certainly, Monsieur Kaven."

So now all that was left of my winnings was 45,000 francs, but there are certain things you've just got to do, your honor, right?

"Would you do me a favor, Monsieur Fabre?"

"Anything you say, Monsieur Kaven."

I gave him the number of Suzy's beauty salon, and asked him to call and give instructions that my suitcases be sent over to Le Monde as quickly as possible. I still had a lot of things at Suzy's. I hoped she wouldn't take her time about sending them over. And I still had to empty my safe.

"I'll attend to it right away." Fabre beamed at me. "You settled things all right with that scandal sheet, didn't you, monsieur?"

"What scandal . . . oh!" He meant the paper with the headline about me.

"There's a whole page with a retraction and an apology, Monsieur Kaven. Didn't you see it?"

"No, I had to fly to—"

Thank God he interrupted me! "To Madrid. With Mademoiselle-Geiringer. How is she?"

"Better. She's in the best hands now."

"I'm glad to hear that, Monsieur Kaven. I really am. Mademoiselle Geiringer is such a charming person."

I took the elevator to the fourth floor and went to Suite 419, closed the door behind me, sat down and looked at my shoes. I thought of Ruth, totally confused at first because my situation was so confused, then I began to think more coherently about what I could do to see her again. And I saw that my shoes were dirty and took them off to clean them, and then it occurred to me that the stuff to clean them with was in one of my suitcases at Suzy's. So I went on thinking of Ruth instead, staring at my socks all the time. Even my socks had been paid for by Sylvia. Everything I had on, except for my handkerchief and shorts, Sylvia had bought for me. They were very fine, dark-blue socks. . . .

29

The door flew open. Joe Gintzburger came storming into the room. I could see Lejeune behind him, and behind the maître, Rod Bracken, and bringing up the rear all the men Joe had brought with him from Hollywood. They rushed up to me, and I was scared to death. Joe was a midget, but the others, husky athletic types every one of them, could have beaten me to pulp. I stood up and stepped back. They came after me. I moved back again. Finally I was against the wall. And I'd left my racing winnings lying on the table, I saw to my horror.

"Now listen, Joe," I started to say, but the little man with the thick white hair interrupted me by bellowing, "Not a word out of you, you son of a bitch!"

I tried again, yelled, "Get out of here!" while the others closed in around me.

"You're to shut your trap, I said," said little Joe. "A son of a bitch! That's what you are! That's what I said!"

"I heard you." I felt especially helpless, standing there in my socks. "You're a super pig, Phil," said Joe, and it sounded almost affectionate, "but a super pig's got to be paid if you need him, and we need you."

At that point I thought I was going to fall over. Suddenly I understood. After Joe had thrown me out, the others had panicked, because Joe was right—they needed me desperately now. Evidently they had discussed every possible substitute for me and had had to drop all of them. They had probably also been scared to death that I'd run to the nearest news agency with the story. I'm telling you, your honor, the prodigal son couldn't have been welcomed more warmly by his father than I was now.

Joe said, "Okay, okay, I'm sorry about this morning. By tonight you'll have your half million."

You must admit, your honor, it was a bit too much to digest within a few minutes. I took a step forward. This time it was Joe and his crew who stepped back. And I walked very slowly over to the chair where I'd left my shoes, because I felt dizzy, and sat down. And they all came very quietly over to where I was sitting, almost on tiptoe, and soon they were all standing around me.

"What's the matter with you?" asked Joe. "Didn't you understand me?"

"I understood you, Joe."

"Tonight. In bills of small denomination. Just what you asked for. Will take that long to get hold of it. It's a lot of money, half a million."

"No," I said.

"What do you mean, no?" said Joe.

"I mean I'm not taking any money," I said, "and I apologize to you, Joe, also to all the gentlemen present," and I looked at all of them one by one.

"What sort of a trick is this now?" Lejeune in his eunuch's voice.

"It's not a trick," I said, "it's the truth."

You see, your honor, after all the thinking I'd done, it had come to me at last how I could get back to Ruth. Not to Babs. I was as indifferent as ever to what was going to happen to Babs. At any rate, at the time I thought I was. But to Ruth! Back to Ruth! And it was really so simple. Why hadn't I thought of it before?

"It's the truth," I said again. "I don't want any money. I only need a little to live on, and Sylvia will provide for that as she always has done. And I'll do anything you want me to do, gentlemen."

Now they were looking at me as if I was crazy, and PR man Charlie said to the doctor, "What's the matter with him? Has he gone nuts?"

Doc stepped forward, looked at me sharply, then he said, "He's perfectly all right." He leaned forward and sniffed. "Smells a little of alcohol, but he's not drunk." After which everyone was silent. In the end I was the one who spoke.

"I will stay with Babs, and with Sylvia. I'll do everything that has to be done. Please step back, doctor."

"Why?"

"Because you're standing on my shoes and I want to put them on. My feet are cold."

" . . . this young man whose funeral we are attending, who was so much loved and the object of so much anxiety and efforts to help, to cure, all of which failed in the end," said Pastor Ernst Hirtmann, pale, somber, shifting his glasses. He was standing beside an open grave, about a dozen people around him. Ruth was there, so was I , and the parents of the seventeen-year-old paraplegic, Tim (*Allow me to introduce myself—Nero!*), who had died at the Sophienkrankenhaus in Nürnberg on December 3, 1971, a few hours before I had arrived from Paris with Ruth and Babs. It was December 7, in the afternoon, a Tuesday.

"In vain and expensive," Tim's father said softly. He was standing beside me, a tall man wearing a fur-lined coat, and his face was red—not from the cold but from anger. In a slightly louder voice he said, "The other day I added up what these seventeen years cost us. In the last three months alone, eighteen thousand marks for this new contraption."

"Be quiet, *please,*" said his wife, the tears pouring down her cheeks.

"Eighteen thousand," her husband repeated. "Eighteen thousand in three months. Because this English doctor insisted that the apparatus could work miracles. Our insurance people said right away they wouldn't pay for it, but you—you said Tim had to have it. And the doctors here? They wanted to try it. I'm telling you, doctors all over the world stick together. Eighteen thousand marks!" he said again, and began to cry.

"He's in shock," Ruth whispered. "He is a good father, a decent man. I've known him for a long time."

"We know," Pastor Hirtmann was saying, "that life must go on. That's a cliché, but it happens to be the truth. Life must go on for every one of us, always bearing death in mind. And when we think that what we do or say daily has a purpose, then we must examine them all to see if this purpose stands up in the face of death. Whether perhaps a lot of what we do isn't nonsense. All of us must die, our chattel scattered to the winds, and not everything said about us after death will be true. But the little pains and the greater agonies are true now, and our grief is true, the grief we feel for this young man."

We were standing close to the crematorium. There were relatives present, and also a few nurses and doctors from the hospital. You could hear the whistle of a locomotive. The tracks of a freightyard by the cemetery, and trains kept passing by.

I had come back from Paris the day before. Sylvia's sleep cure had taken a little longer; Dr. Delamare wasn't taking any chances. Today, if all had gone according to plan, she should have been awake and expecting my call.

"The only thing we may do," Hirtmann was saying, "is help ourselves by honestly admitting our helplessness." It was very cold. Soon it will snow, I thought. "A priest can also admit to helplessness, because he cannot invent consolation. All he can do is pass it on. And I, a simple priest, am telling you here and now: When a farewell is as tragic as the one we are bidding this young man today, then I would rather be standing at the side of you, his parents, than here addressing you. I would much rather be standing beside you both, praying to God that He should not respond to our tears with silence."

Ruth was quite changed. She kept looking over and beyond the cemetery and its graves. A locomotive whistled again.

I thought I had heard locomotives whistling last night in my room in the Hotel Bristol, where I lived now. They had torn me out of disturbing dreams. On my arrival I had shown the desk clerk my German passport, made out in the name of Philip Norton. I was German, residing in the United States, according to various remarks and visas in my passport, which was only three days old but slightly creased and soiled, to make it look used, a forged passport, of course. I shall tell in due course how I got it.

"But," Pastor Hirtmann was saying, "God is not silent, at least not when faced with our tears. His voice, which more often than not we drown out with our chatter and noise, we hear only when we have been made small, very small, by sorrow."

And that was the moment I saw him.

He was very thin, looked about forty-five years old. He had on an open gray duffel coat over a creased blue suit, a white shirt, not very clean, a blue tie, crew-cut black hair, a pale face; and his dark eyes under thin eyebrows were filled with an expression of greed, impudence, ignorance and the shivering fear of a rat. He was standing on the other side of the grave, but he was staring at me. It startled me. Who could he be?

"A life has ended. A child has left us, a child that never knew the restlessness of grown men, the restlessness born of our confused world that leaves us no peace."

Those eyes! The narrowed, cold, merciless eyes of this thin, shabbily dressed man never let me go. Ruth asked, "What's the matter?"

I said between clenched teeth, "That man over there, in the duffel coat, staring at me. Do you know him?"

"A man, according to our teachings," said Pastor Hirtmann, "went forth into a great solitude. The first who experienced his peace called him Christ."

"I don't know," whispered Ruth. "Looks like an American."

"I'm sure he is," I said, trying not to move my lips. The wheels of a freight train again, endless and loud. Hirtmann raised his voice. "Because of this man, no one has to be alone any more."

"What's that bulge under his left arm?" whispered Ruth. "Do you think he's carrying . . ."

"I'm sure he is," I whispered. "Don't look at him any more."

"And we pray in the name of the lonely Christ, the Christ who died for us; we pray for His peace, His quiet, forceful consoling words, but above all we pray for the parents . . ."

The man in the duffel coat stuck his right hand inside his coat. Ruth stifled a cry. I ducked. Several people turned and looked at us in astonishment. The man drew a Minox from under his coat, lifted it and took my picture, once, twice, three times. I wanted to get to him, but it was impossible. I was crushed between people. Meanwhile he was taking pictures of the group around the grave, the pastor, Ruth.

Hirtmann, his back turned to the man, was saying, "We want to cry out to God when we see ourselves so bitterly robbed, but we would be accusing Him who stands beside us, who became one with those who are in pain, who suffers with those who suffer and who must continue to suffer as long as there are sorrowing humans on earth."

The man in the duffel coat turned suddenly and ran off as if pursued, to where the cemetery was wildly overgrown and there were no more graves or paths. In seconds he had disappeared.

"What does it mean?" whispered Ruth.

I shrugged.

"I'm afraid," whispered Ruth. "You too?"

I nodded.

"His love," Pastor Hirtmann was saying, "embraces the dead. It also embraces the living as they face their dead, the living who forget so often to say, 'Lord, teach me to realize that I too must die, so that I may find wisdom.' "

31

I must go back for a moment, your honor, and report on the beginning of a love-hate relationship.

As soon as I had announced, on that ghastly December 4, 1971, that I intended to stay with Babs and Sylvia, Lejeune sent everybody out of the room because he had to speak to me alone. He fell heavily onto the couch, breathed hard, sat with his legs spread because there was no possibility of holding them together, ate some chocolates from a silver dish on the table in front of him and beamed at me. "What are you grinning about?" I asked.

"I'm grinning because I'm looking forward to the next installment of the story." He offered me the dish of candy, more as an afterthought. "Have a piece."

You can imagine what my reply was, your honor. It caused Lejeune to double up with laughter (a *façon de parler*, because he couldn't double up), liberally spraying bits of candy from his mouth. "I'll make a real Frenchman out of you yet!" he declared happily, then, quite suddenly, he was serious. "But first I've got to make a phony German out of you."

"What do you mean by that?"

"Well, you're going to have to lead a double life now, aren't you? Shuttling back and forth between Babs and Sylvia Moran. In Germany your name can't be Kaven, surely you realize that. You've got to put on an altogether different act in Germany. Less ebullient, quiet, depressed. When you appear with Sylvia you're Philip Kaven again, the great lover. You can use your legal papers when you're with her and behave just as you always have; but for Germany we're going to need a new passport for you, and a new image. In Germany you're the poor unfortunate father—don't look at me like that, idiot! In Germany you've got to have a passport in the name of Norton. Not Paul Norton. That was a mistake. Now, if the child dies all of this becomes obsolete, but right now we will get you a passport in the name of Philip Norton."

"Why Philip?"

"Because Babs, if she ever recovers to any extent, which seems to be possible, will call you Phil. That's the name she'll think of if she's ever able to think again at all. Kaven can wait."

"And what about her mother?"

"Children say 'Mama' or something equivalent. She's not likely to address her mother as Sylvia Moran." He picked his teeth and looked with disappointment at the results. "And Mama's still on vacation, isn't she? So . . . you get a German passport with the name Philip Norton, a resident of the United States. All the necessary information and stamps will be in the passport, and it won't look like a new one, either. We must have some photos of you made right away and sent to my friend in Nürnberg."

"Who is your friend in Nürnberg?"

"His name is Vigbert Sondersen, and he is chief of police in Nürnberg. Specialty, homicide."

"Now wait one minute—"

"Sondersen and I are old friends. Once I persuaded homicide here to do Sondersen a great favor. People like us have to stick together, don't we?"

"And you're trying to tell me that a police chief can order the passport office to make out a phony passport for me?"

"Yes," said Lejeune. "Yes, Sondersen can do just that. He is one of the most capable criminologists in Germany. I have friends everywhere. Do you think I could operate the way I do if I didn't? Do you think Mr. Gintzburger would retain me if I didn't?"

I was impressed.

"I've already called him up and talked to him about it. Everything's okay. The passport office is waiting for the pictures. When they have them you get an elegant German passport. For other purposes you have your own. But that isn't all. In Germany you can't be the playboy you are with Sylvia. Don't interrupt! In Germany you're a poor fish with a

247

brain-damaged child. So you won't be wearing suits by Cardin. Some of the luggage, all your good things, stays here in Le Monde. We'll switch the suitcases with Babs's clothes too. The new, cheaper ones, will be sent over today."

"And who arranged all this?"

"Who do you think? I did. I deliver the goods for the money I get, and Mr. Gintzburger pays me plenty. In Germany you must were hornrimmed glassed with clear lenses. Dark glasses are too conspicuous. And you've got to be modest, humble. The Maserati stays here. In case you haven't caught on—from here on in you've got to lead a double life, like Jekyll and Hyde. The comparison doesn't exactly fit, but you know what I mean."

"Yes."

"Then let's get going. No time to lose. I've made reservations in a hotel for you. Nothing spectacular, sorry. But you can stay at luxury hotels henceforth only as Philip Kaven. And now we'll go shopping for your ready-made suits and shoes, and everything else you'll need . . ." And that was the moment, your honor, when my love-hate relationship toward Maître Lejeune began.

32

Just a minute . . . so that I don't get things mixed up . . .

According to my diary, Lejeune and I went off to buy inexpensive clothes for me at the Galeries Lafayette on December 4, 1971, and two suitcases, plastic, of course. On December 5 I finally almost collapsed. I slept all day Sunday and halfway through Monday. I didn't have my German passport yet, so I had to use Sylvia's Super-One-Eleven to get back to Nürnberg. At the airport I said goodbye to the crew, because from now on I'd probably be taking commercial flights. I took the bus to the railway station, and all the way into the city I was cursing Babs, who had let me in for all this. At the same time my heart was beating fast at the thought that I would be seeing Ruth again. From the station I drove to police headquarters, because now I needed my false passport. Lejeune had instructed me to go straight to Sondersen.

Chief Vigbert Sondersen rose to greet me. He was very tall and thin, with the face of a cautious doctor. His steel-gray hair lay like a thick pelt around his bony skull. We shook hands and sat down. He asked me if I had the passport pictures with me. I gave them to him. He used the phone, and minutes later a young man came for the pictures. "It won't take long," said Chief Sondersen. "I hope the child pulls through."

"I hope so too," I said, and thought: But not too soon. "I shall never be able to thank you enough for getting this passport, Chief Sondersen."

"I've not done anything really, Herr Norton. All this is routine. We help other people, they help us. Maître Lejeune and I have known each other for many years. He was able to help me once too."

"Yes. He told me that."

"Of course, things aren't all that simple," said Sondersen. "Through Interpol the police the world over now know that we have issued you what you might call a 'protective' passport. It has a special number in a special series, and a letter stamped on it which is reserved for such purposes only. This is not to imply that we don't trust you. It's simply an international regulation."

"I see."

He rolled a pencil between his fingers and said quite unexpectedly, "I'll soon have all this behind me."

"What?"

"All this here. I'm going to retire."

"But the work you do must be very interesting."

"I used to think so," he said. "It was my ambition to be assigned to homicide, although I had to start as a traffic officer. But murder, capital punishment . . ." He paused. "I had a crazy idea, Herr Norton. I wanted to serve justice."

"Lejeune told me that you've done just that, many times."

Sondersen was looking at me, half closing his eyes. "Yes, Herr Norton, I've done that. But it turned out to be very tiring. When I was young I had another dream. I wanted to further the good things by being a teacher. But then"—he put down the pencil—"that didn't seem to have a future, and I decided to fight evil more directly. You see," he said, "evil—I mean absolute evil—turns up very rarely in our world. Most of those who have done wrong simply didn't have the imagination to realize what the results of their actions would be. But beyond them we have absolute evil, Herr Norton, and I have come in contact with it often, very often. It is my duty to fight absolute evil, and I do the best I can. But it grows increasingly difficult. Do you know the most dreadful thing about absolute evil?"

"What?"

"That one really can't do anything about it. You can punish an absolutely evil human being, but what's the use when you can't make a better human being of him?" He spoke very quietly. "And the worst thing, Herr Norton, is that when I look back on my life and the work I've done, there is so much that I've missed, or failed in, or done wrong. And none of it can be redressed. Everything I was able to do in the past today is worth nothing."

"But there is a continuity of events, surely!"

"No," he said. "There is not. That is your wishful thinking, Herr Norton, and my nightmare. We Germans have talked long and at great length about our irrevocable past, but very few people, and unfortunately I am one of them, know that the past really cannot be revoked. And that is a recognition that in my work becomes unbearable." He looked at me gravely.

"So why are you still working?"

"Two years ago I might have retired, but at the time I had just built a small house. I'm married, you see, and I had to take out a loan. So . . . I stayed on."

The young man who had picked up my pictures came back with my passport. It had been lightly and appropriately soiled to look old, and now my picture was pasted in it and correctly stamped.

"Thank you," I said to the young man, who nodded and smiled and withdrew. "And I want to thank you especially, Chief Sondersen."

"Nonsense. When one can do something to help . . ." He rose with me. "Come," he said, "I want to show you something."

He pulled out the drawer of a file. Two large calendar sheets were pasted against the long sides, showing every day and month of the year; a third sheet was stuck on the front of the drawer, inside. I had to lean forward to see it. They were calendars for 1971, 1972 and 1973. Nineteen seventy two and 1973 had nothing written on them. I could see that Sondersen had drawn the one for 1973 himself. Every day had been crossed out in red on the 1971 calendar, up to December 7. "I'll cross out the seventh tonight," said Sorensen, "before I go home."

"I don't understand. Why . . ."

"Put your passport away, Herr Norton. You see, this is my daily pleasure. On December 31, 1973, I retire. At last."

"And until then you will cross out every day you still work?"

He nodded. "This year's almost over, then there are only two more, Herr Norton. Only two more." And he looked so happy as he said that, your honor. And neither of us knew at the time that Chief Sondersen would not retire on December 31, 1973, because a short time before that date, on October 8, 1973, to be exact, he would be called in to investigate the drama that had taken place in the dirtiest room of one of the sleaziest hotels in Nürnberg. And the man whom Chief Sondersen was to find in this sleazy hotel, shot dead by a bullet from a 6.35mm Walther automatic pistol, Model TPH, Serial No. 128467, was the American actor Romero Rettland, and the woman standing beside him, the pistol in her hand, was Sylvia Moran. Two months before his retirement, Chief Sondersen was forced to face absolute evil once more.

33

"Phil . . ."

"Yes, Babs, yes!"

"Mommy?"

"She's coming, Babs."

"Has she been dead a long time?"

End of dialogue. After that question the World's Greatest Little Sunshine Girl closed her eyes again—she had opened them when I had answered her—her lips parted, little saliva bubbles formed on them, and she went on sleeping. She still seemed to prefer to lie on her side, but stretched out now, not hunched up any longer. There were dark shades over the windows. The only light in the room came from a flashlight that Ruth was holding.

I had driven to the Hotel Bristol from police headquarters with my luggage, then straight on to the hospital, where Ruth was waiting for me. "Come with me, Herr Norton," she had said, taking me by the hand, and she had walked ahead of me to Babs's room. I had stood beside Babs's bed and had called her by name and she had replied, as just described.

I straightened up. Ruth was standing close to me, only dimly lit by the flashlight, which she held pointed down. As I looked at her she smiled. "Well?" And in her voice there was joy, the joy of all the mothers in the world when they see their children. *Their* children!

"Well, what?"

"Well, Babs said 'Phil,' Herr Norton. She recognized you! Isn't that wonderful?"

"Yes," I said, my heart beating fast as I looked at this woman in her white coat. "Yes, Frau Doktor, it's wonderful."

"She isn't disoriented any more. Her fever has gone down too."

"How much?"

"It's one hundred and two. And she can almost lie straight. The spasms are less violent. For three days now her breathing has been normal. There have been no more convulsions since she has been here. Pulse is normal. She is in less pain."

"How do you know?"

"You can touch her without her screaming. Her neck is less stiff. The ear is still suppurating, and the paralysis on the left side is still present, but that too is less. She tolerates all medication, especially the broad-spectrum antibiotic. That's done wonders for her."

"Yes, Frau Doktor . . ."

"As far as we can judge, she is out of danger. We examined her thoroughly this morning—two other doctors and the professor. Babs is going to live."

"Live," said Babs, like an echo.

"But her eyes?"

"What's the matter with her eyes?"

"They're crossed. Didn't you notice?"

"Paralysis of the eye muscles. Don't you remember, in Paris the lids were paralyzed too?"

"Yes," I said, and as I write this, your honor, I remember that faced with this obviously hopeful improvement in Babs's condition, I reacted in a way that you, with your understanding of human nature, will surely excuse. I thought: I wish

Babs well, sincerely, but please don't let her get well right away, let it take a long, long time, because once she is well again she will leave the hospital, and I with her. As long as she is ill, she has to stay here and so do I. *With Ruth!*

"But . . . but I guess it will be quite a while before Babs is up and about again?" I said.

"Up and about again?" Ruth's smile was gone. "Herr Norton, all we have done is get the child out of danger! Everything else will follow slowly. In fact, we have no idea how her condition will develop. You mustn't expect miracles."

"I am not expecting miracles, Frau Doktor. She is out of danger, that's miraculous enough. I thank you."

"Don't thank me," she said.

"Oh, but I must, Frau Doktor," I said. "I have to thank you."

34

"Silky?"

"Yes, my Pepito." Sylvia's voice came somewhat slurred through the receiver. She was speaking slowly. Dr. Delamare had certainly put her under thoroughly if she was still speaking like this. "I've been longing for your call. Dr. Delamare has told me where you are with Babs, and it's my fault."

"Nonsense!"

"It's not nonsense. I simply went to pieces. I'm so sorry, so dreadfully sorry about what I did. How is she?"

"Better, Silky. Much better. She's out of danger. She recognized me and called me by name."

"I know you can't come to me now, Pepito. And that's terrible, simply terrible—but my career . . . you'll call me, won't you?"

"Yes."

"Every day?"

"Every day."

"Maybe twice a day?"

"Twice a day, often, my Silky."

"What does she look like, my darling little Babs? Tell me! Why do you have so little to say, Pepito? Maybe it's all not true!"

I said, "I'm in Dr. Reinhardt's office, Silky. I've just spoken to Rod. He knows where I'm staying and under what name if you want to call me. But I'll be in with Babs most of the time."

"You're a darling. You're the darlingest darling Pepito . . ."

"I'll let you talk to Dr. Reinhardt now, so that you can believe me," I said, interrupting her. "She'll corroborate everything I've told you. And she'll tell you what they're planning to do next," and I handed the receiver to Ruth, fast.

Ruth spoke to Sylvia quietly and calmly, in a voice that had to inspire whoever heard it with confidence. We had stood side by side as I put through my call and spoke to Sylvia. Ruth's room here in the Sophienkrankenhaus for children was just as full of toys, books, records, test material, posters and colorfully smeared walls as her room in the Hôpital Sainte-Bernadette, and there was also the one wall covered with shelves full of books. She talked on and on, never raising her voice, never becoming impatient. There was a second desk in the room. I went over to it and sat down.

"No, Frau Moran. All of us, the director included, have come to the conclusion that your daughter is out of danger. . . ." I could hear Ruth saying. I smiled at her, but she didn't smile back.

"Oh, I'm afraid you're going to have to wait weeks for that, Frau Moran, possibly months. . . ." There was a pause.

"No, Frau Moran, it's much too early for anything like that. This—what is his name?—this Dr. Wolken couldn't do anything with Babs yet. Later it would be nice, of course, if Dr. Wolken could come to Nürnberg . . . , No, Frau Moran, please believe me—her first lessons with Dr. Wolken should take place here in the hospital too. We must continue to watch her. I'm so glad you understand, Frau Moran. . . ."

Beside the desk I could see a pile of water colors. I leafed through it. Evidently someone had had the idea to let the sick children paint animals or humans, all of them carrying a knapsack. Some of the paintings were just daubs, others were perfectly clear, some were quite funny, and all of them were colorful. Some of the figures were bent low, some were crawling, but others looked happy and seemed to be carrying their knapsacks quite easily. I got the feeling that a great deal concerning the child's emotional state was revealed in the paintings.

"But Frau Moran! You are going to have to stay in Dr. Delamare's clinic for weeks. And when you appear in public again, surely that can wait, especially any public appearances with Babs. Aren't you happy enough that Babs isn't going to die?"

And then I heard Ruth say, "Of course. He'll call every day. Absolutely. Yes, yes, I'll tell him. Goodbye, Frau Moran." Ruth put down the receiver and said, "Frau Moran loves you more than she can say, more than anything else on earth except for Babs. She wants me to tell you that." Her face was expressionless.

"Why did she end the call so abruptly?"

"Something fell off the bed and she had to pick it up. I think it was a diamond necklace, Herr Norton."

"Oh."

She looked at her watch. "Tim's funeral is in two hours. I must go to it. Will you come with me?"

"Of course." I sounded a little breathless. "May I . . . may I make a request?"

"Of course."

"I owe you such a lot, Frau Doktor. I am so happy to be in Nürnberg. Are you doing anything this evening?"

"No."

"Would you have dinner with me? Please don't say no!"

"Why should I say no, Herr Norton? Of course I'll have dinner with you. I'll be glad to," said Ruth.

35

After Tim's funeral, Ruth and I had taken a taxi back to the hospital, and I had waited for her to finish the day's work. Before we left the clinic, we went to see Babs once more. She was fast asleep. Every now and then her face twitched, and I noticed that her body was similarly affected. "That's all part of her illness," Ruth explained.

She had on a gray suit that evening, and a sheepskin coat. I can see her now. I was wearing a nondescript winter coat and a gray flannel suit, and my hornrimmed glasses. Until that night, I knew Ruth only in hospitals; now for the first time I saw her elsewhere. When she was outdoors, she did something strange, and she did it so regularly that I began to expect it. At first it confused me, because it was the last thing I would have expected of her. As we walked out onto the street she stood still suddenly and looked at me with an embarrassed smile. "You must think I'm an idiot, Herr Norton."

"Why?"

"I've taken the wrong turn again! I keep going in the wrong direction. It's too silly!"

"You're nervous."

"Oh no, that isn't it. It's just that since a certain time—I wasn't like this as a child—I have a strange idiosyncrasy," she said, and in the cold I could see her breath when she spoke. "I know Nürnberg like my own pocket. I know a lot of other cities. It makes no difference—if I spend a few minutes in a store, or in a church, or just stand in front of a church as I'm doing now, and I want to go on—you can bet your life I'll walk in the wrong direction every time! You can't imagine the things that have happened to me. Not only on foot, but when I'm driving too. I get to a fork in the road or a street crossing, and I may have seen it a thousand times—and it happens! I go in the wrong direction! And the craziest thing about it is that in spite of all this, I always get to where I want to go in the end. And on time! In spite of all the detours I make. I have a reputation for being punctual."

"Perhaps you should let one of your colleagues help you get to the bottom of it." I had taken her arm as we walked along, and now I could feel it stiffen.

"No," she said curtly, but then, right away, she was friendly again. "Here's the Edelbräu Keller. I thought we might eat here."

"By all means," I said, and decided that I had never known a woman like her, and couldn't imagine that there would be a time when she would no longer be a part of my life.

36

The man who waited on us was old and fat. He looked tired. Perhaps he was sick. He coughed a lot, softly, but he smiled all the time and was very polite.

"May I give you some more potatoes, Frau Doktor?" he asked with a smile. Ruth evidently came here often; the waiter seemed to know her. "Yes please, Herr Arnold."

"And you sir?"

"Thanks, yes." We were sitting in the so-called Carp Room, one of the three dining rooms in the famous Edelbräu Keller. The Patrician Room is decorated with the coats of arms of old patrician Nürnberg houses. Students and professors of the Nürnberg Art Academy had hung the walls with three paintings—a group of patricians, the Nürnberg Buttnertanz and the Nürnberg Ship of Fools. Ruth asked me if I knew the Katherine Anne Porter novel with the same name. "Yes indeed," I said. "It's one of my favorite novels."

"Mine too," she said, and looked at me again with her serious brown eyes. "Porter got the title from Sebastian Brant," she said. "He wrote an allegory called *Ship of Fools* sometime in the fifteenth century."

"I know."

While we were eating, Ruth mentioned the novel again. *Ship of Fools*—she used Brant's simple universal symbol—the ship of our world on its voyage to a fool's paradise."

"I know Katherine Anne Porter."

"You do?"

"Yes," I said, and felt so safe with this woman, felt almost like a decent human being, your honor. "Yes. When she gave her interview to the *Paris Review*, we were there."

" 'We'?"

"Well, I and . . . and Miss Moran."

"Oh yes, of course. How stupid of me. And?"

A few hours with Ruth and I had forgotten that Sylvia Moran existed! I stared down at my plate. "And?" Ruth said again.

"And," I said, finding it difficult to go on, "Katherine Anne Porter gave this interview at Le Monde. Miss Moran knew Mrs. Porter, and she allowed us to be there during the interview."

"Oh yes! That famous interview. Does Frau Moran like the book too?"

"Yes," I said, hesitantly, because I didn't want to think of Sylvia. She knew the book only through what I had told her about it; she had found it too long and complicated to wade through. "Mrs. Porter said that the voyage she describes is symbolic. It is a voyage into chaos, because human life itself is in chaos. No one knows how the life he is leading is going to end. In fact—so she said—neither did she, since she too was a passenger on this ship of fools. A lack of understanding and isolation are the natural essentials of humankind. We meet only on these firmly established fronts. All of us are passengers on this ship, but when it finally arrives at its destination, every one of us is alone."

Ruth had been watching me as I spoke. I looked down at my plate. "This carp is very good," I said, and my voice was suddenly hoarse.

"Why did you change the subject, Herr Norton?"

"I didn't. But this carp really is . . ."

"Of course it is," she said, accepting my mood right away. A good doctor. "It's an Aischgründer carp. You won't find it cooked better anywhere in the Old City. I wanted you to have one of our specialties, since you've never been in Nürnberg before."

"Thanks."

"Not at all." And she was still looking at me. "The secret is that it's been baked in fat, not butter, according to a sixteenth-century recipe. What's the matter, Herr Norton?"

"Nothing."

"Nothing?"

"What should be the matter? I'm happy that Babs is better."

"I know you are."

I looked up fast. Her face was expressionless. "And I'm enjoying your company so much," I said.

"And I'm enjoying yours, Herr Norton."

I lifted my wineglass. "And that's just a small part of the truth," I said. "Your health, liar!"

She lifted her glass. "And yours, liar!"

37

I put down my glass. "I think I was always a liar."

"I don't think you were, years ago," said Ruth.

"No, I was. But you weren't. You're different. You—"

"You have to call Frau Moran every day and tell her how Babs is, Herr Norton. And please don't forget it."

"Yes, Mother," I said. "And you were never a liar. No, let me finish, because what I have to say isn't all that complimentary. You were never a liar until a certain area became involved."

"What do you mean?"

"When I asked you why you interrupted your study of history of art on our flight from Paris—remember?" Ruth nodded. "And you said that the way one experiences beauty was a psychological problem, and that because you saw this you decided to begin all over again with the study of medicine." She nodded again.

"I think you lied then, that the reasons were quite different."

An old woman with a basket full of little bouquets of flowers came up to our table, and I chose the prettiest one for Ruth and gave the old woman too much money. The tired old waiter called Arnold came wheezing up to us with a glass of water, and Ruth put the little bouquet in it and said, "Thank you, Herr Norton." She laid her hand on mine and spoke softly. "You're right. I lied to you. But now I want to tell you the truth. I don't know why—not a soul beside myself knows anything about it."

"Thank you."

"I had a brother," she said. "His name was Peter. He was twelve years older than I."

"Why do you say 'was'?"

"He committed suicide," said Ruth.

38

This is what Ruth told me in the Carp Room of the Edelbräu Keller in Nürnberg:

Dr. Peter Reinhardt went to the United States and studied medicine. He worked for years in Oklahoma City, Oklahoma, and became a specialist in the treatment of brain-damaged children. He had a friend the same age as himself, a Dr. George Radley.

One day an ambulance brought an eleven-year-old boy to the hospital. His name was Joe. He had been hit by a car. His head was badly injured, and Joe lay in a coma for three years. All the doctors at the hospital, especially Dr. Reinhardt and Dr. Radley, who were treating Joe, were convinced that there was a chance of Joe's regaining consciousness and eventually leading a more or less normal life—a cripple, yes, but mentally sound. Ruth's brother and Dr. Radley therefore worked over Joe day and night for three years. Other doctors and nurses helped. These efforts cost a lot of money.

Joe's parents didn't have that kind of money, so the state stepped in. During these three years while Joe lay in a coma, the state of Oklahoma spent $120,000 for doctors, nurses, hospital costs, an artificial lung, all for Joe. And this was possible only because a certain medication, developed in Switzerland and used on Joe, had resulted in a marked improvement in his condition, albeit a very slow one. According to the EEG, which showed a gradual but steady improvement, one could assume that the medication would in due course restore Joe to consciousness and life. But there was no way of telling when this point would be reached.

While Ruth's brother, encouraged by the slow but steady improvement, became absolutely fanatic in his determination to see the boy recovered, Dr. Radley became increasingly nervous and impatient. The two friends had endless discussions about whether it was right to work so long for Joe's recovery at such a cost.

One morning they were sitting in the hospital cafeteria,

Ruth's brother exhausted after night duty. Dr. Radley, about to take over, was in a foul mood. The day before he had had to justify the expense and slow results of Joe's treatment to the board of the hospital. Many members of the board, doctors among them, had reproached him and Ruth's brother for their stubbornness. The debate had centered around the question of the relationship between further costs and the determination to preserve a life, however wretched. In the end Dr. Radley had won, but the arguments against him had taken their toll, especially since he had been thinking along these lines himself for quite some time.

That morning, while they were drinking coffee, Radley said to Ruth's brother, "A hundred and twenty thousand, Peter! And the time, the care, the medication, the contribution of so many others!"

Ruth's brother said, "But Joe's EEGs are getting closer to normal all the time. Everybody knows that! For two weeks now he's had periods of spontaneous breathing. That's why they're letting us go on. Of course we'd have the right to let Joe die if the brain were dead and there were no hope for life!"

"Yes . . . but what a life!" said Radley.

"He'll be paralyzed, but he'll be able to think and speak and see and feel, and do some kind of work, but above all look after himself!"

"Sure," said George. "But when, Peter? When? We've been working on him for three years. We've been absolutely possessed by the idea of helping this boy."

"And he is better, George. He is!" said Ruth's brother.

"I know he's better. But *I've* had it!" said Dr. George Radley. "I can't go on. And if I'm breaking my Hippocratic oath a thousand times over—I can't stand the sight of him any more!"

"You need a rest," said Ruth's brother. "Take a week off. You like to fish. Go fishing. You'll come back and be glad to see Joe again."

"I'll never feel like seeing Joe again!" cried Radley. "Never! Do you hear me? I can't go on. The money! The work! The tension! The thought of the other sick children we might have been able to help!"

"But—"

"Now listen to me," said Radley. "What we've been doing with Joe the last three years is insane, absolutely insane! If

261

one of us had turned off the lung right at the beginning, he would have died peacefully within a few hours, painlessly, and you know it!"

The following night when Dr. Radley was on duty, Joe suffered acute arhythmic fibrillations, which were easily corrected. But the next day the staff was talking of nothing but the fact that after three years Joe had developed complications. The night after that Ruth's brother was on duty again. When Joe gave no indications whatever of spontaneous breathing, Ruth's brother disconnected the iron lung. In the morning Joe was dead.

The hospital immediately reproached Ruth's brother for what he had done. The local press reported on the case in detail. The result was a political hassle over the problem of euthanasia. Ruth's brother was in disgrace.

He went on working at the hospital for another six months, then they had to let him go because he had become an alcoholic. He neglected his work, made incorrect decisions, appeared for work drunk or not at all. He stayed in Oklahoma one more year, wandering aimlessly from place to place, became impoverished, and finally suffered a severe alcoholic psychosis, from which he recovered. His only wish became to return to Germany. He traveled tourist class on the cheapest boat.

In the meantime his and Ruth's parents had died. Ruth met him at the pier and couldn't hide her horror—a broken old man got off the ship. She took her brother to her apartment and did what she could for him. During the following weeks he told her what had happened, after which he seemed to feel better. Once he even said that he'd like to work as a doctor again. Only the nights were bad. Peter had nightmares. Ruth woke him up, trembling and sweating, as soon as she heard him cry out. The improvements in his spirits proved deceptive. One night, in a moment of terror, Peter cut his throat. He was buried in the Westfriedhof, where they had buried Tim.

39

Peter's suicide was such a shock to Ruth that she interrupted her study of art history and took up medicine, later specializing in the treatment of brain-damaged children. After she had told me all this, I was able to understand her seriousness and the most exaggerated passion with which she fought for the life of the most pathetically retarded child. I understood her relentlessness when there was a question of preserving human life. I understood her hatred—the word is not too strong—of all those who were indifferent about it. I never spoke to Ruth about it, but I did wonder if her idiosyncrasy of starting off in the wrong direction wasn't somehow connected with her brother's suicide. Was it the result of reproaches that wouldn't die, reproaches that she hadn't helped her brother enough? But how could she have helped him more?

Ruth is self-controlled as is no other woman I have ever met, and yet this faulty sense of direction, this constant going the wrong way—I think somehow it all hangs together, and I believe she thinks so too.

"Peter's friend Dr. Radley has meanwhile become one of the most ardent members of the American Euthanasia Society," said Ruth, looking over my shoulder as she spoke. Waiter Arnold had brought our dessert quite a while before—apple strudel. I hadn't touched mine; Ruth was picking at hers with a fork.

"Never heard of it," I said.

"It's very powerful. It was founded two years after the English one. The society fights for the rights of old and seriously ill people to euthanasia. In Greek the word means 'good death.' The Nazis called it 'merciful death.' There are all sorts of fantastic ideas for legalizing it. There he is again."

"Who?"

"The man we saw this afternoon. He's sitting on the other side of the room. He looks as if he's been sitting there quite a while, but I only just noticed him. Who is it, Herr Norton?"

I turned around and there he was, this pale scarecrow of a man who had been at the Westfriedhof and photographed me and Ruth and all the rest of us, and then run away as if pursued. I got up.

"Stay!" Ruth whispered.

But I didn't stay. I walked straight up to him. "What's the matter with you?" I said. A carafe and a wineglass stood in front of him, nothing else. Again I noticed the crazy look in his eyes. "Do you find the lady at my table so attractive? Or me? Do you want to take some more pictures?"

"I don't speak German," said the man. He still wore the wrinkled blue suit and the crushed, soiled shirt he had worn that afternoon, and the same blue tie. His hair was black and very thick.

"All right," I said, and repeated everything in English. "How dare you speak to me like this?" he said, and there it was again—the cagey fear of the trapped rat in his dark eyes, and an expression of boundless greed. "I don't want to take your picture."

"So why did you take my picture?"

"When?"

"Don't try to make an ass of me! This afternoon at the Westfriedhof. You took my picture during the funeral."

"So what? Are you trying to tell me that's forbidden?"

"Perhaps I am," I said. "And perhaps I'll knock your block off," and I took a step nearer.

He shot up, stepped back, knocking over his chair as he did so, and put his hands in front of his face. "Get out of here!" I said.

He licked his lips, put some money on the table and said, "You're going to be sorry for this."

"Out!" I said. "And make it fast!"

He stepped back again as I stepped forward, then he turned and left the room. A young waiter came to me. "Anything wrong, sir?"

"Nothing's wrong. Just a friend of mine in a hurry," I said. "Do you have a phone here?"

"I'll show you where it is, sir." And he led me to a booth beside the cloak room.

I called police headquarters. I wanted to tell the story of this strange man to the police, if possible to someone I knew. Sondersen wasn't there, but when I said who I was, they gave me his private number. I dialed, and Sondersen answered the phone. I could hear music. Gershwin.

"I'm terribly sorry to disturb you—"

"You're not disturbing me, Herr Norton. What is it?"

"But the music—are you watching television?"

"No. That's a record. My wife and I like Gershwin," said this strange policeman. "That's *Porgy and Bess.* So, what's up?"

I told him what was up.

"Hm," he said. "I'll notify the Americans right away, since you're so sure he's American. Perhaps they know something about him. If he turns up again, and you're in a position to do so—call me."

"Thank you, Herr Sondersen."

"Not at all. We must get together one day, you, my wife and I."

"I'd like that. Now comes 'Bess, You Is My Woman Now.' "

"Yes."

I thanked him again, left the booth and went back to Ruth. She looked worried. "What happened? Why did you take so long?"

"I don't like it," she said when I told her. "You think he's an American. And what with you and Frau Moran both from Beverly Hills . . ."

The waiter came, and we ordered coffee and cognac. "What do you mean?"

"Well . . . I don't want to be indiscreet, Herr Norton, but you told me once that Frau Moran's name wasn't always Moran, and that she wasn't born in the United States, and I read in a magazine that she refuses to say who Babs's father was. I thought that perhaps . . ."

"I don't see any connection," I said, and thought that there might very well be a connection. "Sylvia Moran's real name is Susanne Mankov. She was born in Berlin in 1935. Ten years ago she was playing important roles at the Schiller Theater, but she was well known only in Berlin." The waiter brought the coffee and a bottle of Martell and snifters, and served us with his friendly smile and steady cough.

"Here's mud in your eye!" said Ruth, lifting her glass. "Isn't that what you say?"

"Yes. Mud in your eye!"

We drank. "Go on," said Ruth.

"Then Seven Stars came to Berlin. They were shooting a film that took place for the most part in Berlin, and they were looking for a German actress to play an important part. The lead male was being played by one of their own stars—Romero Rettland."

"Oh, that one."

"Yes."

"A wonderful actor." Ruth sipped her coffee. "I've seen quite a few of his pictures—some I even saw more than once. He was a big star. What's happened to him?"

"That's a sad story," I said. "In those days, when they were filming in Berlin, he was on top. Everyone at Seven Stars made a big thing about finding a good German actress. Well, Sylvia—Susanne Mankov at the time—was lucky. They chose her. She played that first picture under her own name, and was a huge success. Everybody was crazy about the new German actress, most of all Joe Gintzburger, the president of Seven Stars. He's made a lot of stars what they are today. Romero Rettland was fascinated too. They talked Sylvia into coming to Hollywood. She worked very hard, learned English, studied acting with Strasberg, and nine months later gave birth to Babs."

"And has never been willing to reveal who the father is."

"A publicity stunt."

"But couldn't Rettland be the father?"

"A lot of people think so, but he isn't. He can't be."

"Why not?"

"Sylvia Moran—she had meanwhile changed her name—produced a report from a Berlin doctor who declared that Susanne Mankov came to him before Seven Stars came to Berlin and that she was already pregnant."

"She asked for this report when she had no idea that an American film company was coming to Berlin?"

"No. She got it after the child was born and Rettland had declared he was the father. The report was the proof she needed that Rettland couldn't possibly have been the father."

"Why was that so important to her?"

"I don't know. It seems that right after her arrival in Hollywood she had a horrible experience with Rettland. She hasn't even told me what it was. Anyway, she refused ever to appear with him again."

"And Seven Stars was willing to give in to the demands of an unknown actress?"

"She wasn't unknown any more. And something else had happened. Romero Rettland began to go downhill. Rapidly. It started with a double scandal—cheating at cards and the seduction of a minor. There was such a protest against him, there was nothing Joe Gintzburger could do but fire him."

"What happened then?"

"He was ruined. That happens fast in our profession. Drugs, women, alcohol. And worse. You should hear Joe Gintzburger when he gets on the subject. He spent a fortune to make Rettland a star, and then Rettland bites the hand that feeds him. Rettland made a few more films for smaller companies, but then it was all over. That's what I heard. I didn't know Sylvia at the time; I wasn't in the States yet. He turned up once or twice and asked Sylvia for money."

"And did she give it to him?" Ruth sounded interested.

"Yes. But then he began to give interviews, insisting he was Babs's father. And the next time he came, Sylvia threw him out. I have no idea if he is even still alive. Rettland may be dead, and if he is, nobody gives a damn!"

"How old would he be if he is still alive?"

"Around sixty, I'd say."

"And the doctor?"

"What doctor?"

"The one from whom Frau Moran got the report."

"Oh, that one! He died long ago."

"How long ago?"

"Sylvia told me he died a few months after giving her the report," I said, and then we looked at each other. I knew we were thinking the same thing. It *was* a bizarre idea, that Babs was a love child and her mother was never willing to say who the father was. . . .

40

I took Ruth home in a taxi. It had begun to rain softly, and the rain froze as soon as it hit the pavement. It was very cold that night. Ruth sat beside me, holding the little bouquet. Once, she was thrown against me. "Sorry," she said, and withdrew into the corner.

We had talked about a lot of things that evening, we had felt so close, now suddenly we had nothing to say. I could see

267

her face in the lights we passed, reserved, expressionless. We had become strangers.

The driver had turned on the radio. It sounded like the American army station AFN. Somebody was singing spirituals. "Nobody knows the trouble I've seen, nobody knows but Jesus . . ." After a while I said, "May I come to the clinic at eight?"

"Of course, Herr Norton. You may come whenever you like." After that nothing more was said. The taxi stopped in front of a big new apartment complex, not far from the Sophienkrankenhaus. I helped Ruth out and led her to the entrance, because it was very icy here. She said, " 'Nobody knows the trouble' . . ."

"What did you say?"

She took her keys out of her bag and opened the door. "What the Negroes are singing: 'Nobody knows the trouble I've seen, nobody knows but Jesus.' "

"I know the song, Frau Doktor."

"So much trouble," Ruth said absentmindedly, then she turned around and began to walk away. I followed her. "Where are you going?"

"There! You see? I was going to walk away from my own house!"

I laughed. She didn't. I thanked her for the evening and tried to kiss her hand, but she drew it back almost angrily. "No, Herr Norton, please don't." She opened the front door and closed it quickly without looking at me again. I remained standing. The lights went on in the hall, I could hear Ruth's steps, then I heard a door close. I didn't move. A few minutes later the light in the hall went out.

I went back to the taxi, and took it back to the Bristol. I had to ring because the front door was locked. A sleepy night watchman opened up. I took the elevator to the third floor and walked down the passage to my room, number 331, wondering why Ruth had changed so suddenly at the end of the evening.

I unlocked the door to my room, locked it behind me, and turned on the light in the foyer, then walked into my room and turned on the light there. The man with the pale face and the crazy eyes was sitting in the armchair beside the television set. He had a gun in his hand. It glittered blue-black, and it was aimed at my stomach.

41

"What the hell . . ."

"Shut up!" He got up and came slowly over to me. "Hands up, face the wall, head down."

I saw the expression in the man's eyes and turned around obediently and did everything he told me to do. The whole thing seemed like a cheap television show. He had apparently watched too many, I decided, as he frisked me. I've never carried a weapon in my life.

"Okay, you're clean!" Also straight out of TV. He stepped back. "Turn around." He waved his gun. "Over there. Sit down where I was sitting. And no funny business or I shoot."

I walked over to the armchair and sat down. Beside the chair there were glass doors that led out to a small balcony. The fellow walked over to me. He scratched his stomach with his free hand, pressing and shoving something aside, God only knew what. Probably has lice, I decided. And I was sitting in the chair he'd just sat in. He put a finger in the trigger guard of his gun and began to twirl it. "Stop it!" I said. "That thing could go off!"

"Yeah?"

He'd seen too many Bogart pictures too, I thought. "You're telling me!" he snarled. "I grew up with this thing, you dirty son of a bitch!" Yes, definitely Bogart.

We spoke English. "For God's sake," I said, "put that thing away."

"Nervous, eh? Mr. Bigmouth, back in the restaurant. Now you're shitting in your pants." At that the gun slipped from his fingers and fell on the floor. The fellow sat down on the bed. He was suddenly white, and his knees were trembling. I began to sweat.

He tried to get up, but his legs wouldn't support him, and he fell back onto the bed again. Now he was shaking all over, like an old drunk.

"I . . . I . . . I'm sorry, Mr. Norton."

Mr. Norton. Evidently he believed that was my name. I hoped. In which case my suspicions had been wrong.

269

"I feel sick. You don't have any whiskey handy, do you?"

"No."

"Or anything else?"

"No."

I leaned down and picked up the gun. "Thank you, sir," he said, as he saw me holding the gun, aimed at him now. I looked at it. Good God, he'd even released the safety!

"Going to be sick." He managed to get to his feet and stagger into the bathroom. He closed the door behind him, and I could hear him vomit.

I acted fast. I walked over to the phone which stood on a small table beside the bed and dialed Chief Sondersen. He answered quickly.

"Is the man there again?"

"Yes."

"Where are you?"

"In my room. Hotel Bristol, Room 331. This time he doesn't have a camera—he has a gun."

"How is it you can talk?"

"He's in the john, throwing up."

"Hang on to him as long as you can. Talk to him. Try to find out what he wants. I'll call the Amis. Our people too. We'll be there."

"Hurry," I said, and put down the receiver. The sounds in the bathroom were endless. At last he came out, looking jaundiced, yellow and gray, green under the eyes. He fell on the bed, gasping.

I got up and went into the bathroom to see what things looked like there. Clean. He'd even lit some toilet paper and flushed it down the john so that there would be no smell. He'd evidently rinsed his mouth with water from the shower, which was still dripping. I shut off the shower and walked back into the room. He was still lying on the bed, fiddling with his pants at the pit of his stomach. "What's the matter with you?"

"It's my truss. The damn thing's driving me crazy. They told me it was the best I could get. Have you any idea how a truss like that can itch and hurt?"

"You're breaking my heart."

"Go on, make fun of me. I've got it coming to me. Give me hell. But you don't have a hernia."

"No," I said. "But if I did, I'd have it operated on. Nothing to it today."

"Nothing to it?" he whined. "Have you any idea how many never come out of the anesthesia in a hernia operation?"

"Everybody does."

"That's what you think! But I know. It's one of the most dangerous operations. I have a friend. He knows what he's talking about. He told me, *'Don't* let them operate on you!' And I'm not going to. I'd rather wear the goddam thing the rest of my life!" I let him talk. "And in the summer, when it's hot . . . drives me nuts!"

"How old are you?"

"Forty-six."

"And how long have you had the hernia?" Time. I needed time.

"Since I was twenty-six."

"Twenty-six?"

"Baseball."

"You played baseball?"

"Don't believe me, do you?" He began to cry. I swear, your honor—he wept! "Nobody believes me. Not one motherfucker believes me. And I was the best pitcher and outfielder on our team!"

"What team?"

"Varsity."

"What university?"

"I'm not going to tell you."

"Why not?"

"Because it's none of your goddam business! You don't believe I was the best pitcher and outfielder, but that's how I got the hernia. I wanted to get on the Yankees. That was my dream. And I'd have made it if it hadn't been for this goddam hernia!"

"Why not the Giants?" Time . . . time . . .

"Because the Yankees are the better team. A thousand times better. Joe DiMaggio was with the Yankees then. My hero. He was married to Monroe. Man . . . Monroe! And me with my hernia . . ."

"What did you study?"

"Law."

"Don't tell me you're a lawyer!"

"No. I had to quit. No money."

"Too bad. Feeling better?"

He nodded. "But if you don't mind, I'll lie down a little longer." He tugged at his tie and undid his collar button. "My hair is clean. I washed it yesterday."

"How did you get in?"

"Through the window. Across the balcony."

"The window's shut."

"It is now. When I came it was half open. The maid must have left it open. I walked through the lobby and came up in the elevator. The hotel door was still open then. There is no room after yours, nothing but a pantry for the floor waiter. I went in there, then from balcony to balcony . . ."

"You're on the third floor!"

"Doesn't make any difference. I don't suffer from vertigo. I've done bigger and better things than this."

"How did you know my room number?"

"I know a lot about you, Philip Kaven," he said.

42

This I didn't like. "My name's Norton, not Kaven," I said.

"Yes," he said, "and I'm Napoleon. Your name's Philip Kaven, and you're Sylvia Moran's guy, and in Paris you had a fight with a newspaper photographer in the yard of a hospital. I read about it. I don't speak much French, but it was enough."

"You've got softening of the brain!" I said, but I felt uneasy. Who was this guy? How did he know all this?

"I read the retraction too. All that hogwash about the sick governess who had to be flown to Madrid. So why were you standing in that cemetery today and eating with this lady doctor tonight if the sick governess is in Madrid? What are you doing in Nürnberg?" He was looking at me with those crazy eyes again. How had he found me? Who was he, anyway?

"What were you doing in Paris?" I asked.

"What do you mean?" Like an idiot. "How come Paris?" Like a dangerous idiot.

"You said you'd read the paper and the report about Sylvia Moran's lover."

"Yes," he said, "about you. About Philip Kaven."

"I am not Philip Kaven. My name is Norton. Stop being an ass!"

272

Suddenly he laughed. "You think you can put on glasses and nobody'll recognize you! I *know* you're Philip Kaven. My friend told me. And he told me that you were wearing glasses now, so that nobody in Nürnberg could recognize you."

"Where in Paris did your friend tell you that?"

"I was never in Paris."

"Where were . . . what's your name, anyway?"

"You don't think I'm going to tell you, do you? I wasn't in Nürnberg either. I was in—in another city, and my friend called me up."

"From Paris?" I was racking my brains to figure out how he could possibly have found out what he knew. The first person I thought of was Lejeune. He was capable of anything. But he'd arranged this whole business in Nürnberg for me so that nobody should find out what was wrong with Babs, so where was the logic in that? Or Joe, the pig? Or Marone? Or Rod?

Not one of these people had anything to gain if the truth came out. What about Dr. Wolken? Forget it, I told myself—he was too stupid. Clarissa? Maybe . . . because I'd rejected her. By now Clarissa probably hated me. Yes, she was the only person I could think of who would be delighted if there was a worldwide scandal and Sylvia was finished, and me with her. And her love for Babs? Well, that was in the good days when I believed what I was told. All right, then, I thought, let's say it was Clarissa.

All this passed through my mind in a flash as I said, "From Paris?"

"From Paris, yes," said the fellow. Clarissa would have had time to call him from Paris. "Sent me the second paper from Paris too, my friend did."

Forget Clarissa! I told myself. She could have sent him the first paper, she was still in Paris then, but when the retraction appeared she was already in Dr. Arias Salmerón's clinic in Madrid. So she couldn't have sent it from Paris, and you couldn't get the paper in Madrid. But perhaps she had an accomplice in Paris. Suddenly I thought of Suzy and felt hot all over. She hated me because I had left her. So if not Clarissa, maybe Suzy? I could imagine Clarissa doing such a despicable thing more easily than Suzy.

"I am not Philip Kaven," I said again. "I am Philip Norton."

"Sure, sure," said the guy. "You're Philip Norton and my friend made a fool of me. Or he was wrong and I came to Nürnberg and photographed you in the cemetery—all for nothing. And I'm sure all the agencies and newspapers will throw me out when I show them the pictures of Mr. Norton and say they're pictures of Philip Kaven. They'll laugh themselves silly. And here I thought I could sell the pictures because you're Philip Kaven and could do without another scandal right now. The public would go crazy if they read and saw where you are and what you're doing. That's what I thought, and I'd have money again, because you wouldn't have any choice but to collaborate with me."

"I don't think much of collaboration," I said.

"Why not?"

"Let me tell you what I think of collaboration," I said, and thought that by now the Amis and the police should be arriving. "Collaboration," I said, "is when I give you my watch and you tell me what time it is."

"Very funny! So you won't buy the pictures from me?"

"Certainly not. Go to your papers, you fool!"

This made him feel unsure again, and he gave it some thought. At last he said, "Of course I don't have the camera or the film on me."

"Makes no difference to me where they are," I said. I took the magazine out of the pistol and tossed the gun on the bed. "Do whatever you want with your film."

"At the main station," he said, "in a locker. That's where the Minox is."

Through the half-open curtains of the glass door that led to the balcony I could see several cars down the street. "If you don't get out I'll call the police," I said. I lifted the receiver.

The fellow jumped off the bed and grabbed the gun. "All right," he said, but I could have sworn he had no idea if I was bluffing or not. "Have it your own way. Then I'll just have to let them throw me out wherever I go with my pictues. Takes good pictures, that little Minox does. Too bad I was wrong."

"That your friend was wrong."

"Yes. So I'll go now," he said, and didn't move.

"So go!"

"I'm really going," he said, and didn't move.

I picked up the receiver and read aloud what was written on the dial: "Police—one-one-zero." I dialed the one. The fellow grabbed his duffel coat, which had fallen on the floor and ran to the door. He tore it open and it slammed behind him, and I could hear him running down the passage toward the elevator. I stepped out on the balcony, lit a match and waved it back and forth. The headlights flashed on and off on one of the cars parked under the trees.

I stayed on the balcony and watched the end of the scene take place below me. As the man walked out into the open, the headlights of four cars were turned on. The cars moved forward toward the hotel entrance, and suddenly the man was caught in their light. He stood still for a moment, as if petrified, then tried to escape along the side of the building. Men in civilian clothes and in uniform jumped out of their cars. He ran directly into the arms of two of them. He didn't try very hard to defend himself. The men got him into one of the cars; a couple of them waved to me, and I waved back. Among the men waving I recognized Chief Sondersen. "I'll call you soon," he yelled.

"Okay!" I called back, and saw him get into his car. They all drove off. It was 1:30 A.M.

43

"Sorry if I'm disturbing you." Sondersen's voice over the phone, which I'd finally been able to find and answer. "But I said I'd call you as soon as I knew anything."

"Yes, of course, thank you, Herr Sondersen."

According to my wristwatch it was 5:07 A.M. I could hear it raining hard outside.

"Didn't take me long." Sondersen's voice again. "Because the Americans know him very well."

"They do?"

"Yes." I found the switch of the bedside lamp and turned it on. It was a bright light, and my eyes hurt. So did my head.

I really felt terrible that morning. "Roger Marne," I repeated, and the rain was splashing on the balcony. If only I never had to get up again!

"We have his Minox too, and all his film. We went to the station with him, the Amis and I. They gave me the photos and the camera. The films are yours if you want them."

"Thanks, Herr Sondersen. A million thanks. It's so very good of you ..."

"Don't mention it, Herr Norton," in his calm voice. "You know that we're glad to do anything to be of help."

I began to feel better. "Who is this Roger Marne, anyway? Is he crazy?"

"When it suits him."

"I don't understand."

"In my profession, we know the type—the malingerer. We call them 'clowns.' Marne is a man who can be mad, sane, wounded, homosexual, a beggar, a whiner, all according to the situation he's in. He can also be Superman or hysterical. He can play countless roles. The hernia and the truss, by the way, are true."

"Has he ever been examined?"

"Many times. By various psychiatrists. But the reports on him don't agree. He's been in court four times."

I sat up. "Why?"

"Blackmail. Cheating at cards. The head of a call-girl ring."

"A call-girl ring? Marne?"

"I found it hard to believe too. But I found out a thing or two from the Americans. Incredible! How did he ever get mixed up with *you?*"

"That's what I'd like to know. How did he get to Nürnberg, anyway?"

"That's something the Amis would like to know. Herr Norton, every time Marne has been in court his lawyers demanded a psychiatric opinion, and the psychiatrists could never agree on whether he was psychotic or just slightly touched. So he went to jail but invariably ended up in a mental institution from which he always managed to escape."

"Where?"

"In California. He comes from Los Angeles. Everything he's done, with the exception of one incident in Bonn, happened in the Los Angeles area. Beverly Hills, Hollywood, and so on. Only the mental institutions were farther away. The last time he escaped was three and a half years ago. That's when he came to Europe. I'm sure he has false papers." Like me, I thought. "We have no idea what he's up to in Europe. The Americans don't either, except for the thing in Bonn."

"And what was that?"

"They didn't say exactly. Some sort of homosexual blackmail. Must have been VIPs, because they're keeping the whole thing very hush-hush. Marne managed to get out of that one too. The Americans are trying to find out what he's been up to since then, but they want to keep everything as quiet as possible because of the Bonn affair. Then they'll ask for his deportation, and they'll institutionalize him again back in the States. The Amis would be grateful if you didn't bring charges, because of Bonn."

"I can't bring charges," I said. "I'll be thankful if the Amis take care of him."

"That's what I thought," said Sondersen. "But the films are yours in any case."

"How did Marne get on my track? Who helped him?"

"You're not going to find out from Marne," said Sondersen. "I've questioned him. Can't get a word out of him. He's afraid. Terribly afraid."

"Of whom?"

"Yes," said Sondersen. "Of whom?"

44

"Godammit! What's the idea of calling me at this hour? It's a quarter to five!" Rod Bracken was stammering with fury.

I was sitting on the edge of the bed, in my robe. In the glass of the balcony door, I could see myself and a part of the room, mirrored by the light from the bedside lamp. It was still raining hard.

"Shut up, Rod. It's important or I wouldn't call."

"Is Babs dead?"

"No."

"Then what is it?"

I told him. He listened without saying a word. All he said when I was through was, "Shit! Everything that could go wrong is going wrong."

"What do you mean?"

"We've had our share too."

"What's happened?"

"Dr. Wolken's left."

"What? When?"

"Tonight. I can't seem to get to sleep. Two hours ago your friend Lucien woke me up. He told me that Dr. Wolken had just paid his bill and was leaving with all his things. Wolken was still in the lobby and Lucien thought I might be able to catch him, but Wolken was smarter. And quicker. By the time I got down, he was gone. Lucien couldn't stop him, of course."

"Why did he leave?"

"That's what all of us would like to know. I woke everybody up and we had a short conference, and I'd just got back to sleep when you called."

"And Wolken didn't say a word about where he was going?"

"He didn't *say* anything."

"What do you mean?"

"He asked for a flight schedule."

"Where's he headed for?"

"How do I know? Lucien doesn't know either. But he gave him the Iberia schedule.

"Iberia? The Spanish airline?"

"Yes. So the lawyers and I will be driving to the airport later this morning. The first flight to Madrid's at twelve-fifteen. Maybe we'll catch the bastard."

Suddenly I felt hot all over. "I'm coming too."

"What?"

"I'm coming to Paris. On the first plane I can get."

"Why?"

"I'll explain when I see you."

"Why not now?"

"Too complicated."

I heard Bracken catch his breath. "Goddam!"

"What?"

"I completely forgot. This whole thing's driving me nuts. Lucien said one of the operators told him that Wolken had called Spain an hour before he left. She doesn't know who he called. Wolken used a booth. The girl made the connection."

"Then she must have the number."

"She has. Lucien gave it to me. Where did I put it? Just a minute." A humming in the wire, then he was back. "Wolken called . . ."

"Madrid."

"Yes. How do you know?"

"And spoke to the Salméron clinic, where Clarissa is."

Bracken was stammering again. "What does . . . why should he call Clarissa? I don't get it."

"I do."

"Then explain it to me."

"Later. In Paris. Clarissa and Wolken. So that's how they worked it—together!"

"Will you *please* try to behave like a rational person and tell me what's up?"

"All hell's broken loose," I said. "That's what's up! We've got to catch Wolken and shut him up. And Clarissa. Bring Joe to the airport too. We need all the support we can get!"

45

It wasn't raining any more as I drove to the Sophienkrankenhaus, but the driver was cursing because now the roads were icy. I told the night clerk that I would be back soon and was keeping my room. I looked at the flight schedule before leaving the hotel. There was a plane to Paris at 10:15. The clerk reserved a seat for me. This left me plenty of time before and after.

I was at the hospital before 8:00 and had to wait for Ruth. When she came, she was friendly; just as serious as usual, but not as strangely reserved as she had been the night before. She went first to see Babs and listened to what the doctor on night duty had to report, and examined Babs herself. Then I was allowed to go in.

"Much better than yesterday," Ruth said happily. "Temperature a hundred and one. Slept well. No vomiting."

I looked at the little girl lying there with her eyes closed and said, "But the twitching in her face, and her whole body . . ."

"Did you think it would be all over in two days, Herr Norton? Things will go on like this for quite a while, but we are making progress."

"I've got to leave right away."

"Leave?"

"Yes." And I told her all about Roger Marne, and that I had to go to Madrid because I suspected Clarissa and Marne were working together.

"And this Dr. Wolken?"

279

"He's probably in on it too."

"Hello, Phil," Babs said suddenly. Her eyes were wide open, and her face was distorted in what I guessed was a smile. It looked dreadful, but yes—it was a smile. Ruth smiled right away too.

"Hello, Babs," I said, leaning over her. "You're a lot better, aren't you?"

"Not Madrid," she said. Her speech was slurred. Had she heard everything I had told Ruth or only caught the word 'Madrid'?

"You stay right here in bed like a good girl," I said, "and I'll be back in no time. What do you want me to bring you?"

"Nounours."

She had been dragging a little teddy bear around with her for years. His brown pelt was completely worn out in places, but she loved the toy. Jean Gabin had given it to her. In French a little bear is called *nounours,* so that was what Babs had named him. The bear had to be at Le Monde.

"Sure. I'll bring Nounours with me. But wouldn't you like a nice new teddy bear?"

"No. Nounours. I love Nounours."

"Okay," I said. Babs, by the way, was speaking German.

"Becausebecausebecause Nounours," she said, then suddenly she was fast asleep again, breathing deep.

"The bear," I told Ruth. "She's dreaming about her teddy bear in Paris." I stopped, because I noticed that Ruth was staring at me wide-eyed. "What's the matter?"

"You must call Frau Moran, Herr Norton, and tell her how well Babs is doing. But don't mention that there may be relapses, and that we really can't tell how things are going to develop."

"I won't Frau Doktor." I was smiling, but she was all seriousness again. We walked out into the passage together when she said she had to see her other children now. She avoided my eyes. She looked out the window and up at the sky. "It's going to snow soon," she said.

46

"Look for Babs's old teddy bear," I said.

"Why?" Bracken wanted to know.

"Because I need it."

"Buy one. I've got more important things on my mind."

"No. I've got to have her old teddy bear," I said. "You'll find it somewhere in her room."

"Man, you know what you can do!"

"Likewise!" Suddenly I was screaming. "If you don't bring Nounours to Orly, *I'll* go to Le Monde to find him. And the hell with tracking down Wolken!"

"Don't shit in your pants over it!" said Rod. "I'll find the dumb bear and bring him with me."

Both of us slammed down the receiver without saying goodbye. I had called from the Nürnberg airport. I managed to get on my plane just as they were taking up the boarding ramp. It was a nearly empty all-tourist-class flight. I read a Nürnberg paper and found out that the heaviest fighting of the war was taking place in Vietnam, outside Hue, enormous casualties on both sides. By now war in Vietnam was in its thirtieth year ... then I thought that in thirty years Babs might still be crippled and need medical care, and I would be sixty, and Sylvia would be sixty-six, and Ruth ...

At Orly I found Bracken, Lejeune and Gintzburger waiting for me. We went to the airport restaurant and had drinks, and I listened to Lejeune bigtalk, and he had of course been disgustingly smart.

Dr. Wolken, it seemed, had bought a ticket for the 12:15 Iberia plane to Madrid. He had already checked his baggage. Lejeune's "people" were looking for him but hadn't found a trace yet. Lejeune, needless to say, ordered an early-morning lunch while he spoke.

"When we've made quite sure that Wolken is on the twelve-fifteen flight, you, Bracken, and Maître LeJeune leave," said Joe, "on Sylvia's jet."

"Her jet's in Nürnberg."

"Her jet's in Orly, on one of the outer runways. Ordered it here right away when I found out about this latest mess," said Lejeune, his mouth full of the veal cutlet he had ordered, with green beans and *pommes frites*. "Did you bring a suitcase with my Philip Kaven things?" I asked Rod.

"Under the table," said Bracken.

"And the bear?"

"And the bear."

So I went to one of the washrooms and put on my "good things," and packed the Galeries Lafayette stuff in the one plastic suitcase I had brought with me. I put it in a locker and went back to the restaurant, where Lejeune had meanwhile worked his way through to chocolate cake and liqueur. I knew that I should call Sylvia but couldn't bring myself to do it.

At 11:15 they began calling the passengers flying Iberia 871 to Madrid, and a little while later a young man came up to our table and told Lejeune, "Wolken is on his way to the plane. He's just going through immigration checkout." So Lejeune, Bracken and I departed.

The flight across the Pyrenees was turbulent, as usual, but it didn't bother me. Not until we landed did I notice that throughout the entire trip I had been holding Babs's worn little teddy bear in my hands.

47

We arrived in Madrid on December 8, which happens to be a religious holiday in Spain, the Feast of the Immaculate Conception. All shops and offices were closed. I had been in Madrid frequently before my insolvent playboy days, but I'd forgotten the holiday.

We ran into a storm just before Madrid, and in spite of the captain's efforts landed a few minutes after the Iberia plane. But it hadn't mattered. The Iberia plane had been very full, and customs had taken a long time, of course not in our case. Now all we had to do was not lose sight of Dr. Wolken. It was Bracken who spotted him at customs, and we could see that he had three large suitcases. The customs agent inspected all of them. Politely. Spanish customs inspectors are always polite. Believe it or not, your honor, the Spanish customs agents wear white gloves when they examine luggage. I imagine this is intended to impress those arriving with Spanish dignity and refinement.

But dignity and refinement take time to examine three full suitcases, so it wasn't difficult for us to find a taxi and follow the one Dr. Wolken had got into. All of us were sure that he was on his way to Clarissa at Dr. Salméron's clinic, and we didn't want to confront him until he got there. Because of the holiday there was very little traffic, so it was just as easy to follow Dr. Wolken's taxi as it was difficult to remain unobserved in the process.

We arrived at the clinic. All three of us spoke Spanish enough to make ourselves understood. Bracken told our driver to stop about two hundred meters behind Dr. Wolken's taxi. He got out, and the driver carried his three large suitcases into the clinic. Wolken didn't even look around once.

We waited until his taxi had driven off, then ten minutes more, because I wanted to confront him with Clarissa. At last we were ready to enter the clinic. Behind a white desk sat a Spanish beauty, with black hair and black sparkling eyes. She greeted us, we greeted her, then I said, "Our names are . . ."

"Señor Kaven and Señor Bracken and Señor Lejeune," said the Spanish beauty.

"How do you know?"

"A Dr. Wolken was just here. He said you would be coming."

"We—Señor Bracken and I—brought a patient here a few days ago," said Lejeune, without showing any surprise over what he had just heard.

"I know, Señor Lejeune. Señorita Geiringer is in Dr. Salméron's private wing."

"We have to speak to her right away."

"And Dr. Salméron wants to speak to you right away," said the beautiful Spanish girl.

"How does *he* happen to know we're here?" asked Bracken.

"I don't know, señor. He just gave the order that he wanted to see you on arrival."

48

"The little girl talked about death all the time. She often asked for a mirror and looked in it and said over and over again, 'No. I can't go on living. I have to die. Please, please kill me!' "

"How old was she?"

"Nine years old, Mr. Kaven," said Dr. Alfons Wolken from Winterthur, dressed as neatly as ever, with his sharp blue eyes, long narrow face and sparse Van Dyke beard.

"And what did you say was wrong with her?"

"A brain tumor," said Dr. Wolken.

"And?" said Bracken.

"The doctors in the Zürich clinic treated the child for three years—that is to say, they kept their Hippocratic oath concientiously, which in my opinion is a contradiction in terms, since the Hippocratic oath demands that the doctor preserve life and alleviate suffering, and in a case like this, one duty contradicts the other, Mr. Bracken. Then the child came down with pneumonia. This was not treated, as happens in thousands of clinics in similar cases, and the child finally died," said Dr. Alfons Wolken.

He was standing in Dr. Arias Salmerón's office, and if you think, your honor, that Babs's tutor had exhibited the slightest embarrassment when we appeared, then I must disappoint you. I never saw a man more assured or determined.

"That's a lot of bullshit!" I said. "Babs doesn't have a brain tumor. She has meningoencephalitis. So what are you driving at?"

"The child I am talking about went into such a decline that it made you feel physically sick to look at her. Nauseating, Mr. Kaven. I saw her. She was a pupil of mine."

"And the sight of her nauseated you?" said Bracken.

"Yes, Mr. Bracken."

"If I have to look at you much longer, I'll be nauseated too. I'll throw up in your face, you fucking bastard!" Child of the Bronx, your honor. You could depend on Bracken.

"Please, gentlemen, please," said Dr. Salméron. He was the only one of us who was seated, behind his big desk with a statue of the Madonna on it which I would have liked to own. He was about fifty, I decided, tall, slender, with a bold hooked nose in his narrow sympathetic face, and graying hair. He had greeted Bracken, Lejeune and me in a most friendly fashion on our arrival. Dr. Wolken's greeting had also been friendly, and he had informed us hastily that he was happy to be able to "explain everything" to us here, so to say on neutral ground. He told us just as politely that he had called Dr. Salméron four times to ask his advice, and the doctor had suggested that he come today, on the 8th, since it was a holiday and he would therefore have more time to talk.

"And why didn't you tell anyone in Paris that you were coming here?"

"That must be obvious, Mr. Bracken," said Dr. Wolken, bowing and jiggling up and down. "You saw that I brought all my things with me."

"You're clearing out, right?"

"I would express it in a little more genteel fashion, Mr. Bracken, but it would come to the same thing. I am leaving. And for very specific reasons."

"And what are they?"

"We'll get around to that in a minute," said Dr. Salméron.

"And would any of you at Le Monde have permitted me to 'clear out,' as you put it?" asked Dr. Wolken.

"Not so easily," said Bracken.

"Well, you see," said Dr. Wolken, and from that moment on he didn't bow any more, he didn't jiggle up and down, he didn't lower his head humbly. He spoke in a firm, almost aggressive voice, looked everyone straight in the eyes, and at last sat down. I found it ridiculous to go on standing and sat down too. Bracken looked at me and followed suit. Lejeune had been sitting for some time.

I said, "I find it absolutely incomprehensible! What induced you to leave and come here of all places, and what on earth does it have to do with your pupil who had a brain tumor? Her case has nothing whatsoever to do with Babs, because Babs doesn't have a brain tumor and is no longer in great pain. Babs is afflicted with meningoencephalitis, and she is improving daily. She is not suffering from any pain now that could possibly arouse your pity. Her condition will continue to improve; we may even see a complete recovery."

"No," said Dr. Wolken. "It is not going to be like that, and you know it. You and all the rest of you have built a colossal edifice of delusion and deceit around this pitiful child, and what is most despicable of all—you have done it for commercial reasons. And as far as I can see and from all I've heard you intend to continue doing so. Babs will come out of this, at best, a heavily brain-damaged child—"

"She will *not!*" I shouted, jumping to my feet.

"Please sit down, Mr. Kaven," said Salméron.

I sat down but went on yelling, "Babs is getting the best care possible! She was also in your charge once, Herr Doktor, and I would very much like to know the true motives for your behavior."

"They are very simple. I don't want to be a party to such deceit."

"You filthy . . ." Bracken started to say, then, in a total about-face, "Okay. What's your price for staying? All of us know you can ask what you like. We'll pay."

"If you do not apologize immediately for this insult, Mr. Bracken," Dr. Wolken said quietly, "I shall beg Dr. Salméron to ask you to leave the room."

In the silence that followed I could hear church bells. "Well, Mr. Bracken, how about it?" Salméron said calmly, and it was quite evident that he was prepared to throw Bracken out.

"I'm sorry. I apologize," said Bracken, almost choking on the words.

"Good," said Dr. Wolken. Then he began to speak animatedly. "My mother died of cancer of the larynx. My mother was doubly unfortunate in that my father was a doctor, and a fanatic—I can't think of a better word—a fanatic Catholic. And a further misfortune—*he* treated my mother. In a clinic in Basel. As a fanatic Catholic he demanded that my mother, who was also Catholic, experience her death 'consciously,' as he put it. He therefore gave her no morphine, not even when the pain became unbearable and she begged him to make things easier for her. All the other doctors at the hospital loathed him. I did too, naturally. But nobody dared give my mother morphine, because my father was chief of staff."

Red spots had appeared on Dr. Wolken's cheeks; he spoke fast, his hands were fists. "And so my father let my mother die 'consciously.' "

"What did he mean," I asked, "by 'die consciously'?"

286

"My religious father explained to me, and I shall never forget it," said Dr. Wolken, stumbling over the words, "that one must not rob a human being of his own death, the most noble experience he will ever have, one that will give him the clearest and most valuable answer. That was the belief of my religious father, Mr. Kaven, and this in a case where there was the most excruciating pain, as Dr. Salméron can corroborate. You, gentlemen, haven't the faintest idea of the pain my father forced my mother to bear. Am I right, doctor?"

"He is right," said Salméron. "If people had any real idea of what pain those who are fatally ill endure, they would give us clear-cut instructions not to permit such suffering."

"I don't get it," I said. "I can't see any connection. In our case—where is the indescribable pain? What makes you give such an opinion, doctor, and above all why has Dr. Wolken come to *you?*"

"I was one of the doctors at the Basel clinic where Dr. Wolken was chief of staff, Mr. Kaven," said Salméron. "I was witness to the unbearable torment Dr. Wolken's mother had to suffer. Two years later, Dr. Wolken developed cancer of the stomach, and when he implored me to give him some relief from his pain, I gave him an overdose of a certain medicine and put him out of his misery. During all this time and long afterward, until I left Basel, I knew Dr. Wolken—as a boy, as a young man. And I was a comfort and support to him, if I may say so, Dr. Wolken?"

"You must say so, doctor, and I have something to say too. Without your efforts to help me get over the tragedy of my mother's tortured death, I would have committed suicide." Wolken turned to face Bracken and me. "So that's how it is, gentlemen. At that time, Basel; today, Madrid. Can you understand now why, in my dilemma and faced with the suffering of that poor child, Babs, I turned again to the man who had once saved my life?"

Nobody said a word. The church bells rang. "You especially, Mr. Kaven, have been exposed—I am sure for a very good reason—to a bitter opponent of euthanasia," said Salméron. "I mean Frau Doktor Reinhardt, an admirable woman whom I respect highly. And yet, the problem of mercy killing, active and passive euthanasia, is a double-edged sword—as you can see."

49

Lejeune looked out of the window. I looked at Bracken. At first he shook his head, then he shrugged. I felt the same way. First impression: Dr. Wolken was behaving for personal motives and wasn't connected with this 'clown,' Roger Marne. Second thought: Or was it possible? There were several things to be said for that—Wolken's childhood trauma, his hatred of all doctors like Ruth, thanks to his own experience, and Salméron's correct—or incorrect—declaration that euthanasia was a double-edged sword. He corroborated what had just passed through my mind when he said, "I asked Dr. Wolken to inform me about the seriousness of Babs's illness and the whole situation. I must say that I am *not* for putting an end to the poor child's misery, certainly not at this point. But I have also come to the conclusion—and you know this better than I do, Mr. Kavin—that her health will never be completely restored, never, and that at best she will have to live out her life badly handicapped—that is, if she continues to progress."

"Everything is going to be . . ."

"Let me finish. In a way I can understand your position and that of your colleagues, which is not to say that I approve of a reaction without a single humane thought, only the thought that business must go on. It can happen any time—and you know this as well as I do—that Babs's condition can become critical again, if, as according to you, it isn't critical right now."

"She *is* out of danger!"

"In that case," the doctor went on, "everything will be done to prolong Babs's life, am I right?"

"You are."

"To prolong a human life today is a relatively simple matter," said Salméron. "The only thing we don't know is—what does the patient get out of it?"

"What's going on here, anyway?" From Bracken. "It isn't our fault that Dr. Wolken's father behaved like a bastard!"

"So you would have given Dr. Wolken's mother an overdose of morphine?" asked Salméron.

"Certainly."

"Ah, but things aren't as simple as you think, Mr. Bracken," said Salméron. "Professor Werner Forssmann from Düsseldorf, who received the Nobel Prize in 1956, foresaw the specialist who kills on request, and equated him with the paid executioner of the death penalty." He was looking at me. "I'm afraid I am very much impressed by the last lead article in the German magazine *Der Spiegel*. Did you read it, Mr. Kaven?"

"No."

"That's a pity. The title was 'Mercy Killing: Euthanasia—Compassion or Murder.' An excellent article. I will quote it frequently as we discuss this matter, because I can't get it out of my mind."

Salméron had plenty to say and he continued. "The Bonn neurosurgeon Peter Rottgen predicted years ago that if neurosurgery were to go to the limit of its technical possibilities, we would have a hospital inferno of Dantesque proportions! And this is true not only in the case of neurosurgery. An uncompromising rejection of every type of euthanasia could have the most macabre consequences, Mr. Kaven. A dying human being, for instance, whose body has been almost totally devoured by cancer, could easily be saved. All you would have to do is separate his head from his cancerous body, and let it live on by itself."

"For God's sake, stop!" cried Bracken.

"I have no intention of stopping," said Salméron. "In Japan they have succeeded with dogs in separating the head from the body, and it can be done with human beings too. The head is placed on a frame and connected by tubes to machines that take over the functions of heart, lungs and kidneys. Such a headless body could even speak."

"Such insanity will never be practiced!" I declared vehemently. "Never!"

"I have to contradict you," said Salméron. "It will. There can be no question about that any more. Two hundred years ago the German philosopher Immanuel Kant gave us the answer. 'If we desire the goals, we also desire the means to reach them.' "

"So you are perfectly willing to help the dying to die?" I said. "As you did years ago with Dr. Wolken's father."

"Certainly," said Salméron. "And I would do it again today, because in many incurable cases the services of mankind can turn into the terror of mankind. Now I am quoting your German theologian Helmut Thielicke. All this in the *Spiegel* article I can't forget."

"You are a Catholic?"

"Yes."

"In a Catholic country. What does the Vatican say?"

"In 1957, Pope Pius XII said, 'When a narcotic serves two purposes—namely the relief from pain and the shortening of life—then it is permitted . . .' "

"You don't say!" From Bracken. "So the Holy Father—"

"But only," Salméron interrupted him, "when there is no connection between the shortening of life and the will of any interested parties. And then, again . . . a month ago the Vatican paper *Osservatore Romano* declared euthanasia as the final step away from the Gospels, because only God has the right to decide life and death."

"And with that we are back to Dr. Wolken's father who let his poor wife die a 'conscious' death."

"That's right," said Salméron. "But, Dr. Kautsky—a practicing Catholic like myself—considers the *Osservatore Romano*'s statement thoughtless. According to him, if it were true that one could not interfere with God's will, then it would *never* be possible to prolong life at all!"

Bracken groaned and clutched his head, elbows on knees.

"Yes, the whole problem is neither pleasant nor simple," said Salméron. "Paul Bockelmann, the Munich jurist, believes that the doctor must do everything possible to prolong a patient's life, even if it is a case of only hours or minutes, even if during that period the life preserved isn't worth living."

"This is driving me nuts!" said Bracken.

"If every doctor were to do this," said Salméron, "he could let no patient die. He would have to attach him to every life-sustaining device known to man. And hospitals would not be able to function! In support of Kautsky, gentlemen, I ask you, what is there to be said against the idea that a man whose duty it is to master his life should not also be permitted to be the master of his death, and that his doctor should be permitted to help him?"

"Goddam idiocy," said Lejeune, "that's what it is!"

He got up and walked over to the window, turning his back

to us as he went on speaking. "Goddam idiocy!" he said again. "What are you trying to say, doctor? We are living in insane times; in a time when half a dozen guerrillas who will stop at nothing can paralyze entire countries and blackmail them. In a time when three-quarters of the people on this globe are starving while the other quarter are stuffing themselves to death! Like myself. Or have become totally incompetent politically and morally. We are living in the age of the cobalt bomb, the ballistic missile, and racial hatred. In a time like this *I* am pleading for a law to mete out severe punishment to anyone bringing children into this filthy world! And that, in my consideration, is the only sane course: Let the old die and see to it that there are no offspring to follow them!"

I turned to Dr. Wolken. "I understand your attitude, based as it is on your own tragic experience, but I can't understand what made you leave *us*. In Babs's case you can rule out any thought of a mercy killing."

"At the moment, yes," said Dr. Wolken.

"Never!" I said, and had no idea how near the time was when I would have to decide—not to help Babs die, not that, your honor, but to let her die.

Dr. Wolken said, "Babs is every man's child. She is the child of the most famous film actress. Since birth she has been captive in this singular position, in an industry in which nothing counts but money, money, in which everything thinkable will be done to preserve her life. I would have stayed with you, Mr. Kaven, if the whole thing hadn't been such a repulsive conbination of life or death and business."

"Now I've had it!" cried Bracken.

"Shut up, Rod," I said. "Go on, Herr Doktor."

Dr. Wolken went on. "How would things be if Babs were not the daughter of Frau Moran? If her mother were the wife of a laborer, a washerwoman?"

"Let's not go into the social aspects," said Bracken.

"The social aspects," Salméron said slowly, "are of the greatest interest to everyone speaking out against the insane amounts of money spent on brain-damaged children. The cost of such intensive medical treatment *per day* is eighteen hundred marks! For one day! And costs are going up all the time! From one to two hundred people in starvation areas could subsist on that amount of money *per diem*. So there you have a human being who barely earns the designation on the one hand, and on the other a hundred to two hundred starving humans. Who is more deserving of help, Mr. Kaven?"

"Babs is still a child," I said.

"All right, then let's talk about children. But we don't want to forget those who are starving, do we, Mr. Kaven?" Salméron was stroking the head of the Madonna on his desk. "We are faced here with a colossal moral dilemma. Leszak Kolakowski, the Polish philosopher, asked once: Why should affluent societies spend fortunes to keep retarded and crippled children alive when millions of normal children are dying of starvation or for lack of adequate medical care?"

Bracken and I spoke simultaneously. He said, "I've had it!" I said, "I don't want to hear any more!"

Lejeune asked Wolken, "So you won't come back to us under any circumstances?"

"Not under any circumstances," said Wolken. "I know you are afraid that I'll talk, that I'll tell what I know. I can assure you that this is something I shall never do!"

50

She was sitting in an armchair beside the window as I came into Room 17. "Mr. Kaven!" Clarissa's pale face reddened as she rose to greet me. How wonderful of you to come see me!"

"Dr. Salméron told the head nurse to let me see you. Everything seems to be very well organized here. No reporters?"

"None, Mr. Kaven."

Clarissa Geiringer, twenty-seven years old, pretty, very blond, wore a warm robe and bedroom slippers. She had been reading. She was still holding the book in her hand; now she put it down on a small table beside her. *King Lear.* "Sit down, Mr. Kaven," she said, and sat down again herself. "How is Babs?"

"Much better. She's out of danger. Dr. Reinhardt is very pleased."

"She couldn't be happier than I am," said Clarissa. "And you and Miss Moran, of course."

"Of course," I said. "And we can never thank you enough for all you have done for us, Clarissa."

"Mr. Kaven." She blushed again. "You know that there isn't anything in this world I wouldn't do for you and Babs—and Miss Moran."

"It could take some more time," I said. "You may have to stay here awhile longer."

"How long?"

"I don't know yet," and all the while she was staring at me. I turned my head aside.

"You don't have to look away, Mr. Kaven. I swear I'll never bring it up again or bother you in any way."

"Now stop talking nonsense, Clarissa," I said. "I know what a decent girl you are, and under different circumstances . . ." And that's life, I thought. Only a few days ago, when she had thrown her arms around me and declared her love, I had been determined to get rid of her as quickly as possible. And after her performance in Delamare's clinic, when she had visited Sylvia, I could have strangled her. And now—and that's how changeable things like this can be, your honor—there was only one thing on my mind, that she remain loyal to us and above all—silent! I said, "Listen, Clarissa. Babs is as well as can be expected. I planned to call you today"—never!—"but then something happened and I had to come to Madrid with Bracken, and this lawyer, Lejeune."

"What happened?"

I told her the whole story. When I had finished, she got up, walked over to the window and looked out for a long time. Then she said, "I think we must understand what Dr. Wolken did, after all he has been through."

"We do understand," I said. "We're not going to try to hold him. How could we? He's flying back to Switzerland today."

"And you're quite sure he'll never betray us?"

"Positive. Lejeune will see to that."

51

An icy wind was blowing. Bracken was standing beside me at the entrance to the Estudios Sevillas Films lot, and like me he was freezing. Our taxi driver was waiting some distance away. After leaving Dr. Salmerón's clinic, we had driven out here because Bracken wanted to show me where a greater part of the most expensive picture Seven Stars had ever financed was going to be filmed. Preparations had been going on for some time. The script was finished and had been approved. Actors, technicians, architects and cameramen were under contract.

On this December 8, 1971, it was already growing dark. Everything looked deserted and dead. The entrance was locked. I looked through the fence at the vast lot—not a tree in sight, not a bush, nothing. The earth out here was red and the terrain seemed to stretch out, endless and empty. Soon, in a few months, it would be teeming with workmen and no longer endless and empty. Instead it would be covered with palatial buildings and poor farmyards, stables, a place for armored riders, triumphal arches and gallows—a whole city! The powerful columns surrounding the huge courtyard of an ornate palace, seat of Governor Georgi Abashwili, ruler hundreds of years ago of the province of Grusinia in the Caucasus, would rise up into the sky of Madrid in the year 1972. American and Spanish architects and Spanish laborers would create this imaginary world. In the offices of the administration building, American and Spanish cameramen and propertymen would be working, American film directors would have settled down, the makeup rooms for the extras would be ready, and the single dressing rooms for the stars.

I clung to the iron fence and looked out across the red earth as far as I could see, into the dim void, into a dim infinity. A brain-damaged child. Ruth. Sylvia. Twenty-five million dollars. *The Chalk Circle.* Producer: Philip Kaven. Seven Stars. Lawyers. Doctors. Joe Gintzburger. I am Malechamawitz, the Angel of Death. So many obligations! And so little strength, so little courage . . .

"What's the matter with you?" said Bracken. He hadn't spoken a word until then.

"I'm all right."

"Good. I wanted you to see it. Of course we'll be shooting in Saragossa too, and near Barcelona. Da Cava's assistants have found various locations, but we haven't made up our minds yet. We'll go up in the Pyrenees for snow. But this is where we'll start. We'll be here for weeks!"

The bastard! So this was his boomerang. "I can't be here for weeks, Rod," I said. "You know that. I have to be with Babs."

"So you'll be with Babs some of the time and some of the time you'll be here. Will be strenuous, granted. We're planning six weeks for the shooting. Will undoubtedly take longer. Bad months for you. But you've simply got to be here *and* with Babs, you know that."

"I know that," I said. "But I can't do it!"

"You can't be here and with Babs?"

"Don't be an ass! I can't be producer, not of this monster picture. I have no idea how . . ."

"Of course you don't. But Sylvia insists that you be listed as producer!"

"Listen, Rod . . ."

"You listen!" And the icy wind blew the red dust into our faces so that we had to turn around. "I told you I'd help, and I already have. Of course you can't be producer—you have to fly back and forth from Nürnberg all the time and you don't know a damn thing about it anyway. So . . . Steve Comming."

"What about him?"

"Best man in Hollywood. You don't know him?"

"Of course I know him, idiot!" I said bitterly. Nothing to be done about it—Rod and I were enemies, always would be, even though we had a traitor in our midst. One thing was certain—neither Bracken nor Clarissa nor Dr. Wolken had anything to do with that "clown," Roger Marne. It had to be someone else, and instead of uniting our efforts to find out who, Rod and I were already at loggerheads.

"I called Steve," said Bracken, "quite a while ago. Long before things went wrong with Babs. He understands the situation, and he's ready to work as assistant producer under you, and do all your work. And you still get your fat salary. Agreed?"

We glared at each other, enveloped now by the red dust. Our eyes were watering. I nodded.

"And now let's go. We've got to get to the airport. God knows what's been going on in Paris since we left. And in Nürnberg. We'll pick up Lejeune at Salméron's clinic."

At mention of Salméron, it came to me. "King Lear," I said.

"King Lear? What're you talking about!"

"I was reminded of him because I can't get that conversation about euthanasia out of my mind. It's driving me crazy."

"Pull yourself together," said Bracken. "So what's it all got to do with Lear?"

"In Shakespeare's play, King Lear is a very old man. He has three daughters and nothing but one tragedy after the other. He's ill, he goes mad, and he has only one friend, a man called Kent."

"Like the cigarette?"

"Yes ... like the cigarette. What Kent said about the tragic old man at the end, when Lear was sick and riddled with pain, fits in with everything Dr. Reinhardt and Salméron said for and against mercy killing or the prolongation of life."

"If you're going to start hallucinating now," cried Bracken, "we're finished! So what was it? What did Kent say?"

"He said, 'Let him pass! He hates him that would upon the rack of this tough world stretch him out longer ...'"

"Are you trying to tell me that those who are for euthanasia are right because they love the sick patient and those who are against euthanasia are wrong because they hate him?"

"I don't know," I said. "I don't know anything any more."

52

Kaleidoscope. Brockhaus. Volume III. J-NEU. Page 53, first column, lower left. "Ka-lei-do-scope (Gr.) An optical toy, containing loose irregular fragments of colored glass. Changes of position display its contents in a variety of symmetrical varicolored forms, most frequently as hexagonal stars. Invented in 1817. Symbol of constantly changing impressions."

That was what I was looking for: a symbol of constantly changing impressions. I just got the volume out of the prison library. Kaleidoscope. Yes. When I think back to what took place after that first flight to Madrid I see it as a time in which events piled up more and more, faster and faster, so that in the end I felt as if I were reeling through life. Some situations have remained fixed in my mind because of their profundity or sweetness, their intimacy and beauty, their dreadful and evil aspects, and their perils. I shall report on them in detail, your honor. As for the rest . . . I shall use my diary for a while.

Wednesday, December 8, 1971. Lejeune, Bracken and I flew back to Paris and reported to Joe and his lawyers. Sylvia had already called three times from Delamare's clinic. So I called Sylvia.

"My darling Silky! Babs is doing very well. Her doctors are more than satisfied. Please stop worrying!"

"Where are you?"

"In Paris. At Le Monde."

"Why are you in Paris?"

"Don't get excited. Babs wanted Nounours, you know—the teddy bear Jean gave her."

"Oh, God!"

"You see, she's fully conscious. She remembers everything. She's getting better every day. That's what I had to tell everyone here. And I needed some winter things. It's terribly cold in Nürnberg. I'm flying back tomorrow, then I'll call you right away, as soon as I've seen Babs."

Thursday, December 9. Take an early plane back to Nürnberg as Philip Norton (wearing glasses). Straight to the clinic. Tell Ruth everything that has happened. Ruth says, "I can understand your Dr. Wolken. I know all the arguments for euthanasia and the debates about the cost of caring for the sick or for the healthy children doomed to starvation. And it's all so terrible, because there's so much truth on both sides. But I can't see the other side and I never will! I shall plead for the sick and the helpless children as long as I live!"

We go to see Babs. She hugs the little bear. Not a word about Sylvia. Am I going to stay with her now? she wants to know. Of course, I tell her, and she falls asleep with shabby old Nounours in her arms. And I see Ruth smile again.

Friday, December 10, to Thursday, December 16. I stay in Nürnberg. See Babs daily. She progresses slowly but surely. Medication changed. Temperature down. She can stand light now. Muscular weakness in left arm and foot less pronounced. Constantly on the phone with Joe, who has decided to stay in Paris until Christmas just in case something happens; with Sylvia, whose voice changes all the time. She isn't putting on an act constantly as she used to do. She sounds happy. But she is very lonely. I let her go on believing that Babs will be fully restored.

Tuesday, December 14. During the night, a phone call at the Bristol. Suzy, from Paris. Since she knows everything anyway, Rod gave her my phone number. Sloshed, she tells me, "My count has come back!"

"But I thought he was staying on in Acapulco."

"Couldn't stand it—longed for me! Don't laugh!"

"I didn't laugh."

"Phil?"

"Yes."

"May I marry him now?"

"What a silly question, *mon petit chou!* You've got to marry him. Why are you asking my permission?"

"Well, because I . . ."

"You're stoned, Suzy, my pet!"

"Yes. And I'm going to go on drinking, because I . . . I never stopped hoping that . . . that you'd come back to me. But you can't, can you?"

"No, Suzy, I can't."

"Because of the child?"

"Yes."

"How is she?"

"A little better. Anyway, she's not going to die. I'm sorry, *mon petit chou,* but I really can't. Forget me. Be a good countess."

"Don't call me *mon petit chou!*" she cried. "All right then, I'll be a countess!" And she hung up.

Babs can eat normally. No more fever.

Thursday, December 16. Joe tells me to come to Paris. Something's happened. Commercial flight as Philip Norton. In Orly take my Maserati Ghibli out of the garage and race it all the way to Le Monde, like a madman. Transformation into Philip Kaven. Joe's problem: He has an agreement with Carlo Marone to premiere Sylvia's last film, *So Little Time,* in Rome because he, Marone, knows from an absolutely reliable source that Alfredo won't live till the opening, which is scheduled for May. He is in a clinic in Rome. Sensational,

298

naturally, if Alfredo was to die before the premiere. I told Marone when I spoke to him about it in Rome that he'd have to meet Joe halfway financially if he was to get the world premiere. I was right, and he and Joe had come to an understanding. Now I'm sitting with Joe in the bar of Le Monde.

"This damn dago's cornered us, Phil. I've just received a report on Alfredo's illness by his doctor. My men copied it in Rome, never mind now."

"So?"

"We're in trouble. Alfredo's condition is improving daily."

"That bastard . . ."

"You've got to come to Rome with me right away. With Lejeune. It's too late today, but early tomorrow morning . . ."

"Okay. I'll call Sylvia and tell her how well Babs is getting along, and sleep in my bed at Le Monde for one night."

Friday, December 17, Rome. "You lied to us! You are a swindler and a scoundrel! You got a lush contract out of us through fraud, and Mr. Gintzburger signed it because he thought you were honest!" Lejeune to Marone.

"I am not a scoundrel and a swindler! I didn't get a contract out of Mr. Gintzburger with anything but the best intentions. When Mr. Kaven was here on the night of . . . I don't remember the date . . ."

"December second."

Lejeune knows everything. That's why Joe lets him talk. We don't open our mouths.

"December second. All right. That was when I told him . . ."

"That was when you told him that Alfredo Bianchi didn't have three months to live. Today, on December seventeenth, I'm telling you that we have reliable information that Alfredo Bianchi's condition is improving daily. He can start shooting his next picture in April."

"You're misinformed! Alfredo is in terrible shape! He's half—"

"Shut up!" Lejeune barely lets Marone get in a word. "Where are your copies of the contract?"

Our position isn't exactly rosy. In the contract between Joe and Marone there is, of course, no mention of the fact that Alfredo Bianchi's death is to precede the world premiere of *So Little Time.* Therefore there can be no question of taking any legal steps against Marone if this unwritten demand is not fulfilled. If Marone insists on the premiere taking place in

Rome, it will. That's why Joe had me come from Nürnberg. That's why we flew to Rome. That's why Joe is so excited. When he's excited, he takes deep noisy breaths through his nose, and he's excited right now, and justly so. A Moran picture world-premiering in Rome, not in the States? Unheard of! It will cost Joe a fortune if Bianchi isn't dead by then. Marone shoves two copies of the contract across the table. "Where is the third?" asked Lejeune.

"What third?"

"Monsieur Kaven," says Lejeune, "you're the youngest man here. If you don't mind . . ."

"With pleasure," and I walk around the desk.

"No!" Marone cries, and suddenly the third copy is lying on the desk.

"Well, there you are!" says Joe.

"Just a minute!" Lejeune. "The bastard may have copies that he can give to the papers and cause a scandal. And we don't need a scandal right now."

"It isn't true!" cried Marone. "I have no copies!"

"Monsieur Kaven," Lejeune again. "May I trouble you once more . . ."

My hands are fists. I've been wanting to wipe up the floor with Marone for quite some time. Marone, both hands protecting his face, says, "In the safe behind the Gobelin."

"Open it!" says Lejeune.

So Marone walks over to the Gobelin, folds it back, opens the big safe, in which we can see—and we take a good look—five copies of the contract, innumerable rolls of microfilm, bundles of letters, photos showing men and women in explicit situations, keys, two pistols, jewelry . . . Marone hands over the copies.

"We don't have much time," says our fat lawyer. "I'm sure the bastard has microfilms of the contract too. And I'm sure that's not his only safe. So let's get to work." He takes a pile of papers out of his attaché case, slams them down on Marone's desk, and says, "Sign!"

"But I can't just . . ."

"Oh yes you can!"

"No!"

"Monsieur Kaven, if you don't mind . . ."

Marone takes a gold fountain pen out of his jacket and starts to sign, fast. He is signing a new contract to the effect that he will have the rights to the world premiere of *So Little*

300

Time in Rome if by March 1, 1972, he and Joe Gintzburger, head of Seven Stars, have come to complete agreement on two controversial points, known to both sides (but *not* stated in the contract). Point One: Alfredo Bianchi must be dead and buried by March 1, 1972. Point Two: If Point One is fulfilled, for the world premiere in Rome Marone hands over twice as much of the box-office receipts as had been agreed upon with Joe in Paris. The punishment must fit the crime. Joe has already signed the contract. Marone may keep three copies.

"I swear by the Holy Mother that I was told Bianchi's condition was hopeless. I swear I told Mr. Kaven the truth!"

"And now the truth is a lie," says Lejeune, closing his attaché case. "Now his condition is improving. The doctors are doing their best. You have no idea what ways there are to prolong life."

"To prolong it!" Marone is screaming. "I can't help it! *Madonna mia*—what do you want me to do? Go to the hospital and ask them to let Bianchi die?"

"Signor Marone, what exactly do you mean by that? Would you agree to the doctors' ending the life of a great actor if it suited your business interests? If it were possible, would you be willing to hasten the death of this poor sick man, through a criminal use of euthanasia, so that he might die at a time convenient to you, and the world premiere could take place in Rome? You don't have to stammer. I find you repulsive, signore. Messieurs, everything is settled. Let us leave."

So we leave. But not straight to the airport. Lejeune knows a restaurant. "We can't leave Rome without a meal here. Besides I'm starved. Gentlemen, they have ravioli, baked in vegetables, with a piquant meat sauce, your choice of vegetables . . . beans, broccoli, sprouts, leeks . . . I recommend the broccoli . . ."

Kaleidoscope . . .

Friday, December 17, 1971. Arrive in Paris from Rome in the late afternoon, on Sylvia's jet. Call Nürnberg. Talk to Ruth. Babs's condition continues to improve. Call Sylvia. Report on Babs, am even more encouraging. Sylvia happy yet at the same time depressed. To be alone at Christmas. Everything she says relates to herself. And I have just heard Ruth's voice. . . . I console Sylvia. She cries. Self-pity. I tell her I'll call regularly. Say whatever comes glibly to mind. How much I love her of course. Joe is flying to Los Angeles tomorrow with his lawyers, the doctor and PR man Charlie. So that they can be with their families at Christmas. Very cold in Paris. Rains all the time. Order a gigantic orchid corsage for Sylvia for the 24th. Buy something for Nürnberg. Takes me a while to find it. Get back to Le Monde, soaked. Hot bath. Change into my Nürnberg outfit. Don't forget your glasses, Herr Norton! Drive to Orly in the Maserati, with my plastic suitcase. Leave the car in the garage. Lufthansa flight 9:30 P.M. from Orly. *Very* tired. From the Nürnberg airport straight to the Bristol and to bed.

Saturday, December 18, 1971. It is snowing. To the hospital right away. Babs sleeps all day. According to Ruth she is still very weak. Ruth! I am with her again. In the hospital all day. Christmas preparations here too. It frightens me. There's to be a Christmas party for the children who have to stay in the hospital. Call Clarissa and Sylvia in the evening. Report how well Babs is getting along. Gross exaggeration. It's snowing in Madrid too. Call Bracken. Joe and his crew have left.

Sunday, December 19, 1971, to Thursday, January 13, 1972—summary of my diary entries. In Nürnberg, at the hospital all day. Always near Ruth. Call Sylvia and Bracken every evening from the hotel. Find talking to Sylvia more and more agonizing. Can't seem to find the right words. Long pauses. Embarrassing. Start feeling afraid of the nightly calls. Does Sylvia notice?

On December 24, the Christmas party in the big lecture hall. Much worse than I had anticipated. The children who don't have to stay in bed walk, are carried or are wheeled in; doctors, nurses and orderlies all present. The children sit in the rising rows of seats, many held by nurses and doctors. I see Ruth with a paralyzed boy in her arms. In front of the first row, two dozen children in wheelchairs. Babs, of course, has to remain in bed. We'll go to her when it's over. The hall and the hospital are decorated with fir branches, tinfoil and colored balls.

Samy Molcho, the famous Israeli mime, has come to entertain the children. He dances for them in a fantastic costume, imitates animals, tumbles and leaps; he has prepared a whole program for them, all funny numbers. The grown-ups laugh. A few of the children laugh. Very few. Not one of those in the wheelchairs. I can see the sweat form on Samy Molcho's forehead; he works harder and harder. Every child has been given a paper bag filled with fruit, candy and nuts. Only a few can hold their own bags. Adults hold them for the children who can't. Some of the bags fall on the floor. Oranges, tangerines, nuts roll down the steps. Some of the children have fits and the doctors carry them out. Others vomit. Samy Molcho has never worked so hard in his life. Fewer and fewer children are laughing now. In the end—none. Silence. Then the record player plays "Silent Night." That on top of everything else! More children have to be carried out. Some start screaming and thrashing out at the doctors or nurses holding them. My shirt is wet with perspiration when this nightmare finally ends and all the children have been taken away. Suddenly I am all alone, because Ruth has left too, with the paralyzed boy. I look for her and find her in the corridor. "This Christmas party," she says. "Every year the same thing."

"So why in God's name do you do it?"

"Orders of the administration and the Board of Health. We've begged them to discontinue it, but they won't."

We pass one of the waiting rooms. The door is open. Samy Molcho is sitting on a bench, still in his colorful costume with the ruff around the neck, his makeup running down his face. Samy Molcho is crying. He is crying so hard, he doesn't even see us. We walk past him quietly.

Pastor Hirtmann is there. He knows that the children and their parents need him. I see him every now and then, in a corridor, in a waiting room, at the bedside of a lonely child, talking to the parents. I imagine that Pastor Hirtmann is speaking to each one in a way that they can understand and that perhaps can console them.

In the ward where little Sammy lies, he who believes he is Malechamawitz, the Angel of Death, I see beds with no adults beside them. Ruth explains that many of these parents have stopped coming long ago. They are happy to be rid of their stricken children while knowing they are well taken care of. I see only a few adults in Sammy's ward and children excitedly opening their packages. Sammy cries, "Come here!" when he sees us. Sammy has no visitors. "Sammy is an orphan," Ruth explains softly.

We walk up to Sammy's bed. He is lying on it, still dressed. He shakes hands vigorously with both of us, then, his eyes bright, he tells Ruth, "I have a present for you."

"For me?"

"Yes!"

Sammy jumps up and disappears halfway under his bed. "Everybody gets a present today!"

"The children, not the parents!"

"And what if a child doesn't have any parents?" Sammy emerges, his face red. "There doesn't always have to be a father *and* a mother, does there? Fifty percent is enough, isn't it? Father *or* mother. I've chosen you to be my mother."

"Me? Why? I see so little of you. You're in a different section . . ."

"Would be nice if you were."

"Were what?"

"My mother," says Sammy, handing her a clumsily wrapped package.

Ruth unwraps it, Sammy dancing around her excitedly. There is a box in the package. Ruth opens it. In the box there are ten little men made out of black rags, a little string and paper, a little paint. Ten little dolls with ten little hats on their heads. I try not to show how baffled I am and pretend to be all admiration. Ruth has no trouble reacting the same way.

"It's wonderful, Sammy!"

"You know what they are, don't you?"

"Ten men reciting the Kaddish. There always have to be ten."

"Yes, yes, yes! I made them for you!" There are tears of joy in Sammy's eyes. He jumps from Ruth to me and back to Ruth again, drags our heads down level with his and embraces and kisses us. And cries out to Ruth, "Thank you! Thank you! I made them for you! Thank you!"

Sammy is thanking us for the fact that *he* gave a present. "What does it mean, reciting the Kaddish?" I ask.

"It's a Jewish custom. The Kaddish is the prayer for the dead. Only men can recite it, and there always have to be at least ten."

"Prayers for the dead?"

"Well, of course. He is Malechamawitz, isn't he? The Angel of Death."

"The Kaddish! The Kaddish!"

"Sammy, this is a beautiful present!"

"Thank you very much! Thank you very much!" Sammy cries and embraces and kisses Ruth all over again. She kisses him and strokes his head. "Thank you very much! I made it for you!"

And then we are with Babs. She is fast asleep, holding her shabby old bear with both hands. She looks so peaceful. It is 8:00; all visitors have left. In the corridors it is quiet. Ruth says, "Merry Christmas, Herr Norton."

"Merry Christmas, Frau Doktor. And what are you going to do now?"

"I'm on night duty. I'm not married, you see, I have no family, so I said I'd look after things tonight."

"May I . . . may I stay with you? I don't have anybody either."

"Of course, Herr Norton." Ruth feels Babs's pulse. "Almost normal," she says, "and no fever."

I think of how I would like to kiss her, that there is nothing in the world I want to do more than kiss her. My mother told me once that there were two types of women: mothers and whores. I can feel myself being drawn ever closer to Ruth, who radiates so much motherliness. I am perceptive enough to recognize that I have taken on the role of patient, a patient who is being treated by a good psychiatrist. But all the perception in the world doesn't protect you from love. Does Ruth know what is happening to *her?* I keep looking at her. At last she looks up and says, "I must go back to my office so that they can reach me if they need me."

"Yes," I say. "I have a present for you too, Frau Doktor," and think—but none for Babs.

A lot of small packages are lying around in Ruth's office, a lot of bottles, gift-wrapped, many letters. Ruth tells me that she, like all doctors, gets presents from the parents at Christmas. She'll open them later. But there is one present she will open at once. From Tim.

"But Tim is dead!"

"He got it ready for me before he died," says Ruth. "His parents brought it to me today."

She draws an envelope out of the pocket of her white coat, and we sit down on opposites sides of her desk. Ruth opens the envelope, takes out a folded piece of paper and says in a moment, "Tim has written a poem for me. Shall I read it to you?"

"Please."

A little fir candle holder stands on the desk, a red candle in it. The candle is lit, otherwise the room is dark. And Ruth reads Tim's poem to me by the yellow candlelight:

"I tried to explain it to you,
I really tried,
I tried to explain to you
That life isn't worth the pain.
You didn't believe me.
All you said was: Incurable.
Yet when the end comes,
You will be as I am—
Robbed of everything and broken.
And you will have to go on living
A life of living death.
I am imprisoned in my wheelchair,
And what about you?
I have no more pride,
Not any more.
The same thing will happen to you,
And you will want to fight.
But you will realize soon
That it's a fight for losers;
That people are waiting eagerly
To see you shattered at their feet.
Oh, how I hate to say it!
I tried so hard to explain it to you."

Ruth puts the paper down. I say, "Poor Tim."

"Happy Tim," says Ruth. "He is saved. Of all the people I know, Herr Norton, this paraplegic boy understood me more profoundly and correctly, and evaluated me far better, than I was ever able to."

"Poor Ruth. And now he is happy and you are alone."

"Every human being is alone," she says. "When he is born; when he dies. And one has to face up to it. I believe that only if one can live with one's loneliness can one live with others. I believe that the person who can't live alone can't live with others either."

She is silent. A little while later she says softly, "Why are you looking at me like that, Herr Norton?"

"Because I love you."

"Stop it! Stop it at once!"

"No," I say. "I shall never stop loving you with all my heart." I walk over to my coat and take a square envelope out of the pocket. "But I promise not to mention my love for you again until you permit it. Or want it. May I give you your Christmas present now?"

306

Ruth nods.

I walk over to the record player, because my present is a record. I had bought it in Paris. I put it on the turntable, and turn it on. John William's voice: *"Ô Dieu, merci pour ce paradis, qui s'ouvre aujourd'hui à l'un de tes fils ..."*

Suzy's favorite record, the favorite record of my little whore with the beauty salon, the record I smashed that night when Babs was so desperately ill. Now I had bought it for Ruth. She sits motionless and listens.

And now I don't look at Ruth any more but out into the white, snowy night. *"On Golgotha there stood a cross, there stood a cross, and you were there, oh Lord, on the cross ... stretching your arms out to me ..."*

So much snow. I have never seen so much snow ...

"Yes, it was you who stretched out your arms to me, the poorest of your children ..."

The snow is so white, I think, and the ten little men Sammy made for Ruth are so black, the ten little men reciting the Kaddish for the dead ...

"And I feel a fire of joy burning within me, and I cry out: O God, thank you for this paradise ..."

I am sitting on the floor. Now I turn around, and Ruth is looking at me. She doesn't turn away. The candle flickers and we listen to the song until it ends. I get up and walk back to the desk. Ruth gets up too, says, "Thank you, Herr Norton. Thank you very much."

"And I thank you."

"For what?"

"You know what for." And she turns away and says, "Shall we go to Babs again?"

"Yes."

The corridors we walk through are empty.

Babs is asleep. Ruth and I sit opposite each other on either side of her bed. After quite some time, Ruth finally speaks.

"Dr. Bettelheim was possessed with the idea that a lot of psychiatric clinics make their patients sicker if only because of their atmosphere. He has tried to make his Orthogenic School comfortable and beautiful, like a home."

"I imagine he does this," I say, "so that the children feel they are in a normal home and can hope to be normal again. You're talking about psychotic children, now, aren't you? The thought centers haven't been destroyed, they're simply confused. Am I right?"

"If they're lucky—yes."

"And these children can still think, or if they can't do that they can at least sense that one loves them and is treating them like human beings. But in many psychiatric clinics they don't operate that way—right?"

"I can't answer that, Herr Norton. I can only give you an example. While I was with Dr. Bettelheim, we had a beautiful old peasant cradle."

Babs sighs in her sleep.

"You see, Dr. Bettelheim insisted on having a cradle large enough for an eight- or ten-year-old to stretch out in. But he couldn't find one large or strong enough for his purpose."

"He could have had one made."

"Certainly. But that would have meant having a cradle built for a mentally ill child, and that was just what Dr. Bettelheim didn't want. Because that way the difference between a mentally ill child and a healthy one would have started in the cradle."

"I see."

"So Dr. Bettelheim had to find a cradle that had given many normal children a sense of security for centuries. It took him a long time to find that cradle. Finally he did, in a peasant home. And it was made in the seventeenth century."

We remained by Babs's bedside all night, saying little. Ruth was not called away.

Kaleidoscope! Kaleidoscope!

I am leafing through my diary. This time I stayed in Nürnberg until January 13, 1972. There is still so much that you ought to know, your honor, and we have so little time. I'll try to condense the events.

The first thing I see is that I forgot to call Sylvia on Christmas Day. After staying awake all night with Ruth I went to my hotel and slept until well into the afternoon. The telephone woke me. It was Sylvia. Reproaches and fear. What was the matter with me? I say what I've been saying all along—that Babs is getting better daily, which makes Sylvia happy. But why hadn't I called before? Because I had spent the entire night at Babs's bedside, which made me the darlingest Pepito of all the Pepitos in the world!

I was finding it increasingly difficult to call Sylvia. Her baby voice, all the silly endearments, my feelings of growing oneness with Ruth ... Sylvia's way of talking exclusively about herself after comments about Babs ... She is bored to death ...

I can see from these entries that I'm starting to be really afraid of these calls.

In the hospital I get to know new helpers of those who live in the dark. I spend all my days at the hospital, mostly with Babs. She has no more temperature, the paralysis is almost completely gone. She is still cross-eyed, but not nearly as badly as before. Her mind is perfectly clear now but she never mentions Sylvia. I ask Ruth. She says she's not sure. I think she's perfectly sure but doesn't want to tell me.

When Ruth has night duty I stay in the hospital all night too. Then she often plays the record I bought for her at Christmas.

Bad news from Hollywood. The woman who has been Sylvia's stand-in for years is seriously ill and won't be available for *The Chalk Circle*. A new stand-in will have to be found, preferrably in Spain. Not easy.

Sylvia is recovering so fast that they intend to let her leave the clinic on February 1. She is happy. The rest of us are not. Once free, she'll want to see Babs. Bracken reports that Joe Gintzburger is very depressed about the whole thing and is trying to find a solution.

The ten little rag-doll men reciting the Kaddish have been standing on Ruth's desk since Christmas Eve. She carries the little lamb with her constantly. She is worried too. What will happen to Babs when Sylvia is ready to face her public again? Can one speak sensibly to Sylvia? No. One can't speak sensibly to any woman who is the mother of a sick child. This talk takes place in the course of a long cold walk one afternoon. We decide to return to the city by streetcar. In the streetcar, a boy of about fourteen. The car is very full. The boy is seated. A fat woman is standing in front of him and is indignant. "The big boy's got to sit! He's got to rest, poor thing!" I want to say something, but Ruth stops me. Instead of me, the conductor speaks. He knows the boy. "Look here, if you're not steady on your feet, standing up in a streetcar is hard to do."

The fat woman is furious. "Is that all you have to say? You're on his side?" Everybody in the car is staring at her. Another woman recognizes the boy and says, "That's Lenke's oldest boy. He's not . . . you know," and she taps a finger against her forehead. Now everybody stares at the boy. They mumble to each other, a few louder voices speak up, again for the boy, whereupon the fat woman cries indignantly, "How was I to know that? Why don't these idiots have some sort of identification, like an armband? Then at least one would know!"

Ruth's hand in mine is a fist now. She sees that I want to intervene. "Don't, Herr Norton," she says quietly. "Millions think just like that woman. Now you've seen it for yourself."

"But something's got to be done about it!"

"Something *will* be done about it," says Ruth.

On the following day Ruth feels that the time has come to give Babs a series of tests to find out exactly how far she has progressed. I may be present. The tests were developed under the direction of Professor Curt Bony from the Psychological Institute of Hamburg between 1963 and 1968. They are known in Germany as the *Testbatterie für geistig behinderte Kinder* TBGB, or Evaluation Test for Brain-Damaged Children. Many of the tests have been derived from American research.

Intelligence test: Among various colored objects on a large card, the child has to show the one that doesn't go with the others. There are a hundred cards, but the test is to take no more than forty minutes. The questions get progressively more difficult. For instance: colored houses and things that belong in them, then, suddenly, a hand, next to things that belong in a house.

Babs gets through the hundred cards in twenty-two minutes without making a mistake. She says, "Baby stuff!" Her speech is still fairly slurred.

Next day, another intelligence test: In forty-six different problems, Babs has to fit the pieces missing in a geometric pattern: triangles, circles, semicircles, segments of circles, and tiny pieces, some with quite complicated shapes. Babs has no difficulty fitting in all the pieces correctly. In the end Ruth and Babs are beaming.

Next day—vocabulary test: Seventy questions from the Peabody Picture Vocabulary Test by Dunn. Babs has to respond to a word spoken by Ruth by pointing to the matching picture on the card. For instance, one card shows a stocking, a pencil, a butterfly and an apple. Ruth says "pen-

310

cil." Babs must then point to the pencil. She does. She does the right thing often. But she also makes frequent mistakes.

Next day—perception test: Ruth works on "obeying instructions." Nounours plays an important part. "Take Nounours in your arms.... Put Nounours under the bedclothes.... Take Nounours out from under the bedclothes...." The first instructions are comparatively easy, and then get more complicated. Babs doesn't make a single mistake, although the test takes a long time. They work with other objects too—with Ruth's wristwatch, with the little lamb, with a toy trunk—putting the lamb into it, taking it out again. Now all of us are beaming. There are beads of perspiration on Babs's forehead.

Next day—motor impulses: There is a paper with a hundred circles printed on it. In one minute Babs is to put a dot in each circle, and the dot is to be as central as possible. Babs finishes off eighty-nine circles. Nearly all the dots are well centered, scarcely one at the edge, not one outside the circle. But Babs still can't speak clearly, and her sentences are very short. "That's going to get better too," says Ruth.

Thursday, January 13, 1972. Bracken calls me at the Bristol. I'm to come to Madrid the next day. The staff has begun working on *Chalk Circle* in the offices of the Estudios Sevilla Films. Since I am the producer I have to be there. Steve Comming, the associate producer whom Rod has found for me, is arriving tomorrow too. I say goodbye to Babs. She is almost gay. Not a word about her mother.

Paris. Le Monde. Bracken has already flown to Madrid. I change clothes and suitcase and am Philip Kaven again. To Madrid on Sylvia's jet. Bracken and Steve Comming waiting for me at Barajas. Steve has been associate producer of many big Hollywood productions. I know he's the best man Bracken could have gotten. Steve knows the truth, also the role he and I are going to play. We shake hands, a long handshake. "You can trust me, Mr. Kaven. Always."

Friday, January 14, to Friday, January 28, summary of my diary entries. Madrid. We're staying at the Hotel Castellana Hilton. Very busy days. Spend most of my time at the Estudios Sevilla films. It's colder than ever in Madrid. The wind blows the red earth across the lot. Workmen and Spanish and American architects working together to get a start on covering this huge area with the appropriate structures. The heating is on in the administration buildings, but not enough. We're freezing. A lot of us have colds. The American scriptwriters have arrived, and so have the tailors and seamstresses, and the technical and financial staffs are moving into their offices. More phones are being installed. Joe and Rod mistrust all European developers, so at the end of every day the film will be flown to Hollywood to be developed and copied, and the prints flown back to Madrid.

Spanish extras have been hired, a lot of them. I help da Cava choose them. Have no idea how to go about it. Da Cava is a world-famous director. He knows what he wants. Exterior acquisition men in bitter negotiations with peasants and horse farmers. We need a lot of animals, especially horses for the armed riders. Three translators are working for us. I have to be all over the place, giving my opinion. Steve tells me what opinion I'm supposed to have. The bookkeeping office is negotiating with the Spanish Bureau of Finance. Foreign-exchange problems. Don't know a thing about them. Steve explains, gives his opinion. Then I have the final say. The same applies to all insurance questions.

I have never really worked in my life, but now I sit with Bracken and Comming, and plans for financing, building and shooting have to be discussed. They've given me a huge office. I know I won't be using it much, but it's furnished and overflowing with files and plans. Steve has attended to that. No one is to have the slightest suspicion that things aren't what they seem.

The time flies. I phone Ruth. Babs's condition satisfactory. On February 1, Sylvia will leave Dr. Delamare's clinic, and when Sylvia appears in public again—*what then?*

We puat a prominent ad in *ABC*, the Madrid daily paper, for a stand-in for Sylvia Moran. The ad appears on January 28, 1972, a Friday. I have to be in my office on that day at 3:00 P.M. Bracken, Comming, da Cava, cameraman Roy Hadley Ching are with me. Kate and Joe Patterson, Sylvia's cosmeticians, are also present. We find out later that 114 women and girls turned up that afternoon to apply for the job. The whole procedure lasts from 3:00 P.M. until 2:00 the next morning! By that time my office is reeking of tobacco smoke and the tables are covered with glasses and bottles of beer and whiskey.

As the hours pass I feel increasingly miserable; my head

begins to ache, my eyes to tear. Then at 2:15 A.M. I squint through my sore, red eyes and lean forward. Like me all the others stare uncomprehendingly at the young woman who has just walked in.

"You . . . you are . . ." I start to say, but get no farther. The young woman looks at me anxiously.

Bracken says, "You're not Miss Moran's double. You're the absolute image of her!"

All I can do is nod. Sylvia Moran is standing before me. This young woman looks exactly like her!

Da Cava asks her in Spanish, "What's your name?"

"Carmen Cruzeiro."

"Where do you live?"

"In Madrid."

"And where do you work?"

"With Spanex."

"And what is that?"

"An export-import firm. I'm a secretary in their foreign department. I speak English, French and German."

Steve looks at me and nods slightly. "You're hired," I tell Carmen Cruzeiro, whereupon the girl bursts into tears. Bracken gives her a drink. At last she calms down. When everything is settled and Carmen is saying goodbye, we shake hands. There is a little card in hers. I keep it in my hand.

Now everybody disperses. Rod and I drive back to the Castellanas Hilton together and go straight to our rooms. Then I look at the card Carmen Cruzeiro slipped into my hand. Written in longhand I read: "I am living at the Hotel Cervantes, Plaza de las Descalzares Reales, Apartment 12. Please come tomorrow morning before noon. Carmen Cruzeiro."

It is near noon and I am sitting opposite Carmen Cruzeiro at a table in a tiny living room, drinking Chato, a good cheap red wine. Carmen has put a platter of sharply spiced pieces of meat, olives, peppery sausage and tortilla between us, and I've eaten quite a lot.

A woman will never understand these pages. A woman couldn't understand why I went to see Carmen Cruzeiro. A man can. Men can understand that a man can love a woman as I loved Ruth and still, from time to time he simply *has to* sleep with another woman. This has nothing personal whatever to do with the woman he sleeps with. There are women who can think like men and can sleep with a man without its affecting their souls in any way. I know a few, but not many.

But one thing is strange. The idea of having to sleep with Sylvia again disturbs me, but the idea of sleeping with a woman who looks exactly like her makes me raunchier than I've been for a long time.

Carmen is wearing a red dress, cut very low. It is Sylvia sitting in front of me, talking to me; still, it is a quite different woman, and all the love of which I am capable belongs to yet another woman far, far away in Nürnberg. Carmen has told me that she knew a woman had to go to bed with any film man who has hired her, so, just in case, she had written the little card before coming to the audition. She had had no idea at the time whom she would give it to, and it had turned out to be me.

She evidently looks upon it as a fantastic opportunity to sleep with Philip Kaven. Nothing dangerous about it; she'll never mention it to a soul. I'm perfectly safe with her. Like all foolish film aspirants, she thinks she's started on the ladder to a roaring success. If she talks, she knows what it means: back to the foot of the ladder. She always wanted to be a movie actress; now she's positive she'll make it. Some bigshot or other will see her working as Sylvia Moran's stand-in and then . . . well, it's quite clear, isn't it? The way to Hollywood will be wide open. Goes without saying.

"Drink some more," she says. She addresses me with the formal "you." She'll do it in bed too, I'm positive. She gets up. "I'll be right back," she says, and withdraws to the bedroom.

I go on drinking Chato. I tried to call Ruth from the Hilton, but they hadn't been able to locate her. And then—and this is really strange, this I don't think even a man will understand, I certainly don't—I gave the operator at the Sophienkrankenhaus the name of the hotel where Carmen lives. And I said I'd be there until very late that evening because I was attending a conference, and that I would like Frau Doktor Reinhardt to call me if anything important happened. Purely routine. Then I called Sylvia in Paris and told her Babs was fine, that in two or three weeks she'd be getting up. Sylvia was very happy. I tried to make the call short, but that wasn't working, so I pretended I couldn't hear her voice any more and kept saying, "Hello . . . hello . . ." until she hung up, and I took a taxi to Carmen, who looks so much like Sylvia she could have been her twin. And that's what I'm thinking

314

of as I drink Chato. Then I hear a sound and turn around, and Carmen is standing in the doorway of her bedroom. She is naked. I feel the blood coursing wildly through my body and stand up to walk over to this naked woman who stretches out her arms to me, and . . . the phone rings.

"Whoever could that be?" Carmen asks.

Against her protest I pick up the receiver and can feel the cold sweat of fear running down my back because I know who it is, who it has to be. Yes, I am Señor Philip Norton.

"A call from Nürnberg for you."

"Hello? Yes?"

"Herr Norton?" Ruth.

"Yes, Frau Doktor."

"Please come. Come as quickly as you can."

"Why? Has something happened?"

"Yes."

"Has Babs died?"

"No. But she . . . please come. As quickly as you can!"

"Is it bad?"

"Yes, Herr Norton."

I drop the receiver and run out into the hall, grab my coat and rush out of the apartment, Carmen after me, naked. I can't understand a word she's saying.

Saturday, January 29, 1972, Nürnberg.

"Babs!"

No answer.

"Babs!" I am kneeling beside her bed. No answer. Nothing. She lies there motionless. I notice that her eyes are more crossed than ever. "Babs! It's me! Phil!"

Suddenly Babs stands up in bed, stands on tiptoe and waves her arm as if she were dancing. She tries to kick me in the face and falls. I look at Ruth, horrified. She has never looked more serious. "What happened?"

I can barely hear her answer. "This has been going on for several days. I thought it would pass; that's why I lied to you on the phone the first time. But I had to call Madrid and beg you to come. In the meantime we've started the medication again. Babs is on Alepson."

"But she was so much better!"

"Yes. But then, five days ago, she suddenly hit me, and fell out of bed. She became terribly excited and tried to get back into bed. I could see that the paralysis on the left side was much worse. She defecated in the bed, just as at the beginning."

"But that isn't possible!"

"Oh, Herr Norton, the best recovery is often followed by the worst relapse. I've seen it happen only too often."

I can't bear to look at Babs any more. Her crossed eyes are too hideous. "She's going to have to wear glasses," says Ruth, "if that doesn't get better." Glasses . . . oh, dear God!

"And look here!" Ruth points to a chair. Nounours is lying on it, the teddy bear Babs loved so much, arms and legs torn out. The head hangs by a thread, pieces are lying everywhere. "She did that today," says Ruth, "this morning. I came immediately and she was screaming insanely. We fought, then suddenly she was silent."

"She didn't say anything?"

"She hasn't spoken a word since then."

"And that can happen too?"

"Yes, Herr Norton. I know that Frau Moran gets out on February first. So we'll have to make a plan. I asked you to come back from Madrid for that reason too. We have three more days. We're going to give Babs a thorough examination, however difficult it may be, considering her condition, so we know where we are. You can stay until February first, can't you?"

"Certainly. Only I must call Bracken at once. May I use your office?"

"Of course."

I look at Babs again and get the feeling that her eyes are more crossed all the time. I have to look away. I see her beloved Nounours, the toy she tore apart. I open the door and let Ruth go out first. "Frau Doktor?"

"Yes?"

"You're going in the wrong direction. Your office is that way."

She looks shocked. "That's never happened to me in the hospital before!" She sounds upset. I'm upset too. What next?

Saturday, January 29, to Tuesday, February 1, 1972. I report to Bracken. He swears obscenely. Will call Joe at once. Joe must come to Paris and be there when Sylvia gets back to Le Monde and finds out the truth. Long-range decisions have to be made.

Although I scarcely leave the hospital the following day, I see very little of Ruth. A whole team of doctors is examining

316

Babs. I sit at the desk in Ruth's office for hours, in front of the ten little rag dolls, waiting.

On the evening of January 31, Ruth is at her desk. I am sitting opposite her. All tests and examinations are over. "Herr Norton, the results are bad."

"How can that be? Babs was getting better all the time."

"The situation has changed completely. That's the dreadful thing about this illness. I mustn't lie to you, Herr Norton, and I don't want to. Babs's illness has left her severely damaged, damage that has only become apparent now. Even we find it incomprehensible. But our examinations are precise."

"What sort of damage?"

"Severe brain damage, Herr Norton."

Then she speaks for a long time, a flood of medical expressions, more than half of which I don't understand . . . postmeningetic syndrome . . . disjointed movements . . . lack of muscular coordination . . . destructive impulses . . . rage . . . constraint of the brain trauma . . . a cretin, therefore, an idiot child . . .

Ruth gets up, takes a bottle of cognac out of the cupboard and pours me a glass. "Thank you." I down the drink in one swallow.

"Herr Norton, it would be criminal if I didn't tell you the truth now. Babs has all the mental and physical handicaps I just mentioned, and others—her eyes—extropia—her sudden mutism, and many other symptoms."

"And things are going to stay that way?"

"Many of these symptoms will stay that way, Herr Norton, for a long time," Ruth replies, "perhaps forever. But I don't think that's likely. It is much more likely that the damage will abate, abate considerably. But only with the correct treatment and care, in special surroundings."

"In . . . in what kind of surroundings?"

"In an institution for mentally handicapped children," says Ruth, and standing on her desk are the rag dolls that pray the Kaddish for the dead.

Tuesday, February 1, 1972. Sylvia's eyes are open wide, her black hair is glossy, her skin is clear, white and taut. Professor Delamare is a magician! A genius! Sylvia Moran—the Beauty, the Madonna. Her voice is exquisitely modulated. She speaks the classical King's English. "Joe, you dirty son of a bitch! If you don't shut your fucking mouth and let me finish, I'll kick you in the balls, so help me God!"

Even the lawyer Lejeune is impressed. He is present too, naturally. All of us are there, the whole happy family, in the salon of Suite 419. Even old Dr. Lévy. I arrived in Paris from Nürnberg and changed to Philip Kaven as fast as I could. Joe, his lawyers, PR man Charlie, the American doctor and Bracken were already waiting, Lejeune and Dr. Lévy too. I had insisted on resting before Sylvia's arrival. They understood that.

I bathed and changed. But I didn't lie down. I called Nürnberg and asked for Ruth. She was there at once. "Nothing new, I suppose."

"Nothing, Herr Norton. But things aren't worse either."

"It's bad enough as it is."

"When does Frau Moran arrive?"

"It's four o'clock now, isn't it? She's on her way to Le Monde. In about half an hour you can pray for me. You pray sometimes, don't you?"

A long pause, then, "Herr Norton?"

"Yes."

"Do you remember Christmas Eve?"

"Yes."

"You said that you loved me."

"And you forbade me ever to mention it again."

"Yes."

"So?"

To which Ruth replied, "In the last few days so many terrible things have happened. You're so unhappy about Babs; I am too. Last night, when I had to tell you the truth, it was worst of all. It choked me. And this morning you left. But you have to know. Now."

"Know what?"

"That I love you too, Herr Norton."

"That you . . . *what?*"

"I said, 'I love you,' Herr Norton."

"You love . . ." I was stammering. The receiver threatened to slip out of my perspiring hand, my whole body was suddenly wet with perspiration. "You . . . you love me?"

"Yes."

"Frau Doktor, please! Why do you suddenly love me?"

"Not suddenly. I have loved you for a long time. I think it's love. I'm not sure. But I've never felt like this for any man before."

318

"Your brother . . ."

"That was a quite different feeling. I know I love all my children, but that's a different feeling too. What I feel for you is so strange, so utterly strange . . . it . . . it startled me at first."

"Do you mean to say you have never loved a man?"

"I have had men, but love . . . you are the first man I have ever loved." Her voice had grown softer and softer.

"But . . . I don't understand! I mean . . . why?"

"I don't know."

"There must be a reason."

"You were always there for Babs."

"That's no reason. Other men are there for their sick children. Give me a reason, please. Just one!"

A long pause, then Ruth said, almost in a whisper, "Perhaps . . ."

"Yes?"

"*'Ô Dieu, merci, pour ce paradis . . .'*—because you gave me that record."

"Because I gave you a record? But that's crazy!"

"It's not crazy, Herr Norton. No man has ever given me a present like that, at such a time, in such a situation. Yes, yes, it's the little record that made me sure, quite sure, that I love you."

"But I'm . . ."

"I know just what you are. Better than you do. Better than anyone else in the world. I know what I'm talking about. I know what I'm letting myself in for. I love you, Phil!"

"And I love you. I . . ."

"Will you call again today, when you've spoken to everybody?"

"Of course I will, Ruth. Of course. But what's going to become of us? What's going to happen next?"

"I don't know, Phil. Don't be afraid. Somehow things will go on, because we love each other." And she hung up.

I must have gone on holding the receiver in my hand for at least five minutes, sitting there on the edge of my bed. It was the strangest declaration of love I had ever received. And I knew it was going to be the strangest love, a love I couldn't even begin to imagine. But what luck! Ruth loved me!

Half an hour later, Sylvia arrives. Enter the star! Greetings with embraces and kisses, an interminable kiss for me. "My Pepito, my beloved Pepito! I'm so happy, so happy!"

319

"And I'm so happy, Silky," I say, and think of Ruth, who loves me.

"Now we'll never part again. Do you hear me? Never!"

"Never!" I assure her.

Compliments from all sides. Fantastic, unbelievable, what Sylvia looks like! She accepts all admiration, smiling. Not too broadly. Her skin probably still feels tight. Then she notices how many of us are there. Just to receive her?

"Yes . . . no . . . I mean . . ." Joe can't go on. He shuts up. Meanwhile waiters are serving tea, coffee, cognac. Dr. Lévy has been busy filling cups and glasses, and in Sylvia's cup, out of a tiny vial, a few drops of a clear liquid. She doesn't notice. All of us see to it that she doesn't notice.

"Pepito, my sweetheart—and now to Babs. Tell me about Babs, my darling, darling child. How is she? How much progress has she made?"

I drink again—tea—so do the others, Sylvia, automatically, as well, and then I give my report on Babs. The whole truth. I take my time about it, keep drinking tea in between so that the others will too, especially Sylvia. Dr. Lévy said the drops would prevent the worst from happening, and as I say, "There is hope that things will improve, I can assure you of that, but Babs will have to go to an institution where she can get the right treatment," the porcelain cup falls from her hand and breaks on the carpet. Sylvia sinks forward slowly, very slowly, and falls on the carpet too, on her face which has just been so fantastically restored, luckily not on the shards, and lies there motionless. Dr. Lévy and the American doctor kneel, roll her over on her back and examine her; the rest of us watch silently.

"She has fainted," says the American doctor, the one who has been here before, whom they call Doc. "She'll be all right in a minute."

Sylvia comes to fast. Dr. Lévy gives her cognac, again with a few drops, the strongest tranquilizer on the market that doesn't make one feel tired. No, Sylvia must not be tired now. She has to think clearly. And we don't exactly need an outburst of hysteria now.

Sylvia has drunk the cognac. She has sat down on the red velvet couch again and wept for quite a long time. No one has said a word. All of us understand and sympathize with her. Most of us look at our shoes or our hands, or at the fine old prints on the walls. I look out at the twilight.

Then Sylvia begins to speak, very clearly, very slowly, with the tears running down her face all the time. Every now and then she wipes them away with her handkerchief, and I really feel sorry for her. She asks me in that slow clear voice, "Where is my jet?"

"In Orly, Silky."

"We're flying to Nürnberg. I must see my child at once."

The way she speaks, the absolute stillness in the salon when she is done, with so many people present, gives the whole scene an unreal aura.

"You can't fly to Nürnberg now, Silky. I've spoken to Dr. Reinhardt. Babs wouldn't recognize you."

"But I want to see her."

"You can't go to Nürnberg now," says Bracken.

"Why not?"

"Because the Paris papers are full of the news that you've come back from your vacation."

"Without Babs?"

"And that Babs is staying awhile longer, with Clarissa, because the weather's so bad in Paris right now," says Bracken. True. The papers are really buying the story. Bracken has notified all of them.

"I don't care what's in the papers. I want to see my child."

"You can't."

"Of course I can! Who's to stop me?"

"Listen, Sylvia . . ."

"Pepito! Call Orly! We're on our way. They're to get the plane ready."

"Silky, it's impossible. It really is. Babs is to be kept absolutely quiet. God knows what might happen if she did recognize you!"

"Nothing will happen! I'm going! Babs is my child! What do you think I am? Do you think you can do whatever you like with me?"

This sort of thing goes on for half an hour. Even under sedation, Sylvia fights heroically. Finally Joe says in his Bible salesman's voice that now *I* will have to look after Babs whenever possible, that what has happened is terrible but that Sylvia is not only a great actress but also a great human being, and that only the truly great are swept into the hell of life, the others only stand in front of it and warm themselves. And *The Chalk Circle* will make all this self-evident, because Sylvia, however much she may be suffering, will act as she

321

has never acted before. Sylvia keeps saying that she'll never act again, and when Joe again tries to interrupt her with his gentlest voice, Sylvia says, "Joe, you dirty son of a bitch. If you don't shut your fucking mouth and let me finish, I'll kick you in the balls, so help me God!" And she goes on fighting for her right to see Babs, and refuses to appear in front of a camera again.

Without changing his voice, Joe becomes icy.

"Preparations for *The Chalk Circle* have begun, nearly all contracts are signed. If you don't play, Seven Stars will sue you for twenty-five million dollars."

"And a further fifty million damages," says one of the American lawyers.

Another lawyer: "To that will be added the payment of the penalty included in your contract, and that's the highest ever to be paid."

A third lawyer: "At the same time, today if necessary, Seven Stars will withdraw from any further contracts with you, Miss Moran, and will sever all business connections with you for all time."

"Information concerning this will go out to every news agency in the world, today if necessary."

"And what reason do you intend to give for getting rid of me?" Sylvia asked.

"You will be able to read that tomorrow, Miss Moran, in every paper."

Sylvia turns to Bracken and me. "Maybe you two could say something!"

Bracken says, "The man who's blackmailing us with the tapes will read it in tomorrow's paper too."

Sylvia presses her fist to her mouth. Joe gets up and turns on the lights in several sconces on the wall and comes back, hands in pockets. He walks up to Sylvia and says, "That's why the penalty is so high in your case, that's why in all our contracts with you since ... then, we have included this special guarantee, because, when the scandal of the century breaks, when our rivals publish the tapes and we're dragged into the story, the pretty story of your remarkable remarks about mentally retarded children ..." And Joe is off—a shark, nothing can stop him now. "Now you have one yourself. Great! Great for you, great for us! Maybe someday you'll wake up, Sylvia!" He shoves his hand under her chin—the little guy dares to touch her—and jerks her head up sharply, so that she has to look at him. "Get it? At last? You don't have to say anything. I see you got the message. And now shut up! I'm not finished. If from now on, from this very minute, you don't do everything Seven Stars tells you to do, you're through! Through for good!"

I can see a muscle in Sylvia's face twitch. "Then we'll make public what we damn please! Then the last studio around will know all about you and won't dare give you a part, because any film you're in will be boycotted by millions! That was shit you dished up in that dressing room, super shit, my dear! Strictly to vomit, darling, that's what it was! And rest assured that if we fire you, we'll let it all out the open! Every fucking word you said!"

Joe's voice gets gentler and gentler. "There won't be a studio in the world that'll hire you, not even as an extra! Then you can work in toilets and sell postcards of your glorious self! If you can find a place that'll take somebody like you to mop up their johns!" And with that he lets her go, and there is a long, seemingly endless silence.

Sylvia is weeping again, and I think of Ruth and that she has said she loves me, and I sit down beside Sylvia on the red couch and take her hand and say, "My poor Silky." Because after what Joe has said, there are tears in her beautiful eyes again. Everybody knows that Joe has won. Sylvia will do as she's told.

Dr. Lévy says, "All of us must be patient now. Self-control and patience, especially you, dear Madame Moran."

Sylvia nods. Her tone is bitter when she asks, "Who says my child is brain-damaged? Some doctor in Nürnberg!"

"A very good doctor," I tell her. "She saved Babs's life here in Paris, and she isn't the only one who says so. Several doctors at the Nürnberg hospital have been working with her and are of the same opinion."

"Nürnberg doctors!" Sylvia's voice is scornful. "Babs is an idiot and has to disappear in a mental institution because some Nürnberg doctors say so?"

"Of course not!" says Joe.

"But then what *is* going to happen to her?"

"I'll tell you," says Joe. "You naturally want Babs to be examined right away by the best specialists in the world—in the Mayo Clinic, in Switzerland, Sweden, England . . . right?"

"Yes. Naturally."

"And that's what's going to happen," says Joe, reverting to his unctuous tone.

323

"Oh, thank you, Joe! Thank you!"

"Don't thank me too soon, Sylvia," says Joe, dropping the unctuous tone again. "As head of Seven Stars I can agree to that only on one condition. If a majority of these doctors come to the same conclusion as this lady doctor in Nürnberg, then you, Sylvia, must agree to let Babs disappear from all public appearances." And everybody stares at Sylvia. "You must give it to us in writing, right now. Here."

"Here?"

"Yes. Here. Our lawyers are present. We have a notary. And witnesses. Charlie!"

"Yes, Mr. Gintzburger."

"Call downstairs. We need a typewriter, You'll type."

"Yes, Mr. Gintzburger," says PR man Charlie.

It is 6:15 P.M.

At 11:00 P.M. I am back in Nürnberg. I stand at Babs's bedside. She lies there motionless, as if dead. Ruth is standing beside me. I tried to kiss her when I met her, but she turned her head away and said, "No. Not now. Please, Phil!"

I have told Ruth everything that took place, and she is shocked. "But our diagnosis is correct," she says. "Of course there are famous specialists for this disease all over the world, but our diagnosis is correct. Unfortunately."

"Sylvia has been given permission to consult five specialists. Dr. Sigrand is choosing them for us. They may be anywhere in the world. Dr. Sigrand will let us have two doctors and two nurses, and we have Sylvia's jet."

"It's a crime, that's what it is!"

"Why? Can't Babs be moved?"

"I can get her to the point where she can be moved in a few days. But the strain will be tremendous. And we lose time, Phil, precious time! Time during which we could be starting to help her!"

"It's all been decided," I tell her. "I have to do as Sylvia wishes. Her agreement with Seven Stars depends on it; everything depends on it."

"Yes, of course," says Ruth. "How can the future of a child be weighed against that?"

And now we are standing at the bedside of that child. A small lamp spreads a faint light; in the hall outside all is quiet. We stand there hand in hand, Ruth and I, in front of us Babs, motionless, in a deep sleep, lying curled up.

"It's the money," Ruth said bitterly. "The accursed money!"

"I don't understand."

"It is possible to fly all over the world on such a hopeless mission because the money's there—because Sylvia Moran and her film company have so much money! If the money weren't there, if Babs were the ordinary child of an ordinary mother, she'd be luckier. Then we could start with the right treatment and no time would be lost!" Silence. Then Ruth says, "Nothing is more dangerous than a combination of illness and a very rich person."

Kaleidoscope! No, not kaleidoscope, but madness! And what followed was just that—sheer madness!

Monday, February 7, 1972. Ruth has Babs ready to be moved. The condition of her eyes has worsened so that she has to wear training glasses all the time. She looks dreadful with them on. Nobody would dream that she is Babs Moran. She still hasn't said a word. She doesn't seem to know me.

We take her to the Nürnberg airport in an ambulance. The Super-One-Eleven is waiting. Two French doctors and two nurses are with us. Two American detectives from Seven Stars are also to accompany us.

Farewell to Ruth. She is miserable, but there is nothing she can do about it. In her office, in front of her desk, she suddenly kisses me. I embrace her. I can feel her putting something in the pocket of my jacket. Then she says, "Now go, please! Right away! I am not coming with you. I . . ." The sentence remains unfinished. I go, but I keep turning around. Ruth isn't watching me go. She doesn't look my way once.

For the first time in her life, Sylvia has given her checkbook to someone else, namely me. I have to pay the doctors, the flying costs, the salaries of the crew, the daily phone calls Sylvia expects. Not even the salary of a producer suffices for all that.

And it is snowing. When I get to the airport Babs is already in bed, in the jet. She isn't asleep. She is staring up at the ceiling. Twenty minutes later the jet takes off in the driving snow. All occupants have been sworn to absolute secrecy. As the plane climbs, I take what Ruth gave me out of my pocket. A small brass medallion with these words engraved on it: "Peace to all men. —Guatama Buddha."

Wednesday, February 9, 1972. We are in the States. Babs is being taken to the Mayo Clinic. The examination will take two days. Daily calls to Sylvia. Most French telephones have a second receiver, so Joe can listen in every time.

Saturday, February 12, 1972. I phone the results of the Mayo Clinic examination to Paris. It is exactly the same as Ruth's. Prognosis: Herculean efforts will have to be made, innumerable forms of treatment, yet not hopeless. It may be years before there are any signs of improvement. The former mental level will probably never be reached. Absolutely necessary: treatment in an institution specializing in such cases.

Sylvia on the phone, wild! She says the specialists at the Mayo are idiots. She doesn't believe a word of it! She has found out where there is a world-famous specialist for this type of disease, has no further use for Dr. Sigrand's suggestions. She orders us to fly to Philadelphia, to the Disabled Children Center under the direction of a certain Dr. Joseph Lerring.

Monday, February 14, 1972. We arrive at the center. Dr. Lerring receives us. He looks just like a fifty-year-old American film doctor.

Tuesday, February 15, to Wednesday, February 16, 1972. I take a look at Dr. Lerring's incredible mansion in a suburb of Philadelphia, his fleet of cars. I find out he is a multimillionaire.

Thursday, February 17, 1972. In his tastefully decorated office, Dr. Lerring tells me that if Babs stays in his center, he will use a new drug on her, something he alone has permission to use. This drug intensifies the brain action biochemically. The treatment is short and results in complete recovery, in most cases. But no doctor can promise hundred percent complete recoveries. The cost of treatment is horrendous because the drug is so expensive. That is why this treatment of Dr. Lerring's is possible only for those who have the money to pay for it. Which Miss Moran has, of course. But because the treatment has been used on only very few patients, namely those who can afford it, not much is known about it, and Dr. Lerring is no fool—he is not going to give away any secrets.

Call Paris. Talk for almost an hour. Sylvia is ecstatic! Didn't she say so? Lerring is the right man! Never mind the cost. Lerring will cure Babs! I tell her that I think Lerring is an unscrupulous crook. That's how he became a multimillionaire. He has been cautious enough to say that he can't promise anything one hundred percent. So, after Sylvia's lost her shirt, Babs will just be one of the few cases where Lerring's magic failed. Sylvia gets abusive, sounds like a fishwife. She must see Lerring at once, and her beloved Babs. This is followed by a violent argument with Joe, which I listen to. Under no circumstances, and this is in the agreement—oh, wise Joe!—may she leave Paris. I am the one to go with Babs from doctor to doctor. Joe tells me to take Babs to the English specialist next, a Dr. Crossman in London.

Thursday, February 17, 1972. We cross the Atlantic to London. These flights back and forth are exhausting for all of us—doctors, nurses, detectives, even the crew, but most of all for Babs. As we cross the Atlantic she is running a high temperature again, and is having convulsions for the first time in a long time. Her behavior is so wild that the two nurses from Sainte-Bernadette are frightened, and they are not easily frightened. The two French doctors work constantly on Babs. Nobody gets any sleep that night, and all of us look like death when we finally reach London.

Friday, February 18, 1972. London. Babs in a state of collapse. Examination by Dr. Crossman impossible. Five days before he can begin to examine her. During these five days doctors try to restore Babs's strength. Sylvia on the phone, very depressed. She weeps. Joe curses.

Saturday, February 26, 1972. The examination is over. I tell Sylvia the result on the phone: Exactly the same as Ruth and the Mayo Clinic. Big fight in Paris. Joe wants to call the whole thing off. Sylvia insists on the examinations promised her, so we're off again.

Monday, February 28, through Wednesday, February 30, 1972, Stockholm. Dr. Lundstrom, director of the largest hospital for children. I am told that Lundstrom is an excellent doctor, but that he is never precise about his diagnoses, some say out of pity, others because of an overpowering wish not to have to give any brutal verdicts.

Thursday, March 1, 1972. I have to agree with what I have been told about Lundstrom. The diagnosis that I phone through to Paris sounds like it: Professor Lundstrom says (reluctantly) that the prognosis is very bad. However ... cases of an astonishing return to normal have been known to happen.

Sylvia jubilant. Poor Sylvia! I can hear Joe warning her

not to try his patience. Just one more specialist, she implores him. Just one more! Dr. Geller.

Friday, March 3, to Friday, March 10, 1972. Bern. Dr. Geller. Immediately upon our arrival, total collapse of Babs. Dr. Geller, apparently a genius, says it will be some time before Babs has recovered from the critical condition she is in at present. Is furious when he hears what we've put the child through. Confers with his chief of staff. They start a series of treatments to make an examination of Babs possible.

I am staying at the Hotel Bellevue. At the hospital every day. Not allowed to see Babs. Hear that her condition is improving. Call Paris. Sylvia has finally broken down. Cries frequently on the phone, and I can hear Joe comforting her. Call Clarissa in Madrid. Tell her Babs is doing fine. Clarissa should be prepared to come to Paris soon. She'll be given exact instructions. Call Bracken. He has a plan and keeps improving on it, the worst thing he's ever thought up! Call Ruth frequently and report. She is horrified. I tell her that I love her more every day. She says, "I love you too, Phil." And once she says, "Poor Babs . . ."

Tuesday, March 14, 1972. Dr. Geller has worked miracles, he really has. Babs is feeling much stronger and by the end of the week let me stroke her, hugged me. According to Geller the improvement is only temporary, based solely on medication. There will be a relapse.

I call Sylvia in the evening: Dr. Geller gives the same diagnosis as Dr. Reinhardt, the Mayo Clinic, Dr. Crossman, and, with reservations, Dr. Lundstrom. The decision has therefore gone against Babs. According to the agreement, Sylvia must resign herself to it. The odyssey is over. Babs will go back to Ruth and in due course will be moved to a mental institution. Before this happens, however, another gruesome farce is in store for us.

End of the report according to my diary

53

The Blue Salon in the Hotel Le Monde is very big, and Sylvia has given many press conferences there. On Wednesday, March 15, 1972, she gives another. Quite possibly, your honor, you may not want to believe what I am about to describe, but I am writing the truth. I have witnesses.

The conference started late, at 4:45 P.M., and lasted until 7:10, an unusually long time. You will soon see why. Rod Bracken had made all the preparations. The day before, Clarissa had come back to Paris from Madrid on a commercial plane. She went to her room in the hotel and didn't leave it until the press conference. Bracken had been told to tell Clarissa the whole truth about Babs and inform her about what was to happen next. Old Dr. Lévy had given Clarissa enough drugs so that she would look serene. She looked a little too serene!

From Bern I had called my friend the Président Directeur Général of Le Monde, Pierre Maréchal, and told him everything. It had to be done. I had begged him to help us, and he had said he would. But he had to take a few absolutely reliable people into his confidence. Joe, who was insisting on his okay on everything, agreed.

At around noon on the same day, two planes landed in Orly, first a commercial Lufthansa with Ruth on it, accompanied by two other doctors from the Sophienkrankenhaus. They proceeded to Le Monde, where they were given rooms. A little later Sylvia's Super-One-Eleven arrived. Inside it were Babs, the two French doctors from the Hôpital Sainte-Bernadette, and myself. We drove to the inner courtyard of Le Monde; behind us a third car with the Seven Stars detectives. Babs was able to walk, although she limped badly. She was calm and she still hadn't spoken a word. Our plane had left from Basel, and Dr. Geller had explained to me that Babs, if not exposed to too much exertion, would remain in this "normal" state, induced by drugs, for ten hours at the most. So time was against us.

When I walked into Suite 419 at 2:30 P.M., holding Babs by

the hand, there was a horrible scene. Besides Sylvia and Bracken, the following people were waiting for us: Joe, Lejeune, two American lawyers, PR man Charlie, the French doctors and the two detectives. Sylvia was wearing a robe.

Babs walked into the salon, one foot dragging, her face a mask.

"Babs!" Sylvia screamed when she saw her daughter. She ran to meet her, fell on her knees in front of her, burst into tears and embraced her repeating her name, stammering expressions of love and tenderness. Babs stood there, arms dangling, and let three minutes of her mother's hysterical greeting pass. Then Sylvia began to stroke the child's face, still babbling endearments, and tears running down her cheeks. Suddenly she screamed,—with pain, not with horror, not yet! Babs had bitten her hand. It was bleeding.

Sylvia fell to one side. Dr. Lévy and the French doctors took care of the wound. Babs stood there motionless, staring into space. The doctors gave Sylvia a shot, she was still screaming, with horror now. Dr. Lévy gave Babs a lot of pretty little pills—blue, red, yellow. She swallowed them all obediently. She was led into her room. Sylvia remained in the salon.

"Pepito," she stammered, "Pepito . . . she . . . she didn't know who I was!"

"No."

Sylvia began to cry again. "No time, no time," said Joe. "Get going, Sylvia. Into your dressing room. Katie and Joe are waiting."

"I can't!" screamed Sylvia.

"You have to," said Joe, "and you can! And you're going to! Move!"

Sylvia went to her dressing room.

54

Katie and Joe Patterson, who had arrived with Clarissa, had already started to work in Madrid with Sylvia's stand-in, Carmen Cruzeiro, experimenting with makeup under the watchful eyes of the director and the art and historical advisers. Now, because Sylvia kept crying, it took much longer than had been planned to make her up. Her hair had to be fixed, then it took ages to dress her. The shot started working—Sylvia was almost apathetic.

When Katie and Joe were finished, they went over to make up Babs. Babs held absolutely still and let them do what they wanted. They took off her ugly glasses and made her up as if for a film, combed her hair, put on her prettiest dress. They gave her a very chic pair of training glasses, bought for the purpose in Paris, and made according to instructions from Nürnberg. The doctors were in attendance constantly; neither mother nor child was left alone for a moment. When they put on her pretty dress, Babs stood up on tiptoe for a moment and waved her arms, without saying a word, soundlessly. Dr. Lévy gave her a few more red pills. I changed too.

Next to the Blue Salon there is a fairly large room behind a curtain. The Seven Stars lawyer, PR man Charlie, Joe, Ruth, both detectives, Lejeune, Clarissa, Bracken and the French doctors and nurses from Sainte-Bernadette who had accompanied us from specialist to specialist were assembled in it. They had been joined by Dr. Sigrand. He greeted me cordially and expressed his sympathy. Meanwhile the Blue Salon was beginning to fill up. Everything was ready but we couldn't go in because Sylvia had burst into tears again! Joe and Katie had to start all over. Dr. Lévy didn't dare give her another shot for fear that she wouldn't talk straight.

I sat beside Sylvia as they made her up again. She wanted me to hold her hand, which was wet with perspiration, and I thought how sorry I felt for her and how much I loved Ruth.

Bracken came in with Ruth. "Sorry, Sylvia, but everybody's waiting. We're almost forty-five minutes late. Oh, let me introduce you—Miss Moran, Frau Doktor Reinhardt. She just took another look at Babs."

"How do you do, Madame Moran."

"How do you do, madame."

Only French was spoken today.

"I want to thank you for all you have done for Babs," said Sylvia, her eyes on the mirror, Katie on her left, Joe on her right.

"Don't mention it, please," said Ruth. "I was glad to do it." We avoided looking at each other.

"Babs is going back to you now," said Sylvia.

"Yes, Madame Moran."

"I want to thank you again," said Sylvia, then, her voice harsh, "Aren't you finished yet, dammit?"

"Finished, Miss Moran," said Katie.

Sylvia, who had been sitting in her underwear, got up, and Katie helped her back into the pants suit.

55

At last! All of us assembled in the room next to the Blue Salon, 4:45 P.M. "And now let's go out!" said Joe, and I could see him cross himself surreptitiously. He pulled the curtain aside and stepped out onto the small stage. The spotlights were on. He took a few steps forward, then turned and gestured with his hand, and Rod appeared, gestured with his hand, and I appeared, gestured with my hand—enter Sylvia Moran.

She stopped, lifted her hands and blew kisses. I had just left her in Suite 419, ravaged, and now? She is a fantastic actress, your honor! She really is!

Cameras humming, flashes blitzing, a burst of applause. Sylvia walked ahead of us to a chair in the middle of the long table that had been put on the stage. She sat down. I sat on her left, Joe on her right, Rod beside me. Five minutes passed during which pictures were taken. Then Joe raised a hand and stood up.

"How do you do, ladies and gentlemen," he said, in his miserable French. "Greetings. We have asked you to come here because we have something to tell you that I am sure will be of interest to you. I think Madame Moran can tell it better than I." He sat down. I saw that his hands were folded.

Sylvia moved one of the microphones closer, waited a few seconds until there was absolute quiet in the room, then began to speak, so controlled, so at ease, so pleasantly, as if she were going to tell a fairy tale.

"My dear friends here, my dear friends everywhere in the world. As you know, I was on vacation in order to rest before my next film, *The Chalk Circle,* the most important one I have ever undertaken. My beloved Babs was with me, while Phil"—loving look in my direction—"was in Madrid preparing for this production. Now Babs and I are back . . ."

"Where is Babs?" A confusion of cries.

"Just a minute, please. That is why we have asked you to come here. Today we are going to speak only of Babs. I, Phil, Joe, Rod—all of us, like all those people all over the world who know us, love Babs. But now, my friends, the time has come to take leave of Babs for a while." Effective pause. What an actress! "You see," Sylvia went on, "Babs is growing up, and she has reached an age when it wouldn't be right for her to be flying all over the world with Phil and me . . . to Madrid for months, and after that all over Spain. Babs needs quiet, a home, the right school. She shouldn't be taught by tutors any more."

"The right school where?" cried one reporter.

"I'm afraid I can't tell you that."

"Why not?"

My cue. "Because Babs must be left in peace, a peace she could never enjoy if we publicized the name of her school. One item we don't mind revealing: Babs is going to the United States. As for the quiet she needs—Babs has been traipsing around with us for much too long already. She is tired. We really only found out how tired she was when suddenly she needed glasses! Can you imagine it—glasses! The exhaustion has affected her vision. A temporary condition, of course. Soon she won't need them any more. But now you will understand, I am sure, why we don't want to say where her devoted governess Clarissa is taking her now, with me."

"Yes, with Phil," said Sylvia, and laid her hand on mine. It was wet with perspiration, as it had been in the dressing room.

My cue again! I stood up and said, "And now I will fetch

Babs so that she may say goodbye to all you ladies and gentlemen."

I walked across the stage to the black curtain. My legs were shaking, your honor. I pushed aside the curtain, and there they all were—doctors, nurses, detectives, Katie and Joe Patterson, Pierre Maréchal, Clarissa, Babs, Ruth. Ruth was staring at me with wide unblinking eyes. Maréchal lifted both hands over his head and shook them like a boxer.

Clarissa led Babs up to me until she had taken two steps onto the stage and was visible for all to see. No farther. Because, after all, Babs limped. Clarissa had stood on that side for the two steps, so nothing was noticeable from the audience. Now I bent down, like a man very fond of a child, lifted Babs up and held her so that she was seated comfortably in my arms. She was so stupefied by the pills Dr. Lévy had given her that she didn't protest. She was as inanimate as a doll.

I walked back to the table, Babs in my arms, step by step, up to Sylvia. It was a matter of life or death, every bit of it. The doctors had warned us, Sylvia had implored us, not to show the child. But Joe, and his lawyers, and above all Lejeune, had insisted mercilessly. The child had to be produced once more. I had the feeling that everyone at that table and all those behind the curtain were saying their prayers to whatever God was theirs.

A crossfire of flashbulbs, spots, applause. Sylvia smiled. Joe smiled. Bracken smiled. I smiled. And then the most gruesome thing happened. In recollection of so many similar occasions, evidently buried in the poor child's sick brain, Babs lifted her right arm and waved to the reporters. And laughed! *She laughed, your honor!* The artificially, prettily made up, distorted face, which now looked like Babs when she had been healthy, *laughed!* You couldn't see her crossed eyes behind her chic glasses; the lights were mirrored in them.

What a coup for the reporters. And what unbelievable luck for us!

Everybody at the table rose and applauded Babs—her mother, Rod, Joe, and everybody in our audience. I began to count the seconds. Four minutes in all, Ruth told me later. As I carried Babs offstage again there were loud protests. They didn't stop me. There was nothing on my mind but *out!*

There was the curtain, Clarissa holding it open. Into the little room with us. I laid Babs down on the couch. In the very

334

next moment, your honor, she began to thrash and kick. Ruth and the French doctors rushed over to her. I knew they would take care of her. The Super-One-Eleven was in Orly, ready to leave. Babs had to be flown back to Nürnberg at once, and I had to go back to the Blue Salon.

"I'll call you tonight," I told Ruth softly. She nodded.

I hurried out onto the stage and sat down beside Sylvia and put one arm around her. The great lovers. The next hour seemed endless. We had to keep the conference going until we were sure Babs was airborne. Fortunately the reporters had a lot more questions: How did things stand with *The Chalk Circle?* They were also concerned with *So Little Time.* The spokesman they had chosen stepped forward. I was pleased to see it was the AFP man again. According to him, Sylvia's partner in *So Little Time,* was seriously ill. His condition was worsening daily. Did Sylvia know that?"

"Yes," said Sylvia, who had no idea.

"Sylvia sends him flowers daily," said Joe. "She can't speak to him. He is too weak to hold the receiver."

This was news to me. So Alfredo *was* going to bow out in time.

Questions, answers, I look at my watch all the time. The fingers don't seem to want to move! Finally the questioning begins to peter out. And then, when I think I can't stand it a moment longer, the curtain is pulled slightly aside, and Lejeune gives me a sign. The plane is airborne. A few minutes later we end the press conference. The AFP man walks up to Sylvia and in the name of his colleagues presents her with a large bouquet of Baccara roses.

"Thank you, thank you all, ladies and gentlemen," says Sylvia. And then, taking my arm and waving a few times, she walks over to the curtain that leads to the antechamber, Joe and Bracken behind us. The cameras follow us until the curtain has closed.

"I . . ." Sylvia starts to say.

I step in front of her. She says nothing more, but falls forward toward me, the Baccara roses still in her arms. . . .

56

... In her arms a different bouquet of roses now, on the stage, in front of the screen, in the colossal auditorium of the Teatro Sistina, May 18, 1972. It is infernally hot in Rome and in the movie house. The film, *So Little Time,* has just had its world premiere, a huge success. Alfredo Bianchi died on time, Sylvia has given a most touching speech and has asked all those present—millionaires, aristocrats, industrialists, publishers, church dignitaries and worldly statesmen—to stand for one minute of silence in memory of the great actor. Cameras hum, shutters click. In that one minute I have recalled the events of almost half a year.

During these six months Sylvia has worked on the preparations for *The Chalk Circle,* sometimes in Paris, sometimes in Madrid. Babs is still in the Sophienkrankenhaus in Nürnberg, not in bed any longer but limping around, being taught by Ruth and an assistant, and Ruth has got her to the point where she can talk again. According to the latest EEG there is still a slight latent propensity to a spastic condition, especially on the left side. Her IQ, according to Stanford-Binet, is 59, the intelligence of a four-year-old, and Babs is nine. . . .

"We're making great progress!" Ruth tells me over and over again. Great progress . . . dear God!

During these six months I have often gone out with Ruth, to the theater, movies, concerts. She lost her way every time, but in the end always got us to our destination. During these six months I did not kiss Ruth again, never embraced her, much less slept with her. But I never ceased to love her. Our confidence in each other grew, we felt increasingly close. And Ruth's scruples became stronger all the time. I belonged to Sylvia! I did not, I assured her over and over again. "But you do! You do!" she insisted. She didn't know what was going to happen to us. Neither did I.

During these months I was very often with Sylvia, in Paris or Madrid. She was carrying a burden that seemed to weigh more heavily upon her all the time, and I often admired the strength that let her go on with her work.

I don't want to give the impression, your honor, that I was indifferent to my situation—two women, a completely uncertain future, the responsibility for Babs—or that I was putting Sylvia increasingly out of my mind. On the contrary—her strength, her courage and bravery commanded my respect. Only a person like yourself, your honor, who has chosen a profession that judges what is valuable and what is worthless, what is moral and immoral, can understand that. Can also understand why Sylvia refused all intimacies between us although, according to her, she still loved me. Schizophrenic? I don't know. The only thing that I do know is—I love Ruth.

The one minute of silence for Alfredo Bianchi is over. The ovation for Sylvia starts all over again. A madhouse, down there in the orchestra and beside us in the boxes. Joe Gintzburger groans. "Boy, oh boy!" I think this was the happiest evening of his life for some time to come.

57

Three A.M., May 19, 1972. Sylvia and I had been in our suite in the Hotel Bernini-Bristol for half an hour, she in the bedroom, I in the dressing room. The room was so full of flowers you could hardly move. The scent was stupefying. I was packing. The perspiration rolled down my back. I took off my jacket, my shirt, my pants. I could hear Sylvia sobbing at the other end of the suite. She was very drunk and very unhappy.

After the premiere there had been a banquet, arranged by Carlo Marone, the lucky bastard. Sylvia's dinner partner—the Italian president. Hours of eating, hours of drinking, toasts for Sylvia. Toasts for the picture. Toasts for Alfredo Bianchi, for Joe, even for me! I admired Sylvia's poise, your honor. She didn't break down until we got to our suite. She may have been inhumanly controlled before, but now she lost all control. She wailed so that I feared the other guests in the hotel would complain.

"An idiot! Babs is going to be an idiot the rest of her life! And it's my fault!"

"For God's sake, stop!"

I never loved Sylvia Moran, your honor, you know that. But that night in Rome I felt something for her. Suddenly she was a human being, a suffering human being; she was no longer the person or nonperson to whom I had attached myself in order to live a good life. Today I know that this new feeling was somehow connected with Babs, with the mysterious power the weakest have to change everything, something to do with the fact that in the end the softest water can hollow out the hardest stone.

"Please, please, Sylvia, stop crying!"

"I can't," she sobbed. "I can't! Go away! You have to leave anyway. Go and pack. Leave me alone."

So I left her and packed and listened to her weeping. When I closed my suitcase I noticed that the weeping had stopped. I walked into the bedroom. She lay on the big bed, fully dressed. She still had on all her jewelry; her hair tumbled wildly over the pillow, her beautiful face was ravaged by tears. She was fast asleep.

I took the elevator down to the lobby, carrying my suitcase, and told the night clerk that I had to leave for Paris immediately. I made a deal with one of the porters to drive me out to the Leonardo da Vinci Airport in Fiumicino. I had told the crew of the Super-One-Eleven that we would leave at 7:00 A.M. Everything was ready.

PART THREE

Therapy

MR. ANTROBUS: How can you make a world for people to live in unless you first put order in yourself?
—Thornton Wilder, *The Skin of Our Teeth*

1

It was 7:50 A.M., Tuesday, May 23, 1972, when Ruth drove her white VW into a parking area on the outskirts of Nürnberg. "This is where we get out," she said.

I had been holding Babs on my knees during the drive from the Sophienkrankenhaus. Now I lifted her out and got out after her. She had on the heavy, hornrimmed training glasses for her crossed eyes, a cheap pair of glasses. Her clothes were cheap too. Ruth and I had bought them together last Friday. It had been necessary for me to be in Nürnberg that Friday, and I shall explain why very soon.

Ruth lifted the large suitcase packed full of Babs's new clothes from the back seat and locked the car. She smiled at Babs, but Babs showed no emotion. She was calm, but you could sense that she was afraid. I held her hand. We had stopped in front of a long low building with a number of shops in it. Nobody spoke. Babs clung to my hand.

Here, on the periphery of the city, things were already quite rural—low houses, like peasant homes, small stores, horse-drawn carts, blossoming trees at the edge of the road. The last stop of a streetcar line. "Over there," said Ruth, pointing, and I saw the yellow sign of a bus stop. We walked toward it, Babs limping. Two women were standing at the bus stop, one of them holding a little boy by the hand, the other a little girl, and there also was a man with a little girl. Some distance away I could see a second man, leaning against the wall of an inn, a tramp, dirty shoes and clothing, unshaven, his hair filthy. He had the red bloated face of the steady drinker, glassy eyes and only a few blackened teeth. Every now and then he said something and laughed foolishly. I couldn't understand what he was saying. Nobody at the bus stop paid any attention to him.

Finally we reached the little group. Now I could see the children clearly. One of the little girls looked about six. Her face was very round, her mouth was tiny, she had slanting eyes and thick black hair. She teetered back and forth while holding onto her mother's hand. The boy, about twelve, I decided, was wearing training glasses, like Babs. Every now and then his right side trembled spastically. The second girl looked as if she might be about Babs's age. Her head was bandaged and her ears were protected by two large ear pads. The bandages and the pads were painted bright red. All three children were dressed in bright colors and carried their plastic school satchels strapped to their backs.

The adults seemed to know Ruth, because they greeted her cordially. The children greeted Ruth too. She smiled at them; they smiled back. They smiled at Babs and me too, and I smiled back. Babs acknowledged their greeting vaguely. I nodded at the drunken man, but he ignored my greeting.

"Yes," said Ruth, addressing the boy whose greeting had been nothing much more than a babbling, "I have brought you a new playmate, Franz. Her name is Babs. The gentleman is her father." And to Babs, "This is Franz, this is Maria, and this is Anna," pointing them out. "Say hello, Babs."

Babs said, "Hello." Her speech was almost as indistinct as the boy's. The children shook hands, and Ruth introduced me to their parents. I have forgotten their names. Ruth introduced me as Herr Norton. "Why didn't you drive all the way out in your car, Frau Doktor?" asked one of the mothers.

"It's the first day for Babs," said Ruth. She gave me a quick look. "We wanted her to see right from the start how most of the children go to school."

The little girl who looked like an Oriental laughed and cried, "Ride bus too!"

"Smile," Ruth said to me softly.

"Yes," I said, smiling at the little girl with the slanting eyes. "I am going to ride on the bus too."

"Mongoloid," Ruth told me softly.

"Fine," said the mongoloid child. "Fine bus. You like." This time she was addressing Babs.

To my astonishment, Babs suddenly spoke much more clearly. "I will," she said, and she laughed too.

"Many mongoloid children are quite pretty," said Ruth "like this one."

"Babs laughed," I said softly.

"Of course," Ruth replied, just as softly. "She's with children now and you'll hear her laugh often."

"And she spoke German."

"She'll speak German whenever she's addressed in German. That's a natural response. And there are only German children in this school."

"That's what the director told me," I said. And it was because of this director that I had had to be in Nürnberg the Friday before.

Heinz Hallein, director of the school Babs was now going to attend, had been at the Sophienkrankenhaus on Friday and Saturday morning to decide if he could accept Babs in his school. He had talked to her, asked questions, given her a few easy exercises to do; he had spoken for a long time with Ruth; then I showed my false passport and signed various forms, one for instance that attested that I was responsible for Babs financially. Ruth had witnessed all my statements.

Now a big blue bus came up the street. At the same time a man who looked like a clerk came around the corner, pushing a collapsible wheelchair before him. A boy of about ten was sitting in it, dressed colorfully, like the other children, and strapped firmly into the chair. His school satchel hung around his neck. He was trembling from head to foot; his face was expressionless, his eyes gazed vacantly, his legs dangled back and forth with the motion of the chair.

The bus driver blew the horn and slowed down. The wide side door hissed open. The bus looked brand new. There were only six children in it and two young men in overalls. The driver was a huge man wearing a green knit jacket with deerhorn buttons. He laughed and cried out, "There you are! There you are!"

"Uncle Willy! Uncle Willy!" cried both little girls, and the boy babbled his greeting. The boy in the wheelchair didn't utter a sound.

The two young men jumped out. One of them looked very strong, the other was slight. The strong one had a thick, short beard, and they too laughed when they saw the children, and there were hearty greetings all round.

I saw the old drunk pry himself loose from the wall and sway toward us. The young men lifted the girls into the bus, where the driver received them and sat them down on empty seats. Then one of the men lifted the boy, whose right side trembled every now and then and who could only babble, into the bus. At that moment the drunk drew himself up very straight and yelled, "Get going! Get going! The bus is waiting. All idiots aboard!"

I froze. The adults, Ruth included, pretended they hadn't heard. Now the drunk's laughter was a roar. As he turned around, he almost fell, then he staggered away and disappeared around the corner of the inn. Both young men lifted the obviously paralyzed boy out of his wheelchair. I thought it would be difficult to get him in, but the two men evidently did this every day, and it all took place very quickly and easily. The driver helped. The paralyzed boy was lifted onto a specially shaped seat and strapped into it.

I walked up to one of the women. Ruth tried to stop me when she saw how furious I was, but I said, "Forgive me, please, for interfering, but didn't you hear what that drunk just said?"

"Yes, of course."

"And you don't do anything about it? None of you?"

"Don't do anything about it?" said the woman.

"That's Schikora, the biggest drunkard around here," said the other woman. "He stands there every morning, summer and winter, and always yells the same thing."

"But you should do something about it!" I protested.

The four adults stared at me. "Look, Herr . . ."

"Norton."

"Herr Norton. You say we should do something about it. How long has your little girl been ill? Not long, I'm sure."

"No. Not long."

"Our children have been ill for a long time, mine since birth. You know, none of us have the strength left to do anything about anything."

"But—"

"You don't understand," said the man who was collapsing the wheelchair and now handed it to the bus driver. "You don't understand *yet*. But that will come. Oh God, if there were nothing worse in the world than that old drunk . . ."

The driver, who had just caught sight of Ruth, interrupted him. "Frau Doktor! Good morning!"

"Good morning. We're coming with you. This is Herr Norton and his little girl, Babs. I'm going with them. It's their first day."

"Pleased to meet you, Herr Norton," said the driver. "Come along, Babs." I pushed her ahead of me, and he lifted her into the bus. As soon as we were in, the door closed by itself.

"Let's sit at the back," said Ruth, as the bus started off. Now she had Babs by the hand. The adults who had remained behind waved, and the children waved back, the paralyzed boy too. "There'll be a lot more getting in," said Ruth as we sat down in the back, Babs between us, her suitcase between my legs.

The two young men chatted with the children, handed them a doll, a ball, a rattle, out of the luggage rack. All the children knew each other and began to talk. They seemed to understand each other. Suddenly all of them were laughing over something one of the young men had said. After that the laughter and shouts never flagged. Suddenly Babs began to laugh, although she couldn't possibly have heard what the young man had said. The other children turned around and looked at her curiously, laughed and waved at her. Babs waved back. Ruth laughed, and finally I laughed too.

"Who are those two young men?" I asked Ruth.

"Conscientious objectors," said Ruth. "No . . . wait a minute . . . they have another word for them now. Substitute servicemen, I think."

2

During the next hour the bus crisscrossed the countryside on dirt roads, wooded paths and regular highways. We stopped again and again. In one isolated spot was a child in a wheelchair, accompanied by an old woman. The young men lifted the girl in. She was paralyzed too. The driver helped. The wheelchair was collapsed and stowed away. The girl was greeted joyously by the other children and strapped into a specially shaped seat, like the paralyzed boy.

The bus drove on. Then, when one least expected it, off the road and across fields, over the dark earth and meadows covered with little yellow flowers, through dark woods, ten minutes perhaps to the next stop. A village of row houses. Father and mother with a very little girl on crutches. Happy greetings. The child was lifted into the bus.

"This afternoon at four-fifty, Herr Hausmeier?" asked the father.

"This afternoon at four-fifty. I'll bring Agnes back!" cried the driver.

"She has a letter in her knapsack. Please deliver it, Herr Hausmeier. Agnes can say two new words!" cried the girl's mother.

"Agnes! That's wonderful! Two new words *again?* What words?"

Agnes said slowly, painfully slowly, with everybody listening breathlessly, "P . . . p . . . peace. Rail . . . rail . . . railway." And the driver hugged her. "Railway! Peace!" he cried, and Agnes beamed.

One of the young men carried her to a free seat, the other followed with her crutches. The bus drove on. In spite of the straps, the paralyzed boy who had been put on the bus first began to slip. One of the young men hurried over to him, spoke to him gaily, pushed him back into position and fastened the straps again.

The bus drove on as if through an invisible labyrinth, and it was springtime, radiant springtime! Big villages, small villages, stop. A big boy was standing beside a telephone booth, holding a smaller boy by the hand. The big boy lifted the little boy into the bus. The little boy was partially paralyzed. One of the young men took a stand behind him and marched him to his seat, step by step. Both were in a hilarious mood, which resulted in renewed gales of laughter in the bus. "My God, where are you taking us?" I asked Ruth.

"You'll see," she said.

"I see already," I said. "Into another world."

"No," she said. "Not into another world. There is only one world and all of us have to learn to live in it."

Another village. Stop. A little girl standing in front of a church, in a red coat, a red cap on her head. Little Red Riding Hood.

The bus drove on. Stopped again and again. New children. Drove on. "Driving home, yes?" Babs asked suddenly. She looked at me.

I looked at Ruth. "Yes," she said, "we're going home."

Four of the girls had started to sing. I couldn't understand a word. Many of the children in the bus had speech defects, some quite serious, but now they all began to sing, in time. And they were laughing!

A Mercedes passed us, a little girl strapped in beside the driver. He looked up at us, recognized Ruth and waved. To my astonishment, Babs rose suddenly and waved back, with Ruth. The child in the Mercedes smiled.

"Who?" asked Babs.

"That's Jackie."

"In school too?"

"Yes. You'll see her again soon."

345

"Like Jackie."

"I think she likes you too," said Ruth, and to me, over Babs's head, "Mongoloid. Her father's chauffeur brings her to school every morning, picks her up in the evening. I told you there are no boundaries to this thing. It can happen to the poorest and the richest child."

"And this bus?"

"The school rents them. It owns one. They pick up all the children in the county who go to this school. And they take them home the same way. Some fathers bring their children themselves. A lot of the children in the city live in houses that have no elevators. If it's a child who can't walk, he has to be carried up and down."

"And who does that?"

"The school has some taxi drivers under contract. They pick up the children and bring them to the nearest bus stop, and in the evening they do the same thing in reverse."

"But doesn't that cost a fortune?"

Ruth smiled sadly. "It does. Everything that takes place here costs a small fortune."

"So where does the money come from?"

"Actually the school has been bankrupt since the day it opened. But it carries on." Ruth smiled. Babs smiled. I stroked Babs, and she moved closer to me. "That's the first time you've done that," Ruth said softly.

"Yes," I said, surprised over my own action. "That's right. It's the first time I've done it, and now, of all times."

"Very naturally now," said Ruth.

We were driving through a thick forest. A yellow sign with black letters flew by at the edge of the road. Heroldsheid. Right after that I saw a narrow path leading off to the right. The bus made the sharp turn and took the narrow dirt road that led down steeply. As we made the turn I noticed an unobtrusive wooden sign with the inscription "Heroldsheid Remedial School."

I looked through the windshield. We were driving up to a wide wrought-iron gate. Beyond the gate, in the bright sunshine, I could see a gravel parking area with three buses like ours and one smaller one, and a lot of children getting out of the buses, some being carried. And beyond the parking area I could see a little white house that looked like a small palace, built in 1910 style. "Not a bad-looking school," I said, "considering that it's chronically bankrupt."

"If you only knew how we happened to get that house!"

346

Our bus stopped beside the others, and our children were helped out. I could see about eighty children and approximately twenty-five adults. And there was a lot of noise—the adults addressing the children, the children laughing and yelling. Behind the house I could see a field. All the adults were dressed simply. I realized suddenly that nobody was wearing white, no doctor's white coat, no nurse's uniform.

A fairly young man with a friendly face and thick black combed-back hair came up to us. It was Dr. Heinz Hallein, the director. He greeted Babs first by going down on one knee and shaking hands with her. "How wonderful to have you here," he said. "We've all been looking forward to your arrival. A happy, happy birthday, Babs."

"But I don't . . ."

"Oh yes you do," said Director Hallein. "That's the way we do things here. The day a child arrives for the first time is his or her birthday."

"But I have another birthday," said Babs, leaning against me because of the slight paralysis on her left side, and she smiled at the director.

"So then you have two! Every child has two!" said Hallein. "You can do what you like on your second birthday. We celebrate your school birthday here."

"When?" said Babs.

"Later. Meanwhile you get a present." Hallein was holding out a big plastic bag filled with candy, nuts, chocolates and fruit. Babs said nothing.

"Wait," I said. "I'll hold it. It's too heavy for you."

"Quite sure stay here with me?"

"Quite sure," I said, and saw that the drivers were back in their buses, turning the monsters around, and were off again. Only the little bus stayed behind. On its front door I read: "Gift of Operation Handicapped Children. German Television II."

Many of the children and adults had already withdrawn into the white palace when I was startled by the sound of shattering glass. Big pieces of glass fell from one of the windows down onto the gravel. For a moment I saw the distorted features of a boy before a woman dragged him away from the window. "Just another greeting," said Hallein, smiling. "That was Otto."

"But . . . window broken," said Babs.

"Yes," said Hallein. "He does that sometimes. Some of the other children do too. We break a lot of windows here. And tables and chairs and beds and china—all sorts of things." To me he said, "Destructive attacks. Aggressions acted out." He shrugged, and added softly, "The whole thing is an exercise in patience for the staff. We don't mind a certain amount of disorder now and then. But when it's over, order has to be established again right away. And that's difficult because so many of our children don't destroy intentionally. A lot do, of course—toys, teaching materials. We have a janitor. He'll replace the window right away. Unfortunatey glass is terribly expensive."

"Do the children often smash windows?"

"Herr Norton," said Director Hallein, "the maximum since the school opened is fourteen windows in one day, all by the same boy."

"You say that almost proudly!"

"And I am proud of it," said Hallein. "The fact that we permitted this boy to go excessively wild resulted in a turning point in his life."

3

Heroldsheid Remedial School has the utter despair of a couple called Leitner to thank for its founding, two unknown people, living modestly, with no bank account, no Mercedes, no villa, no hunting lodge, no jewelry, no yacht in the Mediterranean. Only a crippled son whom they loved just as much as they loved each other. The father was a minor employee in a very prestigious bank. The name of the crippled child was Alois.

After his birth, Alois's parents visited one doctor after the other with the boy. The story is an incredible odyssey and one gigantic indictment, but I am writing the truth, your honor, as promised.

Alois spent his first year in clinics where they experimented with him. The bank in which Leitner worked has many branches in various cities, and the Leitners had to move frequently. Thus much precious time was lost with wrong treatments, ever-changing methods of various new doctors, or through no treatment at all. The Leitners, humble little people, couldn't do anything about it. They were thankful when Alois was accepted in a home for crippled children. He didn't stay there long. According to what the Leitners were told, he was "unmanageable."

By the time Alois had reached school age, things had gone from bad to worse. He couldn't go to a school for normal children, so he was put in an institution for retarded children. One day Herr Leitner received a call. He was told that Alois couldn't be kept in the school because "there was no possibility for progress." He was not "promotion-worthy."

At the time—this was seven years ago—the Leitners had reached rock bottom. Frau Leitner met another woman with a retarded child in the suburb of Nürnberg where the Leitners had finally landed. And at the Sophienkrankenhaus they met Ruth Reinhardt. Dr. Reinhardt said she was willing, together with a friend, a qualified woman called Wilma Bernstein who had survived six years in a concentration camp, to treat the two children and teach them, but where?

The Leitners knew of a former gymnasium that was no longer being used. They sent a petition to the county administration to permit them to use it, stating what for. The county administration turned them down. Because in order to rent this abandoned gymnasium (Herr Leitner had declared he would be able to take care of the rent), the parents of the two sick children would have to present their petition as a registered organization. So the Leitners and the widow, mother of the other sick child, had founded something they called Menschenwelt, Human World. The name was Herr Leitner's idea. As a registered organization they had a chance of receiving the designation "recognized as in the public interest." If they got that, they would have tax advantages. But an organization consisting of three members and two sick children . . . that was ridiculous! They needed at least seven members!

Ruth had more than enough children at the Sophienkrankenhaus in the same desperate situation, and in the end thirty couples with handicapped children joined forces, among them a lawyer, an accountant, and a man from the Nürnberg city administration. The city government was then willing to help financially, but not for a rundown gymnasium as headquarters! Only for a real school with a qualified staff!

The desperate parents were lucky. In the township of Heroldsheid, near Nürnberg, a doctor died who had been running a nursing home for the elderly in his little palace of a house. It had stood empty for two years because the doctor hadn't been well enough to run the home any more. With the reading of the will, his heirs got a surprise: The doctor wanted his house to be leased for ninety-nine years to an organization that took care of sick children. So there was the school! But what about the rent? The heirs wanted seven thousand marks a month. There were a few wealthy members among the desperate parents, and Herr Leitner, the bank employee, saw to it that they got credit. The house was renovated to accommodate the handicapped; qualified teachers were hired; and the school was soon heavily in debt (and still is!). But after the arrangement with the taxis had been made, and the buses, and hundreds of details worked out, the thing began to function, and now they were in constant communication with the Federal Organization for Handicapped Children in Marburg, with some hope of support from them.

At the dedication of the school, city and county politicians had naturally been present. One of them made a very moving speech. A small orchestra played Vivaldi. Cheap champagne and hors d'oeuvres were handed around. Everybody felt festive, even the heirs, who, faced with the first thirty children, lowered the rent to five thousand marks a month. And that was how Heroldsheid Remedial School had come into being, through the initiative and despair of a married couple and a desperate mother. Frau Leitner once said to Ruth, "Of course we hoped for such a long time that Alois would one day be a healthy normal child. Today we know that there will never be any improvement in his condition. Now there is only one thing worrying us: What will happen to Alois when we are dead?" And Herr Leitner, who was present, had said, "Let it be, Anne. God helped us."

"But I said to him," said Ruth, who was telling me the story, "No, Herr Leitner. Human beings helped you. And they will do it again. Only people can help people."

"Only people can help people?" I asked. "What about God? What about all the gods? What about Buddha? They don't count?"

"Buddha," said Ruth Reinhardt. "Everybody is looking for an easing of the burden, for peace of mind. I found Buddha. He teaches about good and evil. Evil is the satisfying of desire at the cost of other people. Good is a personal sacrifice for any other life whatsoever, even that of an enemy. To love your fellowmen is not part of the church service, it is a person walking the hard path of liberation. It includes a feeling of brotherhood. I have found Buddhism a consolation. It makes the unbearable bearable."

4

Heroldsheid
August 24, 1972

CONFIRMATION

of an allocation to one of the corporate bodies, staff associations and assets indicated in § 4 section 1 item 6 of Corporation Law.

Up to this point the text was printed and the form was in the typewriter on the table in front of me, a typewriter that was driving me out of my mind! The letters got tangled, the *h* and the *r* were up too high, and the return lever was stuck on the *i*! When the letters got tangled, I had to get them back into place with my fingers, my fingers got dirty, the letters I was writing too. During the last days I must have written a hundred letters—to doctors, administrators, parents. I had visited offices, visited parents, been constantly on the go. I was sitting bare to the waist—it was very hot—in a tiny room on the second floor of Heroldsheid Remedial School. It was almost noon. I'd been working since 8:30, as I did every day, sometimes until late in the evening. No, you haven't read wrong, your honor. I was working. In Madrid it had all started on a very small scale, but now things were piling up. My double life! And again and again I had to go away, more often than not to Madrid. Work on *The Chalk Circle* was in full swing, and I had two women, one whom I lived off, the other whom I loved, and I had a child.

When I looked out of the window of my little office, I could see Babs in the field behind the house, with her two friends. One was the little mongoloid girl, Jackie, who had passed us in her father's Mercedes, strapped in the seat beside the chauffeur on the morning we had driven to the school. The other was the boy who was paralyzed and had kept sliding off his seat in the bus. He was Alois Leitner. Alois, now thirteen, would never get better. His parents knew it. Babs, with her training glasses on, still limping, was pushing Alois across the grass. Jackie was helping her, because Babs was still very unsteady on her feet. Jackie walked normally. I could hear the three of them laughing.

I kept looking at the three children, then I'd type again. And all the time I was swearing loudly, "Godammit! This miserable typewriter!"

(1) Herr Walter Kleinheit, Nürnberg, Salomestrasse 234 [Great! the *h* up, the *r* up, disentangle the letters with my fingers!] donated DM 1200 (one thousand two hundred Deutsche Mark) to the Heroldsheid Remedial School on August 20, 1972 for the continuation of his care for his godchild, Heidi Metzler . . .

"This fucking machine! Can't keep anything clean!"

I shifted the form a few lines farther along and went right on cursing. "I must have a new typewriter! Look at these letters!" (To nobody in particular!) "The most important ones we're sending out!" I must show them to Hallein, I thought. He was the only reasonable person in the house. The walls in his office were covered with pictures painted by the children. On his desk there was a framed quotation: "If a man had as much good judgment as understanding, all things would be simpler." Good sentence. Spoken by Nobel Prize winner Dr. Linus Pauling. But he was one of the three Nobel Prize winners, your honor, who suggested that active euthanasia be finally made law in all cases of incurably ill persons, children as well.

To continue: Two years ago Herr Walter Kleinheit had become godfather of a spastic child, Heidi Metzler, age fifteen. An hour ago I had seen two of our conscientious objectors carrying Heidi back from the gymnasium behind the school. She can't move by herself. In the gymnasium, Monica, one of the two physiotherapists, had worked with Heidi on the spastic ball. Heidi has been here for four years. For four years they have been working with her on the spastic ball. Three years ago it looked as if her condition was improving, but that turned out to be a mistake. For four years now there has been no improvement at all, but one has to go on working with Heidi daily. Perhaps in the next four years there *will* be some improvement. Or in six. Or never.

I couldn't seem to concentrate today. So much mail to be

answered! After all, I was employed here and being paid a salary. After deductions, DM 824.50, with free board and lodging. So get on with it, Herr Norton! Any minute now it would be lunchtime, and I had to help downstairs.

Herr Walter Kleinheit, owner of a nursery, needed this confirmation because he wanted to deduct what he had spent on his spastic godchild, Heidi, whom he had never seen and probably never would see, from his income, and he could do this because there it was, in print:

(2) By certificate of the Tax Office of Nürnberg for corporate bodies, dated April 5, 1971 St. No. 53/5320 concerning the support of mentally and physically disabled persons, we have provisionally been sustained as belonging to the corporate bodies, staff associations or assets indicated in § 4 section 1 item KStG, and serving the public welfare and charitable purposes.

"Serving the public welfare and charitable purposes . . ." I stared at the words. Since my return, or let's say partial return, to Germany, the country interested me again. There were other similar institutions, for instance the Cultural Institute in Lochham, Upper Bavaria, or the State and Economic Policy Association of Herr Hugo Wellems, former Reichs Propaganda Chief, in Kowno, Lithuania. After a long struggle, these associations, like the Heroldsheid Remedial School, were also recognized as being "provisionally" in the public interest. I hope you honor understands how this expression—provisionally—is granted in the Bundesrepublik. I don't!

(3) We confirm
      (a) that we shall spend the allocated amount exclusively on the statutable purpose . . .

A bell rang. Lunch. The first seating. Babs ate at the first seating. In half an hour, the second seating. Eighty-one children can't all be fed at once. The three little ones, stumbling across the grass down there, staggered over to the house. The wheelchair bounced perilously. Babs looked up at me. She knew where I was. She could see me and waved.

I waved and smiled when I saw her distorted features with the hideous training glasses. I called out to her, "Coming right away!" and went on writing:

353

We thank you for your sympathy and support, dear Herr Kleinheit, in the name of our retarded children.

Heroldsheid Remedial School
Administration Office

And then I took the form out of the typewriter and signed, "Philip Norton," with the gold fountain pen Sylvia had given me.

5

For lunch there was alphabet soup, vegetables, potatoes, meat and fresh salad. For dessert, various puddings. Everyone had a choice. The adults ate last, after the second seating, because many of the children had to be fed. So everybody was kept pretty busy. All the children, with a few exceptions, had good appetites, especially Babs. She limped up to me when I came into the dining room, smiling, her eyes bright. Things hadn't always been like that, but now Babs was radiant. She had found friends, she was having one of her "good times." Every now and then she had "bad times" too. At first I'd felt I couldn't take it, then I saw that all the other adults were "taking" it, patiently, good-naturedly. I was the only desperate one. The adults here seemed to be composed of nothing but patience. They knew what I had learned in the meantime—every progression was followed by a relapse. When there was progress, everyone was happy, but everyone, myself included now, knew that at some point or other there would be a "bad" time again.

"Croquettes," said Babs. She still spoke very indistinctly. "Puddings. Chocolate, raspberry, vanilla."

"Which will you have?"

"All!"

I had lifted her up, but now she began to kick herself free. "What's the matter?"

"Have to go back. Help Alois," and she limped away.

For weeks now, except when Babs was having a bad time, Jackie and Babs had fed Alois. They did it lovingly and carefully. They smiled at Alois all the time they were feeding him, and Alois smiled, smacked his lips, tried to swallow, swallowed. A few months ago Babs had had to be fed.

I often felt like Gulliver among the Lilliputians at Heroldsheid. The greater part of the house was equipped for little children. Except for where the older children were seated, even the dining hall looked like a dining room for midgets! Low tables, low chairs, small cutlery. Things were no different in the hall, where the hooks and hangers for the children's coats and the racks were very low. Most of the doors had no handles, but on those that had them, the handles were low. The bowls in the washrooms were small and lower than usual, so that the children could use them without help. This also applied to the toilets. In the dormitories it was the same. After lunch each day all the children were put to bed and slept for an hour and a half or two hours. The morning activities had exhausted them. With few exceptions they fell asleep at once in their little beds. In the classrooms everything was arranged so that the children sat comfortably and that everything they needed was at a height where they could reach it. Wherever possible there were ramps on the threshold so that the children in wheelchairs could move easily.

After the noon nap, there were two more hours of instruction, then the buses came and took the children home. Only one child stayed at the school, with me—Babs. We lived in a small house some distance away, at the edge of a wooded area. Until our arrival, the houseman, who also taught shop, had lived there. The director had explained my situation to him. "But of course," the houseman had said. "I'll move out right away!" He had a girlfriend in Heroldsheid who'd be happy to take him in. The name of this accommodating man was Karl Wronda.

"You kissed Babs!"

I turned around. Ruth was standing in front of me. She touched my arm gently. "I was watching you both, and what I saw made me so happy! When did it all begin? Last year you hated Babs, you called her a brat and railed at the fate that forced you to look after her—don't deny it. I know. But now a miracle has happened! Babs always loved you, but as long as she was the healthy darling of the world, you detested her. Now that she is anything but the darling of the world, now that you have accepted all responsibility for her . . ." She stopped.

355

I said softly, "You're right. There are two creatures in this world whom I love—Babs and . . ."

I wanted to touch her, but she drew back. "There's Sylvia."

"Yes," I said. "Yes, yes! And how are things supposed to go on? As usual? We're only human!"

She was silent, looking at Babs while I fed an epileptic child. "She wipes Alois's mouth after every bite," she said. "When I think of the condition she was in when she came to us . . ."

"Not Babs!" I said almost angrily. "How are things going to go on between us?"

"I don't know," she replied. "But things will go on and they will end well."

"You really believe that?"

"I really do."

That was on August 24, 1972, a Thursday. Ruth came out to the school every Thursday to examine the children, and discuss treatment. And every Thursday was a feast day for me!

Dr. Hallein came up to us, walking fast. "Herr Norton!"

"Yes?"

"Telephone. Madrid."

6

The telephone receiver was lying on Director Hallein's desk. "This is Philip Norton."

"Pepito! My beloved Pepito! How is my darling Babs?"

"Where are you calling from, Silky?"

"From the Castellana Hilton. I have a free day. I just couldn't wait until your evening call!"

"Babs is doing very well, Silky. They're all having lunch."

"She's all over the aggressive phase?"

"All over," I said, and thought: Until next time.

"Oh, but that's wonderful! We only have about two months more here, Pepito, then it's off to the Pyrenees. But I'm soon going to ask for two free days, and then I'm coming to see Babs. It's been *such* a long time! My thoughts of seeing her

356

again so soon is what's keeping me going. It's all right, isn't it?"

"Of course it's all right, Silky," I said and knew that it wasn't.

"How are her eyes?"

"Getting better all the time." (Lie.)

"Oh, dear God, thank you! And ... and does she still limp?"

"She's doing calisthenics every day, Silky. The limping's better too." (Lie.)

"And ..." She went on asking, I went on lying. I did the same thing every day. "Everything's going to be all right, even if it takes a long time. But it's going to be all right, isn't it?"

"Yes. I hope so, Silky."

"It is! It is! Don't say 'I hope so'! When are you coming to Madrid again?"

"Next week."

"You can't come sooner, I know. We're telling everybody here that you're doing business for us all over Spain and in Paris, in Los Angeles. By the way, Steve is working out very well. Everybody believes he's your assistant because you're so terribly busy with this film and my next picture. But you've just got to be here for two days once a week or somebody may catch on. Up to now everything's been fantastic! Have you seen the latest *Time?*"

"No. Why?"

"I'm on the cover." Her voice grew firmer. "And I have the cover story. And what a story! 'The Greatest Star in the Greatest Film'!"

"Really?"

"That's on the cover, and in the story they keep saying that I'm the greatest film actress ever! Lots of gorgeous pictures of me! Of you too, and of Babs. From our files."

"Great!"

"*Oggi* called from Rome, and *Paris-Match*. On your way here you must stay at Le Monde. Take my plane. Go to *Paris-Match* and set a date for the article. *Stern* called from Germany. They want to come right away. Rod put them off. Doesn't want everything coming out at the same time. With the *Time* story alone, I can ask for any salary I want, and get it!"

I felt dizzy. In Dr. Hallein's little office I could see simple toys, children's books, records, and through the window, the

357

sunny field. I had trouble grasping what Sylvia was talking about.

"And then you must come here and make one hell of a row! Steve says so. That's something he can't do. He's only the assistant producer. You're the *producer*, Pepito!'

"A row? Why?"

"Because you're here so little and Joe's not here at all. More and more of the people here think they can do as they please. They're fresh and absolutely shameless! Yesterday I slapped Claudia's face."

"Who is Claudia?"

"But Pepito! You know who she is! The wardrobe mistress. The dress Grusha wears when she hides in the palace with the child while the Ironshirts look for her."

"What's the matter with the dress?"

"Claudia's made alterations. Didn't consult anybody. Now it's much too long. Damn her, anyway! She hates me!"

"Nonsense!"

"It isn't nonsense. She told Carmen—Carmen Cruzeiro, my stand-in—she told Carmen that she hated all Americans. She's half Italian. The Italians hate the Americans, don't they?"

"No."

"They do! I know I'm right. And Carmen told me so too. I'm German, but Claudia doesn't know that!"

"She's the best wardrobe mistress we could find. Especially for historic films."

"Could be. But she's stupid just the same. And you've got to give her hell. You've got to promise me that. I've been so upset about it, I thought I'd have a heart attack. You'll tell her off, won't you?"

"Yes."

"And da Cava too!"

"What's he done?"

"He's a bastard! An absolute tyrant! You know the long flight of stairs I have to fall down in the palace?"

"Yes."

"He had me fall down them *eight times*, Pepito! Every bone in my body hurts. I'm just lucky I didn't break anything! He's tried to change the script *three times*! Steve managed to stop him, but he says in the end you're the only one who can straighten things out. Everybody here's so mean . . ."

"It's the heat. And you've been shooting so long."

"It's hatred, that's what it is! They all hate me! You can

imagine how they're going to hate me after they've seen *Time*. Buy a copy right away."

"They don't have foreign magazines out here. We're in a very small place, Silky."

"Then send somebody to Nürnberg. Right away. They'll have a copy there, surely. Will you send somebody right away?"

"Of course I will, Silky. Please calm down. And I'll be with you again soon."

At once a change of tone. "My poor Pepito! I know what you're thinking, but it's no use. I can't. We tried, remember? It's the picture. I'm always like that when I'm shooting a picture, remember? And now on top of everything, my darling's sick. If you love me, Pepito, you'll understand. I'm a woman, a sensitive creature, not an animal . . ."

"I understand everything."

Since Sylvia had left Delamare's clinic, we hadn't slept together once. It wasn't the picture, both of us knew that. It was the guilt both of us felt.

Sylvia went on and on. I wasn't listening any more. I wasn't interested in her reasons. And Ruth had scruples. So I'd sleep with Carmen. No sense in my going crazy too. After all, everything depended on me, and Carmen was ready and willing. She'd always been ready and willing. A strange life, wasn't it, your honor?

" . . . and give my darling a big fat kiss, Pepito."

"I will."

"And I kiss you too, my darling. Once the film's over, everything will be just as it was. Especially if I can see my darling whenever I want to. I love you, Pepito. I love you more than life itself!"

"And I love you, Silky."

"Tonight they're burning the city. You won't be able to reach me. The big crowd scenes, remember? I'll be working. Tomorrow too. We won't be able to talk to each other until the day after tomorrow. But I'm taking you with me in my heart, Pepito. Goodbye, my love."

"Goodbye."

The sweat was trickling down my body. I put down the receiver. If Sylvia knew . . . Then I saw a note beside the phone: "Dear Herr Norton—This morning I heard you swearing about the typewriter all the way from my room. We have put a new one in your office and hope you'll like it! Please forgive us.—Hallein."

7

Dear Frau Kreuzwendedich,

Our most grateful thanks for the check for DM 350 which you were so good to send us to cover the cost of summer clothing for your godchild, Conrad Vetter . . .

I was in my little office again, typing on my new typewriter. A marvelous machine! I was so happy, I called Hallein.

"This is Herr Norton, Dr. Hallein. I wanted to thank you for the typewriter." I could hear him laugh. "What's so funny?"

"You're just too busy, Herr Norton. The new typewriter is one of yours."

"One of mine?"

"Yes. And we have two more of yours."

"I don't understand."

"Three months ago you wrote one of your appeal letters to a typewriter manufacturer, and they sent us three typewriters!" And then I had to laugh too.

"So you see how profitable such appeals can be. What are you working on right now?"

"I'm thanking Frau Kreuzwendedich for her contribution for Conrad."

"Oh yes, of course. People suddenly become generous in the summer."

"Thank God! But they don't all send three hundred and fifty marks like Frau Kreuzwendedich. I also have to get letters out for the ten marks for Helga and the fifteen marks for Peter and the twenty-five marks fifty for Erica. Have you any idea why the fifty pfennigs?"

"They may not have had the extra mark," said Hallein. "All these people who help us are friendly people, and we've got to be friendly back."

I hung up. A great man, this director. The only one here who knew the truth about me and Babs.

The children had just risen from their nap. Such a lot of noise, such happy voices! And in a place where there was so much misery. Ruth was examining them.

There was a lab in the basement of the school, but complicated tests couldn't be done there; for anything serious the child had to be taken to the Sophienkrankenhaus. Ruth got all the reports from those who were with the children daily. All the children here had great difficulty concentrating, Babs too, of course, and they tired easily. Ruth sometimes changed their medication, prescribed new methods. Babs was in Fräulein Gellert's class now, as she was every day at this time.

Fräulein Vera Gellert worked in a room on the first floor. She was very pretty, still young, a psychologist and speech therapist. As I typed I thought of how she had started to work with Babs. It had begun like this: Babs sitting at a table in Fräulein Gellert's classroom, wearing large earphones, in front of her an instrument that looked rather like an old-fashioned telephone. It had a meter and a lot of knobs. In front of it, a microphone. Cards were lying before Babs with various pictures on them, trees, flowers, streetcars, houses, rivers. On some small events were portrayed. Fräulein Gellert put a card down on the table and spoke very clearly into the microphone, her finger on the figure on the card. "This is a boy."

No reaction.

Fräulein Gellert turned one of the knobs and her voice came across louder. "This is a boy."

Still no reaction.

Louder. "This is a boy."

At last Babs reacted. "Isboy."

"This is a boy."

"Isaboy."

Up to now, your honor, I have always repeated what Babs said as if she were speaking more or less normally. I relate the speech lesson here just to give you an idea of how she really spoke. You could understand her all right, though sometimes with difficulty. Since her muteness ended, Babs could at best speak sentences of three words, no more. It left you having to guess quite a lot, but if you saw her daily, you could easily figure out what she was trying to say. Oddly enough Babs never used her speech to express emotions. Those she expressed affectively in gestures. So, once more, "This is a boy." Perhaps ten times.

"How long is this going to take, Fräulein Gellert?"

"Many years, Herr Norton."

"And a class every day?"

"Every day. It has to be built up slowly and cautiously. Never too long at a time, because these children tire so easily."

"You must have a lot of patience, Fräulein Gellert."

"Oh yes, I have, Herr Norton."

She did have all the patience in the world; it was incredible. I never was able to grasp it.

Different cards after reaching a certain level. The next day the same thing. For months on end with ever different cards, then, gradually, other methods. For instance: "Where is the card with the automobile?" Or, "What's on this card?" Or, "Now *you* tell *me* something. Pick your own card." Or an erroneous statement, "This is a train. It is swimming in a river."

"No train. Train no swim."

And Fräulein Gellert was truly happy, I can swear to that, your honor, she and all the others working here, whenever they could see the slightest improvement, a correct reaction, the least sign of progress. There are women who are happy when their lovers give them a mink coat, and there are women—but I found this out only after I met Ruth, after I worked at Heroldsheid—who are more sincerely happy when a brain-damaged child manages to go to the toilet for the first time, after he's been taken there and helped for three, four, eight years, and manages without help. But these men and women live in the dark, the others in the light. And one sees those in the light, not the ones in the dark. . . .

8

Heroldsheid
August 24, 1972

Dear Director Riehlem,

Please don't throw this letter away, or the brochure with it. We know how busy you are, but please take the time to read them.

You have surely heard of Heroldsheid Remedial School. You know therefore—if not, the brochure tells all about it—that this school is the last hope and only salvation for close to a hundred children who manage to live in spite of the most serious handicaps. Many hundreds more would like to come to us. Their parents beg us to take them. They are on a long waiting list. But we can't take any more children.

Three years ago, the fate and future of ninety-four children living here at the time, *learning to live* here, hung by a thread. Our school was on the verge of bankruptcy. Those responsible . . .

The telephone. I picked up the receiver. "Yes?"

"Please come downstairs, Herr Norton. A call for you from Madrid." Dr. Hallein.

"Again? Frau Moran has called once already today."

"This isn't Frau Moran, Herr Norton. This is a man."

I ran down the narrow staircase, past the mysterious, eerie, wonderfully incomprehensible water colors painted by children that were pasted on the wall. A man? What man? What had happened? The strongest of the conscientious objectors, the one with the beard, was carrying Joseph across his shoulder like a sack. He was taking the seventeen-year-old spastic outdoors. I forced my way through the children and adults to reach Dr. Hallein's office. "Yes?"

"Rod."

"What's the matter?"

"You've got to come down. Tomorrow. The jet's waiting in Orly."

"Why? What's happened?"

"Sylvia!"

"Is she sick? I spoke to her only four hours ago and she was fine."

"That's what we all thought."

"What's happened since then?"

"I've called Lejeune and Dr. Lévy. You're to meet them in Paris, tomorrow noon, in Le Monde. They're coming with you."

"What is going on?"

"Plenty! That goddam woman!"

"Sylvia?"

"Yes, yes, yes!"

"Don't yell! I hear you!"

"You can kiss my ass, you goddam liar!"

"Why the hell . . ."

"Telling me Sylvia hasn't slept with you since Babs took sick!"

"But it's the truth! When I'm in Madrid, she locks her bedroom. Has hysterics when I touch her. Hasn't even kissed me! Crazy! But I can understand it. The shock, the guilt, the worry about Babs . . ."

"Shock? Guilt? Worry? Shit!"

"What do you mean?"

"Steve will tell you all about it."

"Why Steve?"

"Because two hours ago one of the electricians came to see him. A Spaniard, a filthy, sweating bum, and he told Steve, 'Señor, I need money, and I don't have any money, but you'll give me money, I'm sure. I need quite a lot but I'm sure you'll let me have it just the same.'"

"Blackmail."

"You're having one of your brighter days!"

"But what for?"

"Your Sylvia, your suffering mother, this unhappy, broken woman who doesn't let you fuck her any more in her overwhelming grief over Babs, lets this freak fuck her!"

"Let's . . . *what?*"

"You got it the first time. And not just once, oh no! Every day last week. Sometimes in his shack, sometimes on the lot in one of the sets! Up with her skirt, unzip the guy, and they're off!"

"I don't believe it!"

"You don't? She admitted it right away when Steve asked her."

"Then she's gone crazy! She needs help! You'll have to stop shooting."

"My God, you really are a shining light, Phil! Crazy? Needs help? Stop shooting? Let me tell you something. Joe's crazy. Everybody here's crazy. Because what they've shot to date is not to be believed! Sylvia was never so fantastic in her entire career. No actress has ever been as magnificent as Sylvia in this picture."

"And I have to come down right away so we can play the Great Lovers of the Century for photographers and reporters before the truth leaks out."

"My, that was fast! Congratulations! Tomorrow P.M. you'll be here," and when I didn't answer right away, "You'll be here. That's an order. Got it?"

"Yes."

"She hasn't gone crazy. This is something that happens in many such cases. Just one more manifestation of guilt and despair," said Ruth.

We were sitting on a bench in front of the little house in which I lived with Babs. It was late afternoon. The buses with the children had left, the adults too. I had told the director that I had to fly to Madrid tomorrow. He hadn't asked why.

"Certainly. Go right ahead. That's why we gave you this job, so that you can always leave for a few days without any problem. Frau Pohl will replace you."

Frau Hertha Pohl was Hallein's assistant, a very active young woman, always immaculately groomed. She was married to an insurance agent, had two pretty children and lived in a small modern house near Heroldsheid. It had been built according to her design, that's what she told me once when I was their guest, which I was frequently, and there was still a big mortgage on it. "But it's ours, and we're happy in it." It was Frau Pohl who had shown me how to handle the business of fund raising.

"And Frau Grösser will look after Babs in the meantime," said Dr. Hallein. The arrangement with Frau Grösser functioned marvelously, thanks to Dr. Hallein. I'll tell in a moment how it came about.

So there we were, Ruth and I, sitting on a bench in front of the house in sunshine and beauty, peace and quiet, surrounded by blossoming flowers, and from inside the house we could hear music, very soft music.

"You mean to say that the way Sylvia is behaving happens often?" I asked, baffled.

"Very often. Some women drink, become tramps, commit suicide, try to murder their husbands. I told you once that no one with a child like Babs comes out of such an ordeal unblemished unless he or she has led a solid orderly life until it happens. Neither you nor Sylvia did." Ruth had stopped saying "Frau Moran" a few weeks ago.

"That we didn't."

"Sylvia is without doubt the greatest living film star, but she has received a body blow. What is happening to her now, starting with denying you, is hysteria, and has nothing to do with the fact that she is a better actress than ever. On the contrary—it is just this hysteria, and the fact that this

365

picture is concerned with a child, that makes it possible for her to give her best."

"But she's endangering the picture, her career, her future . . ."

"Certainly. And it may get worse. What she is doing now is nothing compared with what may yet come." Suddenly there was a slight breeze, ending the heat of the day. The music had stopped. Ruth laid her hand on mine. "It's terrible for you, Phil, I know," she said, "but don't give up. Please don't give up."

"I can endure anything as long as you are with me," I said.

Babs came limping out of the house. She pressed her body against mine and stroked my arm. Then she stroked Ruth's arm, and Ruth lifted her onto her lap. Babs laid her head against Ruth's breast. She didn't say a word, but you could see through the thick training glasses that her eyes were shining.

"How has it been possible for Babs to live here with me for months and be content? Why does she come close and kiss you and stroke you whenever possible, and practically purr like a contented cat when you kiss and stroke her?"

"Because she feels safe with me."

"But she has a mother. She hasn't asked for her mother, Ruth. Not once."

"She doesn't know any more who her mother is. She doesn't know who she really is or what her name is. All she remembers is her first name, and that because we've always called her by it. And she knows your first name. I'm not sure if she knows mine, but she recognizes me. Otherwise she has forgotten everything. She clings only to people who give her love, warmth, a feeling of security."

"Ss . . . scurity," said Babs. Her head rested on Ruth's breast.

9

"Love is a many splendored thing . . ."

The music from the film played by the Ray Coniff orchestra. *Hollywood in Rhythm* was the name of the record. I had bought it in Nürnberg, and others by Ray Coniff, because it was Babs's favorite music. In the school there were many phonographs and records. There was a course called Music Therapy. Brain-damaged children like to listen to music, and it is good for them. Music relaxes, calms aggression; it is a very important therapy.

Now we were in the house—such a simple house, bathroom, living room, kitchen, furnished with secondhand furniture. Everything the way the houseman had left it. Ruth was sitting beside me on an old couch with sagging springs. And "Love is a many splendored thing . . ."

Babs was in motion. With her lame leg she couldn't dance, and with her poor brain she couldn't move in time with the music, but she was so enthralled by it that, sitting on the floor, her legs spread awkwardly, she began to move her body, sometimes in time with the music, then again unrhythmically, swaying from side to side, making big circles with her arms, and all the time laughing happily. She got to her feet, walked a few steps and fell down, still laughing. What she was doing looked dreadful, but neither Ruth nor I saw it that way.

"You are so good," Ruth said softly.

"Nonsense!"

"You are so good," she said again. "So good for Babs. What is it that Sylvia says at the end of the picture? How does Brecht put it?"

" 'That what is there shall belong to those who are good for it,' " I said hesitantly. " 'The children to those with motherly love, so that they may prosper.' "

"Yes," said Ruth.

Then we went on watching Babs's efforts, how she kept falling down and laughing with her dear distorted face, and we laughed and applauded, and Babs went on "dancing" as the record changed to "It Might As Well Be Spring." Then suddenly she was tired, and lay down on the floor, breathing hard.

I turned off the phonograph. Ruth lifted Babs up, Babs threw her thin little arms around Ruth's neck, and Ruth stroked her and kissed her on the cheek, and Babs looked at me. Her glasses had fallen on the floor, her crossed eyes were looking at me, and she was radiant as she said in her garbled speech, "Beautiful?"

"Beautiful, Babs," I said. "Just beautiful!"

10

Night fell. The sky was studded with stars, a light wind was blowing. Babs was asleep in her bed. I had been sleeping on an old couch in the living room ever since we had moved in. We had had supper—Ruth had cooked today. Whenever I was away, Frau Grösser cooked. Otherwise, I did the cooking. I had learned how to in the meantime; the cooks at the school had taught me the bare necessities, and they sufficed. While Ruth got supper I went over to see Frau Grösser.

Frau Beate Grösser wore her white hair combed straight back. She was near seventy, the widow of a civil servant. She lived in Heroldsheid. She had a room, kitchen and bath in the house of a greengrocer. She was a very lonely woman. Her son had been killed in the war, and she had no living relatives. So it had been very easy to arrange everything with her when the question came up of who would look after Babs when I had to be with Sylvia. Frau Grösser had been Dr. Hallein's solution, and he had taken me to see her the same day. She was delighted with the idea. Next day Babs and Frau Grösser met for the first time. "Smells good woman," was all Babs said after everything was settled and Frau Grösser had left. And that was how the problem had been solved. Now I went to see Frau Grösser and told her that she would have to take my place again.

"I'll be glad to," she said, and gave me four big pears for Babs. "Take them, Herr Norton. My greengrocer gave them to me. I have lots more."

Now the four pears lay on Babs's bedside table, and Ruth and I were sitting on opposite sides of her bed. I could see Ruth's face clearly. We were silent for a long time. And then I told Ruth all about myself. I recounted my whole wasted, dissolute life. She listened without saying a word. When I was done, she said, "Now I love you more than ever."

"After all that?"

"Yes. Because now I can appreciate fully what you are doing for Babs."

I said nothing. Both of us looked at Babs, who was fast asleep, breathing deeply and regularly. We were silent.

At 11:00 Ruth said she had to leave. "I have to get up early; so do you. It was beautiful tonight."

"Yes," I said.

Once she was outdoors, Ruth immediately began to walk off in the wrong direction, toward the woods. I caught up with her, took her by the arm and turned her around. I walked her to her VW, opened the gate for her and said goodnight.

"Goodnight, Phil. Good luck. Call me at the hospital if you need me. And . . ."

"Yes?"

"Come back soon, please."

I wanted to kiss her, but she slipped away from me and got into her car. I watched until she disappeared around a bend, then I went back to the little house in which I lived with Babs.

11

It was 107 degrees in Madrid. I felt faint as I left the plane. Rod had come to meet Dr. Lévy, Maître Lejeune and me in Sylvia's Rolls. He drove off at once like a berserk cowboy. He was wearing nothing but a shirt, shorts and sandals. Big sweat stains under his arms. All of us had taken off our jackets and ties. The Rolls was air-conditioned, but you'd never have known it.

"Where is Madame Moran?" asked Lejeune.

"At the Hilton. She knows you're coming."

"How did she find out?"

"Some idiot talked. She's locked herself in her suite and says she won't see anybody."

"Dr. Lévy, we'll drop you at the Hilton. You'll manage to speak to her, won't you?"

"Of course," said Dr. Lévy.

"I've got to know exactly how she is. Where is this electrician?"

"Somewhere on the lot."

"Good," said Lejeune. "Then we'll drive straight to the lot. I suggest we meet between seven and eight in the bar."

"Very good," said Dr. Lévy.

12

Estudios Sevilla Films. Now the vast area of red earth was covered with buildings—gigantic palaces and miserable peasant huts, barracks for the Ironshirts. The extras were wearing plastic armor, metallic-painted. I wouldn't have wanted to change places with any of them, not in this heat. Stables for the horses, triumphal arches, gallows, facades of houses, streets, paths, ancient carts—a whole city, already half burned to the ground. An army of workmen were readying everything for the burning of the other half of the city. They wore nothing but bathing trunks. The perspiration glistened on their sunburned backs.

Rod drove his heavy car into the stall of a stable in a Grusinian peasant farmyard and brought it to a halt so abruptly that Lejeune and I were thrown forward. "Have you gone crazy?"

"The car's got to stay in the shade."

We headed across the lot. Rod walked so fast we could barely keep up with him. There were the administration buildings. Shade! Shade at last! But no relief from the heat. Up a flight of stairs. A young woman dressed in the gray sackcloth of a kitchen maid was coming down them. I recognized her. "Hello, Carmen."

"Hello, Señor Kaven," said Sylvia's stand-in.

We avoided looking at each other. We kept out of each other's way as much as we could whenever I was here. We had never spoken about that afternoon, only about trivial things, and as little as possible about them. As she walked past me I brushed against her right breast and could suddenly feel the blood coursing through my body. I thought: If we ever get out of the mess we're in, I'll do it with Carmen. That was the only solution. *If* we succeed in covering up this latest disaster and finishing the picture with Sylvia, who quite evidently had gone mad. I turned around. Carmen was at the bottom of the stairs, looking up at me. Her large breasts rose and fell. I smiled lasciviously. She smiled blissfully. So . . . everything settled. She looked relieved.

My producer's office, the only one with air conditioning. Soon I was shivering with cold. A heap of papers on my desk—letters, plans, estimates, files—it looked like work. And it was work. For Steve! He came over right away. The man at the gate had told him we'd arrived.

Steve was wearing a sleeveless white shirt, light white pants, nothing on his feet. He came toward us, lanky, and because of his height, slightly stooped. We shook hands. In spite of all the excitement, Steve was polite and to the point. Before Lejeune was able to ask, he said, "Miss Moran is at the Hilton. She will see no one."

"I know. But . . ."

"She will be punctual for the night shooting; she has promised me that. I knew you were coming, Mr. Kaven. I've notified reporters and photographers, for tonight and tomorrow."

"The Great Lovers of the Century," Rod said softly. "You're not here for fun."

"The second half of the crowd scenes in the burning city *must* be shot tonight, and Miss Moran's scene with the abandoned child in the palace. I've made that quite clear to her, Mr. Kaven."

"But you haven't mentioned the stills with me, for tomorrow, have you?"

"No."

"Okay." I sighed.

"Where is the Spanish son of a bitch?" asked Lejeune.

"Locked up in the basement. Do you want me to get him?"

"Isn't necessary," said Lejeune. "What's his name?"

"Pedro Chumez. Here's a file on him. Tells everything."

Lejeune belched. "May I have a telephone book, please?"

"Certainly, sir."

"Thanks."

"What are you looking up?" I asked.

"What do you think? Police headquarters, naturally."

He found the number he wanted, asked if the switchboard could listen in, was told no, was satisfied and dialed. After that he spoke fast in fluent Spanish. The best man Joe had ever picked.

"Maître Lejeune from Paris speaking. I want to speak to the chief of police, Major Mingote."

We sat there speechless, staring at him. Evidently they knew who he was, because he got his connection right away. "Carlos Mingote? . . . Lejeune! Surprised, old man, eh? . . Where? . . . Here in your beautiful city at the Estudios Sevilla Films. Listen, my good friend, you're going to have to get on your horse for me, I'm afraid, and fast. We have a dog down here in the basement, a goddam blackmailer. He went to our assistant producer yesterday and tried to get money out of him. . . . For what? . . . This filthy bastard declares that he has slept with Señora Moran. . . . Yes, frequently . . . that she practically raped him, and to shut up about it he wants money. Carlos—please—the greatest film actress in the world! And what if she has! Isn't it the same here as everywhere else? Don't the police help the blackmailed person . . . under all circumstances? And protect him? . . . Well then, there you are! . . . What? . . . I don't know, but I don't think he's told anyone else about it. He's doing this on his own. . . . Yes. . . . Yes. . . . Yes. Thanks, Carlos. We'll wait. How long can you . . . Six months pending trial and then the trial. Great! Just great! Thanks again, Carlos. Oh, by the way, I suppose you know that that little business with your border guards . . . Yes. . . . It's been dismissed. They'll be getting out tomorrow. . . . Don't mention it, Carlos. Was nothing. You're doing the same for us now. I'll go along with the dog when your people come to get him, and drop in on you. . . . Yes, I'm looking forward to it too." Lejeune hung up, saw our awed expressions and shrugged, a little embarrassed. "Friends. You've got to have friends everywhere."

"The police are coming to get Chumez?"

"Of course. He's not dangerous."

"What if he's talked already?"

"I don't think so. We'll transport him as conspicuously as possible, so that everyone can see he's going to jail. That should help."

"But what if Miss Moran—forgive me, Mr. Kaven—what if

372

Miss Moran has had relations with other men, or still has?" asked Steve.

"I don't think they'll try blackmail, not after this. They—if they exist—won't talk. I believe. And hope," said Lejeune.

"Listen, sir," said Steve. "Miss Moran is deeply disturbed over her daughter's illness. She has become absolutely unreliable. What if something like this happens again, or worse?"

"Don't despair! You've got Papa Lejeune," said our fat lawyer. "Although I must admit your situation is anything but rosy. Twenty-five million dollars is twenty-five million dollars, and Miss Moran is the greatest film actress in the world, and this is her greatest film."

"Yes," said Rod. "That's just it. The film's *got* to be finished, *and* without a scandal!"

"Madame is psychologically deeply disturbed. That's obvious. As soon as I've been to the police I'll see what Dr. Lévy has to say."

"Do you still need us, Maître?" Rod asked.

"No. I can attend to everything myself, Monsieur Bracken. We'll meet at the Hilton."

"Right. See you all later."

13

Bracken and I went together to the Castellana Hilton bar after we had all checked in. Dr. Lévy and Lejeune were waiting there for us. Dr. Lévy was drinking orange juice. A plate of sandwiches and a glass of beer stood in front of Lejeune. The two looked at us silently.

"Have you seen Sylvia?" I asked.

Dr. Lévy nodded.

"And?" I said.

"I am terribly sorry, Monsieur Kaven," said Dr. Lévy, "but madame is very ill."

"What's wrong?"

"Not physically. Not anything I can help her with. She is psychologically ill. If she is to finish this picture, if you want to prevent her emotional state from getting even worse, then she must have the care of a psychiatrist right away. Someone

373

who can be with her all the time. I know an excellent French—"

"No!" said Bracken.

"Why not?"

"If that's the way things are, Joe's got to know. This is going to be the bloody end! Stay here. I'll call Joe right away. Phil, go up to Sylvia."

"Must I?"

"Of course you must!" he yelled.

"Okay," I said. "Okay, okay . . ."

14

She was sitting in the antique furnished salon of our suite, 308. She was wearing a very short, very thin green housecoat, only panties underneath it. She had on no makeup. Her hair was a tangled mass, her hands were trembling. Suddenly she looked so small, so terribly small, especially her face.

"Hello, Phil," she said, and when I wanted to kiss her forehead, "No. Please. Don't be angry, but don't touch me, please."

"It's all right, Silky." I said. "Everything's going to be all right."

She looked past me at a picture on the wall of a wild horse that seemed to be galloping straight out of the frame. Silence.

Her eyes wandered across the other pictures on the wall, across the red and white silk wall covering, the marble mantelpiece, the built-in television set and stereo, finally to a desk near the window with letters, papers, the script lying on it, and back to the candelabra, a table on which—I caught my breath—her jewelry was lying, a heap of it. There was a safe in the room. Why wasn't her jewelry in it? Her eyes passed across a floor lamp with a bell-shaped shade, finally back to me. She said, and her voice was toneless, "You know . . ."

"I know everything. That's why I'm here. The electrician is where he belongs, in jail. Nothing's going to happen."

"But you, Phil . . ." That evening she never called me

374

Pepito, not once. "But you ... you love me ... and I ... I've ..."

"Too much has happened, Silky. You've suffered too much. And the work on the film on top of everything. I can understand that you don't desire me as a man right now. Because you and I ... because we have Babs. I can understand the ... the other man. And what difference does it matter, since I love you?" I said all that, your honor, and every word of it was true. Because, like Ruth, I could not longer withdraw from the tragedy that had overwhelmed this woman, not face to face with her as I was now.

"I don't want you to love me."

"What do you mean?"

"You're not to love me. Nobody's to love me. Only Babs must get well. Please, please, dear God!"

"She will get well, Silky. I've been telling you every day that she's getting better."

"And you've been lying to me every day."

"No!"

"Be quiet. I know. I've been talking to doctors here. They told me what to expect in a case like this. At best."

"So there you are."

"Yes, Phil. But it isn't like what you tell me at all. Babs will never be right again. Never."

"She will!"

"Be quiet, Phil, please. And there's no use praying to God. God has cursed me. And justly so. It's all over for Babs. And for me."

"For you? *The Chalk Circle* is going to be the greatest success of all time!" She shrugged. "Believe me. Everybody says so. Please, Sylvia, don't give up! Do whatever you have to do. We'll cover it up. With money and influence you can cover up anything. And I'll never hold it against you. Never. I understand you. Sleep with as many men as you like."

"Five," she said.

"Five what?"

"I have slept with five different men. Or six. I'm not sure."

"When?"

"Since ... since this happened to Babs."

"Where?"

"In Rome. Here."

"What men?"

"I don't remember."

375

"You must remember. Try! I'm not asking you to remember because I want to make a scene. I'm only asking to protect you."

"It's no use, Phil. I really don't remember. I've forgotten. I've forgotten so much. There's something in my head, like a great emptiness that sucks up everything."

"We'll help you, Sylvia. We're going to get you a good doctor."

"He won't help me."

"He will. I know he will."

"I know what I have to do, Phil. Don't worry. I'll go on working. We're shooting again tonight. I'll be punctual, and I'll do what I have to do. I've been punctual and done the right thing all along, haven't I?"

"Always, Silky darling."

"And you'll be there tonight, won't you? Because of the reporters and photographers. That's why they brought you here."

"I came because—"

"Because they made you come. We'll be there for the reporters and photographers, as we always have been. Tonight. For as long as they need us. All right, Phil?"

"I—"

"Phil . . . please . . . go now."

"I thought you'd be glad to see me."

"I am glad to see you, Phil, but I have to be alone. Don't be angry, please."

"Of course not." I rose and again tried to kiss her forehead, but she shrank from me.

"Don't . . ."

"Of course not, if you don't want me to, Silky. So I'll go now. *Auf Wiedersehen.*"

"Auf Wiedersehen."

"Everything's going to be all right, you'll see."

"Never."

I had walked over to the door and almost closed it behind me when I heard her voice. "Phil."

"Yes?"

"Next week you'll come to Madrid again?"

"Of course, Silky. Of course."

I expected a reply, but there was none. I closed the door softly and took the elevator down to the lobby, and went to the bar. Bracken, Lejeune and Dr. Lévy were waiting for me at a table. I sat down, and a waiter came over. "Two double whiskeys, neat, with ice."

The three were staring at me. "Bad?" asked Bracken.

"Very bad. She has the feeling that something's wrong inside her head. She has slept with other men, doesn't know how many, doesn't know what she may still do. She knows that Babs will never be well again; some idiot of a doctor told her. She can't stand it if I even touch her."

Bracken swore obscenely.

"Did you reach Joe?" I asked.

He nodded.

"What did he say?"

"It's your fault, it's my fault, it's Babs's fault . . . then the old bastard reverted to normal, told me to wait, talked on two phones. A Dr. Lester Collins is arriving tomorrow at noon. And four detectives from Seven Stars."

"Who's Collins?"

"Joe's fire chief on such occasions. He swears by him. Has treated a lot of Joe's stars. If anyone can bring her around, it's Collins, according to Joe. And Sylvia's got to go on filming."

14

That night the rest of the city burned to the ground. Beams toppled, people and animals ran for their lives from the fire, and the Ironshirts laid waste to everything.

The governor's palace. The cowardly flight of his wife, leaving her child behind, a little boy. A meeting of the populace, who were determined to flee too. The child? Let the stupidest, the poorest, the most simpleminded among them take it—Grusha, the kitchen maid. Grusha's conflict within herself as she wants to leave the child lying there but then takes it with her, furious over the burden, Grusha, Sylvia Moran, whom I had never seen give a more brilliant performance and who needed psychiatric care.

A gaggle of photographers and TV news teams, told to be here by Steve and Rod, as well as our own photographers.

The shooting went on until 6:30 A.M. I had never seen Sylvia more disciplined. She did what she was told, even if she had to do it six times. Director da Cava expressed what all of us were thinking. "There's nobody like her and never will be!" In between the filming, hundreds of pictures of Sylvia and me, in street clothes, she in the smock of the kitchen maid Grusha, both of us doing our best. You may have seen one or two of the pictures taken that night, your honor. There were two things we had to keep in mind all night—the pictures had to prove how much Sylvia and I loved each other, and I had to agree to everything she said or demanded. She had only one demand: "I want to see my child." She repeated it over and over again while the cameras clicked. "Certainly, Silky. You'll see Babs just as soon as possible." There was nothing I didn't promise her. After all, $25 million was at stake.

15

More pictures were taken of the Great Lovers all next day. This time in super-elegance; in the Prado, standing in front of a Murillo, Velasquez, Goya, El Greco, French, Flemish and German masters, our arms around each other, cheek to cheek, kissing. Sylvia hadn't a word to say about such intimacies under these circumstances. In front of the Puerta de Alcala, the 1778 triumphal arch—the two lovers; in El Retiro, the beautiful park—the two lovers. All day long, pictures of the two who loved each other above everything else in the world. On the Plaza de la Villa, the Plaza de Oriente, on the Puerta del Sol, the most important site in Madrid. New poses, new ideas, most of them Sylvia's. Embraces, kisses, the love of the century. When I embraced her and kissed her and held her close, I must have seemed to her like a partner in one of her films. She was friendly and silent. Not entirely, though. All day long she said the same thing, "I must see Babs!"

"You will, Silky, you will. I'll arrange it!"

At about noon, the four detectives from Seven Stars and Joe's friend, the famous psychiatrist Dr. Lester Collins, arrived.

We met in our suite in the Castellana Hilton. He was tall and handsome. He stroked Sylvia's cheek, held her hand, said in a kind, calm voice, "Please don't worry, Miss Moran. Don't worry about anything. We'll set everything right. There's nothing we can't set right."

Toward evening, Sylvia and I drove to the airport, behind us a convoy of photographers. They were still taking pictures when I was standing on the top step of the boarding ramp with Sylvia, who was kissing me passionately. You must have seen that picture, your honor. It traveled around the world.

Bracken, who was in charge of the whole performance, now yelled, "That's it, boys! You've had them both for a whole day."

The photographers stopped at once. I wanted to give Sylvia a kiss that was not for show, but she pushed me away. She looked sick, but she was smiling as she said, "I love only you, Pepito. I shall always love you, I swear I will, but if you try to touch me again I'll have hysterics!"

Twenty-five million dollars, your honor. And, "Please don't worry about anything," Dr. Collins had said. And four Los Angeles detectives were in Madrid. And a brain-damaged child in Nürnberg. I had to get back to Ruth!

16

"I'm so happy to be able to talk to you," said Lucien Bayard. He was smiling, but his lips twitched as if he wouldn't be able to keep up the smile much longer. I was sitting in his small room behind the wall with the pigeon-holes for the mail and the room keys. I had joined Lucien at about 10:00 P.M. on a hot evening, August 26, 1972, a Saturday. We had landed in Orly at 8:35 on the Super-One-Eleven—Lejeune, Dr. Lévy, and I. Lejeune had hailed a taxi; I had taken Dr. Lévy with me in my Maserati Ghibli and dropped him at his place. Then I had driven to Le Monde, and as already mentioned, arrived there shortly before 10:00. There wasn't a flight to Nürnberg at that hour, so I booked on the first flight the following morning, the 27th; meanwhile, I had to change at Le Monde and become Philip Norton again.

The hotel was almost empty, Lucien told me after we had greeted each other. He was still working with taciturn Jean Perrotin. I didn't see a soul in the lobby, thank God! So I had gone directly to Lucien and asked him to take my luggage—the good stuff—to Suite 419. Lucien said he had to talk to me, and that was what he was doing now. Perrotin had tactfully withdrawn. He was outside at the desk, and Lucien spoke softly.

"A letter was delivered for you yesterday, Monsieur Kaven."

"By whom?"

"A messenger. The day clerk didn't specify. When I saw the handwriting on the envelope, I was startled, Monsieur Kaven. I know that handwriting, so do you." And I did. It was Clarissa Geiringer's handwriting. I felt warm suddenly as I tore open the envelope.

You see, your honor, since the press conference in the Blue Salon at Le Monde, during which Sylvia had explained that Babs was going to boarding school and would not be appearing in public again for some time—that was on March 15—we hadn't known what to do with Clarissa. Babs didn't need her now and probably wouldn't need her for a long time, but Lejeune had warned us not to let Clarissa go too soon. There could be rumors. So Clarissa had remained in our employ in Paris, incognito. In Rome, at the premiere of *So Little Time*, we hadn't needed her either, so we had shipped her off to Madrid, where she had been functioning ever since as Sylvia and Bracken's private secretary, and traveling back and forth between Madrid and Paris. In Madrid she had stayed at the Castellana Hilton, in Paris at Le Monde. And Lejeune's advice had been good—nobody had paid any attention to her. She, on the other hand, had paid attention to everything, especially to everything that concerned Babs. Sylvia and Bracken had kept her informed. Misinformed, because I never told Sylvia the truth about Babs, and Bracken gave Clarissa the same misinformation. Unfortunately, Clarissa was much too intelligent to believe what she was being told. She grew increasingly unhappy because she knew we were lying. She drove everyone in Madrid crazy with her misgivings and constant needling for information. About a month ago, Bracken had sent her to Paris to stay until further notice. I had called her once in Madrid and told her how well Babs was doing, and she had said, "Fine!"

On my two last visits I hadn't seen her when I had come to Le Monde to change, and nothing could have pleased me more. I was also careful not to ask anyone in the hotel where she was. And now I read her letter, written in her beautiful handwriting on Le Monde paper.

"My beloved! When you read these lines there will be no way of reaching me any longer, not for you, not for anybody."

I looked at the date. "But this letter was written two weeks ago!"

Lucien nodded. "But it wasn't delivered until yesterday, Monsieur Kaven. Mademoiselle Geiringer moved out of the hotel on August ninth."

"And you're only telling me this *now?*"

Lucien looked startled. "You didn't know?"

"No! I thought Mademoiselle Geiringer was still living here!"

"I don't understand. When she moved out she told one of my colleagues that you were sending her on a trip. She said that she probably wouldn't be coming back. Of course we believed her. Why shouldn't we?"

"Yes, naturally. Why not? Did she say where she was going?"

"No."

I went on reading aloud. " 'I never believed that Babs's condition would improve. I know too much about this illness. I realized that I had become superfluous and always would be. I was loyal to you and did everything you asked me to do as long as you needed me. You know that. I did it and I would have gone on doing it because I love you. But I can't do anything more for you. I can't do anything more for poor Babs. I realize that my existence must constitute a great problem for all of you. Out of love, love for you, Phil, I am relieving you of this problem. When you receive this letter— it will reach you much later—I shall no longer exist.' "

I stopped. *"Merde alors!"* said Lucien, to whom I had confided everything about Babs and the situation in Madrid. " 'I shall no longer exist,' " I read again, and went on. " 'You can authorize as many people as you like—they will never find me. I hope that with this I have alleviated your difficult position to some extent. But what I am doing is no selfless thing. I can't bear the position I am in any lnger. One last request: No matter what happens to Sylvia or you, never, as long as you live, never forsake Babs. She needs you. I realize

381

this reads like the last wish in a will, and in a way, that's what it is. I shall always love you, Phil, here on earth and in the beyond, if there is a beyond. Don't be angry with me, be grateful. Your Clarissa.'"

My hand holding the letter dropped to my side. "What does it mean, Lucien? Has she committed suicide?"

"Perhaps."

"But then why make such a production of it? Why didn't she do it right here in the hotel, or somewhere in Paris?"

"Because she loved you. Isn't that what she says? She didn't want to make trouble for you."

"Or perhaps she's still alive?"

"Perhaps."

"Somewhere on this earth."

"It's possible. I'm just as upset as you are. What do we do now?"

"Telephone."

I went to the booth in the lobby and called Lejeune. He had been asleep and was furious. "What's happened now?"

I told him, and he was awake at once. He had me tell him, down to the smallest detail, what Clarissa had done while she was with us, when she had told me she loved me—everything! "If any of this gets out," I said, "We have a helluva scandal on our hands."

"Nobody's going to find out," he said, "except the police. They've got to know. Send the night clerk with the letter over to me tomorrow morning. Too many fingerprints on it already. Wrap it in cellophane."

"What are you going to do with it?"

"Give it to the police with all the information we can give them. We have to let them know or we're culpable. Don't worry. They are discreet. I'll attend to everything. You have to be back in Heroldsheid tomorrow. I have friends at the Quai des Orfèvres. The right kind. They'll start looking for Mademoiselle Geiringer tomorrow, and not only in France. Worldwide. What if she wrote the letter under duress and has been abducted, and the next thing we get are the demands of the kidnapper?"

I said nothing.

"You're not saying anything. You don't get my point?"

"The world is a big place."

"The world is much smaller than you think."

"There are so many ways of disappearing and committing suicide."

"Fewer than you realize. What's the matter? Doesn't a worldwide police search satisfy you?"

I said nothing.

"So it doesn't suffice. What more do you want?"

"I want to know what's happened to Clarissa."

"If you're not satisfied with a police search, put a private detective agency on the case. But it must be an international agency. I'll grant you that considering the number of people who disappear in the world every day, a police search might not be very intensive. They have a few hundred thousand more such cases."

"That's just what I mean."

"So you want a private detective agency?"

"Yes."

"Tell me one thing—did you love Mademoiselle Geiringer?"

"No. It's . . . it's something quite different."

"What is it?"

"A feeling of guilt," I said. "You wouldn't understand. I don't know why, but where this woman is concerned, I feel guilty."

"Who says I don't understand? Lejeune understands everything. I know several international agencies. If you like I'll get hold of the best one and arrange it for you. Is that what you want?"

"Yes."

"The best, of course, cost the most. Things like that are expensive. Madame Moran gives you money for your flights, phone calls, hotel bills, plus a little more for extras, and you have your salary as producer. And your salary at Heroldsheid. Do you think you can pay for such an agency?"

"Leave that to me, maître. You'll get the money."

"Where from?"

"I still have a few things. They're mine. I'll sell them. Don't worry."

"I'm not worrying," said Lejeune. "*You're* the one who's got to worry. All right with me. I'll put an international agency on the job. If they're lucky they'll find out how Clarissa committed suicide and where."

"Or if she's still alive."

"We'll see," said Lejeune, and hung up.

I went back to Monsieur Lucien. I said to my good friend, "Here are the keys for my Maserati. Do you think you can sell it for me? It was an expensive car."

"I know, Monsieur Kaven. But why?"

"I need the money. When you've sold the car, please give the money to this lawyer." I wrote down Lejeune's name and address. "And tomorrow you take him Clarissa's letter and answer all his questions, also any questions the police may ask. Nothing will happen to you."

"I'm not worried, Monsieur Kaven. I'd do anything for you. But . . . but you loved your car."

"Oh, what the hell!" I said. "A car's nothing but a heap of metal."

"As you wish, Monsieur Kaven. I think you're doing it out of superstition. Babs will get well, or get better, if you sell your car, the most precious thing you have."

"You're fantastic, Lucien!"

"Why?"

"Because you may be right," I said. "One of the richest men in the world once said to me, 'The great thing about the stock market is that a gambler can win a thousand percent but never lose more than a hundred.' Look upon me as a gambler. I'm betting on an improvement in Babs's condition."

Three days later Lucien Bayard sold my Maserati. I called him from Heroldsheid and he told me that he had given the money to Maître Lejeune. From then on a renowned international detective bureau was working for me. As I look back I think that I did this crazy thing because Clarissa loved not only me, but Babs as well. Because at the time of the conversation with Lucien, I really no longer believed that Babs would ever recover or even that she would improve.

Neither the detective agency nor the police was able to find a trace of Clarissa, dead or alive. To this day I don't know what became of her. She managed her exit very cleverly.

17

On August 27, 1972, a Sunday, I was in Heroldsheid again. I had called Ruth from Paris. She met me at the airport, and when I got past the barrier, she threw her arms around me and kissed me. Then she stepped back quickly. "Come," she said, and walked on ahead of me, in the wrong direction, of course. I caught up with her and turned us the right way.

In the car I told her everything that had happened. She listened silently, then she said, "Not good."

"What isn't good?"

"That she wants to come here and see Babs. The child isn't ready for it. Babs hasn't seen Sylvia for a long time. As far as I can make out, she has forgotten her mother."

"Yes," I said. "But Sylvia is still her mother."

"Not according to your passport. I think the passport office might be able to help us here."

"You don't know Sylvia. She'll raise hell in Madrid. She'll refuse to go on filming. It's maddening! No. That was unfair. It's sad for Sylvia."

"You know," said Ruth, turning into the wrong street, "in the last analysis everybody is more or less sad if he gives a thought to anything beyond earning his daily bread. But none of us could live without that basic sadness, and there can also be no joy without it. What's the matter?"

"You just took the wrong turn."

"I've been here thousands of times and still I make the wrong turn. But we'll get to Heroldsheid. It'll just take a little longer. Or should I turn around?"

"No. We have time."

"But I *will* turn around," said Ruth, furious with herself. "I can't go on like this!" She started to make the turn. "Of course we can't stop Sylvia from coming to see Babs. We'll manage it as cleverly as we can, with the least possible risk to both of them. She can't come to Heroldsheid. I hope she realizes that. Everybody would recognize her." She had completed the turn and was about to drive on when I said, "Stop!"

385

"Why?"

"There's a little animal . . ."

"Where?"

I drew her to me and kissed her, a long kiss. Two cars passed us. Young people, waving and laughing.

"You know," said Ruth, when she finally slipped out of my arms, "in spite of everything, we're very happy, we two, aren't we?"

"Hm."

"And that's bad. Because we'll come to no good end."

"Why?"

"Because we're doing something bad. You belong to Sylvia."

"I belong to you!"

"And it *will* come to a bad end!"

"Yes," I said. "I'm sure it will."

When we finally reached Heroldsheid and I had unlocked the gate, which was always locked on Sundays, Babs came limping to meet me, her glasses on, in a hurry, laughing. "Phil!"

I knelt down and threw my arms around her and held her close. "My goodness, my goodness!" said Frau Grösser. "Whenever I see how much you two love each other I have to think of my Hansl. He was such a loving child too." Hansl hadn't really had time to grow up when he had died, far away in Russia.

Babs had a surprise for me. She showed it to me proudly as soon as we got into the house. The living-room floor was covered with smeared, crushed paper. One piece, though, was lying on the table, and on it lay a flower. With gestures and words that were very difficult to understand, Babs explained that she had picked the flower and what the present was that she had prepared for me. It was cheap paper, and on it, in single printed letters, very shaky but perfectly legible: PHILIP

I knew that Babs had been learning to write for months now, and that she had found it terribly difficult. "Babs! That's wonderful! That's perfectly marvelous! You can write first-rate!"

"Always write—yes?"

"Yes!" I cried, and lifted her up, and she kissed me on the cheek.

18

During the following week I worked from morning to night. There was so much to attend to, above all letters to the various government offices, differences with mayors and nitpicking tax collectors, all of them doing their duty, I had to admit, didn't I?

During these days a group of children, Babs among them, had been given an intensive writing course. It had begun with tracing the letters printed on a board with their fingers. Then they learned the sound of each letter and its place in a word that represented a thing which in turn had to be recognized, together with the word that belonged to it. After endless repetition of various teaching methods, this little group was now ready to write their own names, their addresses, perhaps a few other words.

In the evenings I called Madrid and went on lying. Sylvia really sounded better, more optimistic and energetic, and she attributed all this to the wonderful treatment she was receiving from Joe's friend, Hollywood psychiatrist Dr. Lester Collins.

"You know, Pepito, the man gives me courage. And strength. I'm calm and hopeful again."

"What does he do with you?"

"Oh, he's a psychoanalyst, not a psychiatrist. So we talk. That is—I talk. He listens."

"What about?"

"Whatever I happen to think of. Nothing set. Just associative."

"I see!"

"He's there when I'm filming because I feel more secure when I know he's there, and then, every evening, he gives me an injection."

"What does he give you?"

"Paronthil."

"What is it?"

"A miracle drug. It works like a brief anesthetic, and while it's working, Lester talks to me."

"Who?"

"Dr. Collins. He wants me to call him Lester. He calls me Sylvia. That's good for a relationship of trust."

"And what does *he* talk about?"

"Pepito! You know that as Lester's patient I can't tell anyone what we talk about, not even you. Otherwise the whole narco-analysis wouldn't work."

"I see."

"And when I wake up, I'm happy. I feel so lighthearted, and at last I can sleep. You want to know something? I don't wake up once all night! They have to call me when it's time to get up! Lester is wonderful, Pepito. When you come down next time, he wants to talk to you."

"Very good, Silky."

"And how about my visit? Sometime soon—I don't know exactly when—I have two free days. That's when I'll come. I'll let you know in good time. Then at last I'll see my darling again!"

"Yes, Silky."

"Give her a big fat kiss from her Mommy."

"I will."

"And one for you too." The sound of a kiss in the receiver. "I love you so much, Pepito. I couldn't live through another day if I didn't have you."

"Nor could I, Silky, my love. Good night."

"Good night, sweetheart. Goodnight."

19

"Taking all things into consideration, Hitler wasn't so wrong. He'd have gassed creatures like that."

"You're right. My Paul just graduated from high school. I had to work like a dog to get him through it, my husband being dead and all that. Now he has his diploma but would have to wait till there's a place for him at the university. I've cried my eyes out. So what does he do? He joins the army."

"Yes. Your boy has to join the army and these bums here, the cowards, substitute servicemen they call them now—they

388

live it up. My boy's still in high school. Has to take the train to Nürnberg and back every morning. And these idiots are bused from door to door!"

Friday, September 1, 1972, 10:30 A.M.

The bums, the cowards, our two conscientious objectors, listened unmoved and pretended not to hear. The ones whom Hitler would have gassed were nine children, Babs among them, her friends Jackie and Alois, another child in a wheelchair, a little girl—the children who had practiced and practiced the writing of a few words for such a long time and with so much excitement and enthusiasm.

The place was the new and much too large post office of the little township of Heroldsheid. Everything had been prepared long in advance. The teaching plan prescribed—so did the common sense of every sensible person—that our children be taken out of the safe surroundings of the school into the world around them, be taught how to deal with everyday duties which they would have to face later in life. So for days now they had been making packages, tying them with string—very difficult—and writing their names and Heroldsheid Remedial School on labels. It had taken hours, days, until all the labels had been addressed and pasted on the packages—shoe boxes, cheese cartons, candy boxes, with something enclosed in every one of them.

We had taken the small bus donated by Television Station II. In the post office, they walked, limped, or were wheeled up to the counter to mail their packages. The children helped each other. Every move they made was an achievement. Babs, with her weak left arm, was obviously having trouble, but I didn't help her. All of the children had to learn what a post office was for and how to behave in it.

Three counters were open, women behind two of them, a man behind the third. They knew we were coming and were ready for us. The man called out to the adults whose conversation he had overheard, "Don't you have hearts? What if they were your children? What would you have to say then?"

He was shouted down by the enraged man whose son had to commute to Nürnberg every day by train. The clerk turned to me. "Nothing like this has ever happened before, Herr Norton. Never!"

One of the women cried, "For God's sake have some compassion! These are children, poor children. What kind of people are you, anyway?"

389

"You shut up!" another woman yelled. "We have to support these wretches. For this sort of thing the state throws our taxes out the window! And our own healthy children—does anybody spoil them like this? Like hell they do!"

"Now listen—" I started to say, but a big man forced his way through to me and threatened me with his fist. "You shut your big mouth, yes? The woman's right with every word she says!"

"Be merciful! Behave like human beings, please!" cried a little gray-haired lady in the background.

"And you shut up too, yes?"

Babs clung to me. "So angry. Why?"

A few of the children were crying loudly. I saw a man gesticulating wildly, telephoning from a booth. I could imagine with whom.

The first woman: "I worked as a cleaning woman for years, all for my Paul. He's a genius, that's what he is! If he could study physics, he'd get the Nobel Prize. But they don't have room for him. Nobody helps him. Only these idiots here get taken care of!"

So there it was again, the word "idiot."

"They can't walk, they can't talk, but of course they have to be given every advantage. Our children, no!"

"Afraid . . ." Babs was looking up at me. She was at the counter now, in front of the nice male clerk. Her hands were shaking as she pushed the package across the counter to him. Gave him her money. He gave her the change. She had no idea, of course, if he had given her the correct change or not; none of the children did, more and more frightened all the time.

A siren shrilled, came closer. A VW stopped outside and two policemen stormed into the post office. "Who called?"

"I did," said the man I had seen in the booth. "Do something! We don't have to put up with this sort of thing. These children belong in a home, not here!"

"They have to come here," said one of the policemen.

"Have to? What's the matter with you? You're a policeman. You have to see to law and order!"

"That's what I'm doing."

"Don't make me laugh."

"If it doesn't suit you," cried the mousy little woman with the gray hair, in a paroxysm of rage, "go to East Germany!"

"The gentleman will find the same thing going on there," said the policeman.

"You're a communist! And our taxes are paying for this sort of thing!" screamed the man.

The quarrel among the adults threatened to become violent. The children were forgotten. Fearfully and helplessly they laid their packages on the counter. There they stood or sat in their wheelchairs, their so laboriously packed and labeled packages in their hands.

The second policeman yelled, "You're to behave like rational human beings! This minute! The children can't help the way they are!"

"And what's that got to do with me?" cried a fat woman. "I've been waiting for half an hour because of these cretins," and she pushed Babs. Babs turned, and before I could stop her, screamed and kicked the woman in the shins.

"You started it!" I said, holding her at arm's length. Babs never stopped screaming, and the others began to tune in. Packages flew through the air.

"I'm sorry, Herr Norton," said the first policeman, "but you'd better leave."

"Yes," I said, and gave the conscientious objectors a sign, and we led, carried and wheeled the children to the exit.

"I'm going to bring charges!" Still the fat woman. "You saw her kick me."

"I saw nothing," said the first policeman.

"So you're siding with them? Our police?"

"Come, Babs." I lifted her up.

We managed to get away. The clerks and a few strangers helped us. The rest were still cursing us, the police, or the postal clerks, or were shouting at each other.

At last we had all our children back in the bus. They were very excited. An old woman with a market bag full of fresh vegetables stared at us in astonishment as I was about to get in. She stopped me. I whirled around. "What do you want?"

"My God . . . I . . . you lost something."

"What?"

"It fell out of your pocket." It was the little metal disc Ruth had given me. I said, "Excuse me. Please understand . . ."

"I understand," said the old woman. "The world isn't good."

"Please get in, Herr Norton!" the conscientious objector who was driving us called out. He wanted to get away. I got into the bus and drove off. I stumbled through the swaying car with its screaming children and hit my head. "But on Sunday they all go to church, of course, and they vote for . . ."

"Oh, for God's sake, stop!" I told him. "What good does it do?"

I sat down next to Babs and stared at the little metal disc that had fallen out of my pocket, and read, "Peace to all Men—Gautama Buddha."

20

Thursday, September 7.

"Hello! Hello! Monsieur Norton?"

"Oui. Qui est là?"

"Mon petit chou! Don't you know my voice any more?" Early in the afternoon. I had been called to the director's office. A call for me.

"Suzy! How are you? What's going on? Why are you calling?"

"You mustn't be angry . . ."

"So go ahead and talk—I won't be angry."

"Mon petit chou! I had to call! An hour ago it was decided when I was going to marry my little count." She began to sob. "On . . . on . . ."

"Suzy!"

"On October first. At the registry office and in church. In one of those little rural towns where he has one of his castles. The biggest one! We're going to live in it. *Mon petit chou*—it's in the wilds of Normandy. I have to leave Paris, my beloved Paris!" More sobs. "I'm liquidating everything! On October first I'll be a countess! *Finis!*"

"My heartiest congratulations, *chérie!*"

"Congratulations—shit! I must see you before it happens! I've got to! Just once more, please!"

"But . . ."

"Please, Phil!"

"You know . . ."

"My little idiot of a count has to go on ahead, to prepare everything. What a production! All counts and countesses! I can't take it! I could puke! I've simply got to see you again before I do this disappearing act! If you still love me, just the least little bit, come to Paris before the first, so that I have something I can dream about up there in Normandy."

"All right, Suzy." She had always been so sweet to me, and so helpful.

"Thank you, *mon petit chou*. Thank you. When will you come?"

"I don't know yet."

"The best thing would be just before the first. Then he certainly won't be here. But then I won't have the apartment in the Place du Tertre any more. I'll be staying in his town *palais* . . . but we two, we'll go someplace nice, won't we?"

"Yes, Suzy."

"I knew you wouldn't let me down. You've got my number? You'll call, won't you?"

"Yes."

"Thank you, thank you, *chéri!* Oh, by the way, how's the child? Still a mess?"

"Yes."

21

"Lapses of memory," said Sylvia. "All of a sudden, lapses of memory." It was Friday, September 8, in the afternoon.

The sun's rays were slanting into Sylvia's dressing room through the venetian blinds. She was looking at herself in the mirror as she wiped the makeup off her face with a soft cream. My plane had arrived two hours before, and I had driven straight out to the studio. Sylvia's call had been followed by one from Bracken. New trouble. I'd find out soon enough when I got there. I simply had to come down. So I came down.

"I used to be able to memorize any dialogue, Pepito, right? The longer the better."

"Yes. And now?"

Now I'm starting to forget my lines. I get stuck . . ."

Well, that was indeed good news!

"It's not a catastrophe. Not yet! But I need cue cards or I'm lost. But it's nothing to worry about, really, Pepito."

"Of course not, Silky."

"Julio, Steve, Rod . . . none of them are worried about it."

"But these lapses of memory, Silky ... there must be a reason for them."

"Of course there's a reason for them. Lester explained it to me."

"Lester?"

"Dr. Collins. He says they're a result of the Paronthil injections."

"Great! Joe will love it. The man must be an idiot!"

Somebody came running down the passage outside, a girl, screaming in Spanish that she'd had it, enough, more than enough! Let the producer find somebody else to do the masks if Señor and Señora Patterson were going to pick on her all the time! The whole thing was taking too long anyway!

And it was going to take a lot longer. It was always the same thing—first they all loved each other, then they got irritated, and by the time the filming was over they couldn't stand the sight of each other.

Sylvia was talking. "Lester isn't an idiot. He's a genius! I have him to thank for the fact that I'm so calm and even-tempered in spite of poor, poor Babs, in spite of everything. Joe knows that. I've told him. He had a long talk with Lester yesterday, on the phone, and Lester explained everything to him. Joe understood it all and thanked Lester."

"Thanked him?"

"Yes, Pepito. Where is ..."

"Where is what?"

"Where is what what?"

"You just said ... oh, never mind."

She was wandering aimlessly around the dressing room, didn't know what she was looking for, probably her dress, but seemed to have forgotten.

"So Joe thanked Lester."

"Yes ... you see ... there it is! The mierable rag! You see, Pepito, Lester had to give me injections." She pulled a yellow summer dress over her head. "Had to. To calm me. The first thing he did was narcohypnosis, during which he gave me orders. They made a human being of me again, short hypnosis sessions with Paronthil. Ask anyone you like. I never acted so well, better than ever."

That was true. Rod and Steve had told me the same thing on the phone; they had also told me that they were worried to death about Sylvia, just because of this psychiatrist. They couldn't do a thing about it; maybe I could.

Sylvia went back to her dressing table and began to comb her hair. "Well, I guess he gave me one or two too many, Pepito. You know what I mean? And I did need a lot or Lester would never have gotten me back into condition the way he has." Now she was putting on her makeup, haphazardly. "It's not a disaster, according to Lester. Da Cava says so too. So does Joe. Everybody says so. It's not going to stay that way. It'll pass."

"When?"

"When . . . what?"

"When will it pass?"

"When will what pass?"

"Nothing. Go on."

"Paronthil is a miracle drug, but there are side effects. Then one has to stop it at once. So Lester stopped it. And now comes the actual analysis, Pepito."

"And the lapses of memory?"

"Oh, they'll clear up in a few days. And then . . . where are you going?"

"To have a talk with Lester."

"You don't know where he is!"

"Oh yes I do. He's in the coffee shop. You just told me. Ten minutes ago."

"I did? Yes, that's where he is. He's a marvelous person, Pepito. You have to admire him. I'm sure you will. I do."

"Yes, I'm sure I will."

22

Out in the passage I started to swear, in German. I tore down the steep stairs to the ground floor and came face to face with . . . Sylvia! Not Sylvia, of course. Carmen Cruzeiro, her stand-in. She was wearing a thin short robe and had already removed her makeup.

"Hello, Carmen!"

"Hello, Mr. Kaven."

I stared at her and could feel the blood pulsating through my whole body. Crazy! Absolutely crazy! I had just seen

Sylvia without feeling a thing; now I was looking at her double and could have torn her coat off her and taken her right there on the stairs. Her nipples protruded under the thin material of her robe. I walked up to her and crushed her in my arms. I cupped her breasts and rubbed her nipples. She moaned. Then my lips were on hers. I was beside myself. If anyone came and saw us! I didn't give a damn!

"I'll come tonight." I could scarcely speak, I was so aroused. "At nine."

"Yes, yes!"

She tore herself away from me and ran up the stairs. I saw her legs, her thighs, her buttocks, and could have . . . but no.

It took a while before I could breathe evenly again. And move. I walked into the coffee shop. Dr. Lester Collins was sitting at a table near the counter. He had on white shoes and white socks and was wearing an elegant white suit, blue-striped shirt, and a blue tie, and a silk handkerchief, same color, was stuck in his breast pocket.

"Hi, Lester!" I said.

He looked indignant. "How do you do, Mr. Kaven."

"What are you drinking?"

"Gin and tonic."

I beckoned to the waiter behind the bar and ordered the same. "Congratulations, Lester," I said. I was lusting for Carmen and enraged with this doctor, a dangerous mix of emotions. "You certainly did a good job on Sylvia!"

"My dear young friend," said Dr. Collins, crossing his legs, carefully easing his pants up first. "I must ask you not to call me by my first name and not to be so impudent. Otherwise I shall have to complain about your behavior to Mr. Gintzburger. The reason why you find Sylvia in such excellent condition—"

"You call her Sylvia, she calls you Lester! What's going on here?"

"Complete trust between doctor and patient. Sylvia trusts me implicitly. That she is in such excellent shape may be attributed solely to—"

"In excellent shape? Forgets her lines! Forgets everything! Has to have cue cards!" We were speaking English. The waiter brought my gin and tonic. I drank it down in one go, I was so furious.

"My young friend . . . I don't want you to worry for one moment. As a layman you can't understand what's going on. Through narcohypnosis and with Paronthil I have succeeded in taking Sylvia across the first hurdle: a general calming down. Let's call it 'peace of mind.' This peace of mind may look to a layman like you as if Sylvia were not entirely well mentally."

"That's right."

"Let me finish, if you don't mind, Mr. Kaven. The specialist, however, knows that this is not the case but that he has simply created the basis on which he can uncover what has been forced into the subconscious, and recognize the various complexes." He sipped his drink and jiggled his crossed leg up and down.

"Complexes! Oh my God!"

He chose not to hear what I had said but went right on. "In Sylvia's case it is mainly a regression into an early development stage out of which a new personality can be formed. And that is my job, Mr. Kaven, now that we have arrived at the analysis."

"The hell it is!" I said. "Get out of here, and fast! I've had it with you!"

He readjusted his silk handkerchief. "Mr. Kaven, it is the express wish of my old friend Joe that I continue treating Sylvia. He knows of my many successes. In any case, we can do without you at this point much better than without me. I would therefore advise *you* to—as you so delicately put it—get the hell out of here." Another sip, a tug at his handkerchief, foot swinging up and down. "I refuse to sit at the same table with a primitive type like you."

"Then I suggest *you* leave."

"All I would do is go to the phone, call Joe, and tell him of your unqualified impudence. I have the feeling that Joe would also recommend that you leave." I stared at him. "Go, Mr. Kaven. After all, you have to think of your future too." I got up; my hands were fists. "And it would definitely be the end of you, Mr. Kaven, believe me, if you were so much as to touch me, shall we say accidentally?"

So I left, and called Joe, and told him how I felt about the whole thing, and he assured me that Lester was a genius; he was the only one who could get Sylvia through the picture; my role was a secondary one for the time being. I was to be sensible, please, and apologize to Collins. After all, we were one big happy family, weren't we?

"And when I think that all I'd have to do is tell about Babs . . ."

"Nobody'd believe you, Phil." Oh, that gentle voice! "Babs is enjoying perfect health in a private school in the States. If necessary we can name the school and let the reporters see Babs."

"What in God's name . . . Babs is in Heroldsheid!"

"That isn't Sylvia's Babs. That's *your* Babs. Sylvia's Babs is perfectly healthy, as I already told you and as I shall tell everybody, and if necessary I can prove it!"

"But that's impossible!"

"You have no idea, Phil, what is possible. Did you think we've been sitting back and twiddling our thumbs all this time? We can produce a perfectly healthy Babs anytime, if required, and you'd look very bad, Phil, very bad."

"What have you done?"

"That's none of your business. You must think we're fools, Phil. And now go back to my friend and apologize," and he hung up.

I was sure he wasn't bluffing. Something had happened, something I knew nothing about, and I wasn't to know for a long time—not until the catastrophe. And then there really was a completely healthy, happy Babs in a private school in the States, however insane that may sound. So . . . I went back to the coffee shop and told Lester, who was smoking a pipe, that I was sorry, and apologized. He nodded amiably and looked past me. He didn't say a word.

23

"You're just too excited. Believe me, Phil. It's an old story. My God, when I look at you, a man like you . . . it's nerves, that's what it is. Relax, darling, please. Just relax completely and you'll see. That'll do it."

"I've relaxed three times and it didn't work three times. I'm sorry, Carmen."

"Sorry? Don't ever say that! Come, I'll . . ."

"No. I don't want that. Besides, it wouldn't work either."

It was about 10:30 that same evening, and I was lying stark naked, bathed in sweat, on Carmen Cruzeiro's broad bed in her apartment. Only a lamp with a red shade was lit. Real cathouse illumination. Carmen, naked like me, was crouched beside me, trying bravely to smile and stroking me gently.

"Leave me alone!"

"I . . . I just want to help you." She seemed truly worried.

"I swear, Carmen, nothing like this has ever happened to me. Today, in the studio, I could have raped you, I felt that crazy. I haven't slept with a woman for months!"

"That's just it." She had lit a cigarette. "Abstinence, nerves, so much work and responsibility. You're a stallion, I tell you! I've seen it happen so many times."

"Nonsense! I'm impotent. That's what's the matter. A little early in life."

"Stop it!" she cried. "You and impotent! Madonna! I've never seen"—she put it her way— "one that size in my life! My poor darling. My sweet darling. Let me help you!"

"No!"

"Please! I . . . I feel so guilty!"

"Now don't you start!"

She was a good girl, she really was. She talked about everything under the sun, brought me something to drink, then a vibrator and a few other items, and gave a little performance, all to help me. But she couldn't help me. Nothing could. I felt absolutely ridiculous. In the end I couldn't stand it any longer and took a bath and got dressed. When I came back into the bedroom, Carmen was sitting on the bed, the vibrator in her hand, weeping. It was too much. I kissed her hair and said a few nice things, but she went on crying and choking over every word, saying how ashamed she was, that she had failed . . . *she!*

24

It was 2:30 A.M. when I finally got back to the Castellana Hilton, and I could hardly walk, I was so drunk. I'd filled up in three different bars, and in one of them the girls had stolen my money. The night clerk looked at me curiously as I gave him my key. We had taken an adjoining suite. Bracken had attended to that. Alleged reason: While filming Sylvia needed absolute quiet and liked to retire early. That was why we now had separate bedrooms.

I took the elevator up and removed my shoes. I walked through our two salons on tiptoe, to Sylvia's bedroom, pressed down the door handle . . . the door was locked. I listened, and could hear Sylvia snoring. I went back to my bedroom, took a quick bath and went to bed. But I didn't sleep more than three hours that night.

Sylvia found me up and dressed at 7:00 A.M. She was dressed too. We breakfasted together and chatted and joked, all nonsense. And of course we talked about Lester. I told her I thought he was simply fantastic. Then I drove her to the studio in her Rolls-Royce and escorted her to the Pattersons. Carmen was there. All of us greeted each other cordially; Carmen was especially friendly to Sylvia, to me too, but in a way only I could notice.

I stayed in Madrid two days, played the producer, was on the lot all day, and the reporters and photographers came again. I admitted my helplessness about Collins to Rod, Steve and da Cava. They were furious.

At the Hilton, Sylvia and I ate in our rooms. Then Sylvia kissed me on the cheek or forehead and withdrew to her bedroom. She always locked the door.

When I left, Sylvia saw me to the airport; the reporters and photographers came along and stayed until the last minute. Sylvia told me that she was going to have her first analysis session with Lester that day. "It's going to be fantastic, Pepito, isn't it?"

"Of course."

This conversation took place at the bottom of the boarding ramp of the Super-One-Eleven, and they were still taking pictures.

"And please, Pepito, arrange my meeting with Babs. You said you would. We're not going to be in Madrid much longer, and later I won't be able to come to Germany. I get my two free days while I'm still here."

"I'll arrange everything," I said, "only we've got to be very careful . . . you realize that, don't you?"

"I'll be very, very careful, Pepito! Oh, how I'm looking forward to my darling!"

In Paris I drove to Le Monde, changed to Philip Norton—how many times had I done that?—and flew to Nürnberg.

Ruth was at the airport, and when we were finally seated in her VW, we kissed, and this kiss made me forget everything that had happened since I had left her—the fiasco with Carmen, my defeat at the hands of Dr. Lester Collins, Joe's unbelievable story of a healthy, happy Babs in an American private school. I told Ruth about it. She said, "They've done something to protect themselves in case the truth leaks out."

"Yes, but how could they? Where could they find a healthy Babs?"

"They have a lot of money, don't they?" said Ruth. "If you have a lot of money, anything is possible. They have to protect themselves. We'll find out what they've done, you'll see. But the best part of everything—Babs is in such a good phase! Better than I've ever seen her. I'm going to drive out to Heroldsheid with you. I want to be there when you see how much better she is, and so suddenly!"

She drove off. For a while I said nothing, just looked at her until she noticed it and laughed helplessly. "It's getting worse all the time!"

She turned the car around, and both of us laughed, and I thought, Oh, my God, how I do love this woman!

25

"How many apples are there on the table?"

"One."

"Right."

Frau Phol, the director's assistant, was in a classroom with Babs. Ruth and I were standing in the background. Frau Phol laid a second apple on the table. "And how many apples are there now?"

"Now two," said Babs.

Ruth took my hand. I knew that the next question was the critical one. In spite of all efforts Babs had not yet learned to count beyond two. Months of work, in vain. Whatever methods Frau Phol tried—and she tried many—in this respect there was no progress. Now she laid a third apple in front of Babs, who was wearing a jumper dress and her training

401

glasses and was concentrating like mad. Frau Phol said, "Wonderful, Babs, just wonderful! Yes, those were two apples. And how many are there now when I add another one?"

Babs was silent. She closed one eye and looked at us helplessly. We remained expressionless.

"Well, how many are there now, Babs?" asked Frau Phol, stroking Babs's head.

"Ah ... ah ..."

"But Babs, it isn't so difficult. At first there was one, then there were two, how many are there now?"

Babs began to sway from side to side with exertion. Any moment now I was afraid she would burst into tears. But suddenly she laughed. She picked up one of the apples, looked at Frau Phol, grinning from ear to ear, and declared, "I'll eat this one, then there'll be two again!"

"Bravo!" cried Frau Pohl.

"Bravo!" cried Ruth.

I was speechless.

"What did I tell you?" whispered Ruth.

I nodded, then I walked over to Babs and lifted her up, and she clung to me and kissed me over and over again, wet kisses, and I kissed her. What happiness, your honor, what joy! Babs was so much better! She couldn't count to three but that didn't matter. Because in a first visible and audible effort *she had thought logically.*

26

"Stop, *mon petit chou,* please stop!"

"Just once more!"

"But *chéri* ... no ... please!"

"Be quiet!"

I was beside myself. Never in my life had I experienced anything like this. Three hours, with a few brief pauses, and I couldn't seem to get enough. Suzy, my sweet little whore with the long blond hair, firm little breasts, and the most beautiful behind I had ever seen in my life, lay still. A while ago she had been just as insane as I. Now she didn't move. But her quiescence only made me wilder than ever! When I reached the next climax I thought my head would burst wide open. I sank down on her and lay still, panting. Then I rolled to one side, and for a long time neither of us spoke, lying there in her ornate bed in the ornate town *palais* of Suzy's little count. Thursday, October 28, 1972, around 10:00 P.M.

At last Suzy got up and filled our champagne glasses again, the finest cut glass. The silver ice bucket stood on her bedside table, and the champagne was Dom Pérignon 1961, one of the best vintage years, your honor. I took my glass, we drank, and Suzy said, "What's the matter with you, *chéri?* I've never known anything like it! Not even with you! You're . . . you're absolutely mad!"

I said nothing but emptied my glass and held it out to her, and she filled it again. I drank and was overwhelmed with a boundless sense of relief. I was *not* impotent! I think on that evening in October I performed as I'd never performed before, and I have quite a few good performances behind me, your honor.

In Orly the crew of the Super-One-Eleven was waiting, and here I was, sitting on the count's bed after the wildest three hours of my life, courtesy of his countess, drinking his champagne. I put on a pair of his silk pajamas because I felt cold, and Suzy ran naked into the bathroom. I could hear her washing herself, and I went after her and washed too.

"A while ago," said Suzy, "I thought I was going to die. And I thought: Let me die now, dear God, please!"

"It's the most beautiful death," I said. "Something I've always wished for when the time comes. Since all of us have to die, that's the way I'd like it to happen."

"So would I," said Suzy. I had brought along our glasses, and there she sat on the bidet, and drank, and I drank and put my glass down, and Suzy laughed.

"What's so funny?"

"My count doesn't want to die."

"Not that way?"

"Not any way. Not at all!"

"What do you mean, not at all?"

"I told him once—when he was boasting about how immensely rich he was—I told him, 'Whatever you've got, you can't take it with you.' So what do you think he said? 'If I can't take it with me, then I just won't die!' And he really meant it!"

"No!"

"I swear he did! He . . . he . . . oh God, when I think of him I could puke. The way he's built . . . must have had rickets as a child, and his head, much too big. So degenerate!"

"But so rich!"

"Yes," said Suzy. "So rich!" After which both of us were silent for a while, I in the count's dressing gown, Suzy in her short terry-cloth robe.

"I'll never forget tonight," she said finally. "Not if I live to be a hundred."

"Neither will I! And you know what gives me special satisfaction?"

"What?"

"That I'm wearing his clothes and drinking his champagne, in his bed. It really is a rather wonderful thing to cuckold a man!"

"Oh, *chéri,* what a shame it is that in this world the right people never get together."

"True."

"But anyway, now I've got something to dream about for a long, long time. May I write to you?"

"Whenever you like."

"We mustn't just forget each other."

"No." I looked at the clock—marble and gold. "I've got to go."

"Just fifteen minutes more, please, please!"

"I can't, *chérie!*"

I stayed another hour.

27

"What do you mean by 'let yourself go'?" said Rod Bracken. "That's supposed to be a good thing, isn't it, doctor? You told me yourself that during one of your sessions Sylvia practically unzipped your fly and tried to rape you!"

Dr. Lester Collins turned purple. That morning he was wearing a brown suit, a beige silk handkerchief in his breast pocket, beige shoes, a brown tie and a beige shirt. He smelled of eau de cologne. It was 9:00 on October 29, a Friday, and we were sitting in the salon of my double suite in the Castellana Hilton. After what had happened, Bracken had called me to Madrid.

Rod and Collins were sitting opposite me, watching me breakfast. Sylvia had left for the studio some time ago.

"I forbid you to use such vulgar language!" said Collins.

"Well now, did she or didn't she?"

We had just put through a call to Hollywood. It was still night there, I had pointed out to Rod. "So we'll wake Joe up. If Collins wants to leave today, Joe's gotta know, and know why."

The call came through, and I took it. Joe's voice, sleepy, annoyed, upset and therefore breathing stentoriously through his nose. "Have you gone crazy, Phil? Do you realize what time it is?"

I handed Lester the receiver. "Go ahead. You tell him, Lester."

It didn't bother him in the slightest. He greeted his old pal heartily and said he would never have called if circumstances hadn't forced him to do so. After which he said, "Look here, Joe, you know how often I've helped you out. . . . That's right. . . . Well, something's happened here. . . . The transference was too strong and I'll have to stop the therapy. . . . No, oh no! I'm not abandoning a sick woman. Our beloved Sylvia is fine, but I can't go on with the sessions. . . . No. Do keep calm, Joe. I assure you it won't happen again. I'm taking off at noon. Please don't worry. . . . Well, of course, Joe. I'm terribly sorry about it, but Sylvia evidently lost control. She . . . Yes, yes, the same thing that happened with Lore. You remember? And I had to stop treatment then too. After all, there are ethical considerations. The two gentlemen here—Kaven and Bracken—don't seem to understand that. But you do, I'm sure. I've brought Sylvia to her senses again, and now you speak to Mr. Kaven," and he handed me the receiver.

And there was Joe's gentle Bible salesman's voice. "Phil, my boy, if you or Bracken have anything to say, any single little thing, against this remarkable doctor, you're in trouble. Got it? Lester has worked a miracle, and not for the first time."

"Okay, Joe," I said. "If that's the way you feel about it."

"I don't feel any way about it—I know! And tell Rod to keep his big mouth shut or he'll get to know a quite different side

405

of me. Lester is . . . is . . . is a saint! We should thank him on bended knee! What just happened doesn't mean a thing. A too-strong transference."

"But Joe! Sylvia actually had—"

"Not another word! What do you know about psychoanalysis? Not a damn thing! So shut up. Nothing like this will happen again. Lester has cured her!" He hung up.

"I apologize, Dr. Collins. Mr. Bracken apologizes. We're terrible sorry that we were so rude. But after all, we're laymen. I'm sure you understand."

"What the hell . . ." Bracken was speechless. "Sylvia humped him, didn't she?"

"Shut up!" I said.

"But she told me so herself, and he corroborated it!"

"It's all okay, says Joe. Can happen, says Joe. Dr. Collins is a saint. He has cured our beloved Sylvia!"

"You've got to be out of your mind!" cried Bracken. "And what if our beloved Sylvia now starts fucking every electrician in sight?"

"You're to keep your big mouth shut," I said, in a mixture of rage, amusement and fear. "Sylvia's not going to do anything like this any more. Isn't that right, Dr. Collins?"

He let me ask the question twice, then he said arrogantly, eyebrows raised, "Of course not. Not after therapy with me."

"But then there's one more thing that interests me," I said.

"And that is?"

"What does it mean: 'too-strong transference'? I'm an idiot; still, I'd like to know."

The man didn't have a spark of humor in him; all irony was lost on him. He leaned back, pressed his fingertips together and held forth with great dignity: "The transference was too strong on both sides; the relationship too close. That can happen. You see, I have an exceedingly strong personality. This is not entirely thanks to myself. Because of the many years of treating exceptional people such as actors, especially actors, I have been constantly exposed to exceptionally strong personalities. And this reflected on me, and my personality became increasingly impressive. In some cases—Joe knows this—the transference between patient and myself was so strong that such incidents as took place between Sylvia and myself happened. Is that clear?"

"No," said Bracken.

"Absolutely clear," I said, and suppressed the question

whether Lester had succumbed to similar strong transferences with the same results when treating male stars.

"So now I shall go and pack," said Collins. He rose. "Who gets my bill?"

"We do. Syran Productions."

Collins looked at us as if we were vermin and withdrew without another word. For the first time in my life I saw Rod Bracken struck dumb. I went on eating. It was quite a while before he spoke. "He didn't even shake hands!"

"Why should he? As far as he's concerned, we're cretins. You didn't even get what he was talking about."

"Neither did you! It's a lot of bullshit, everything he said. And what if Sylvia starts fucking around again?"

"She won't."

"Who says so?"

"Dr. Lester Collins. A saint."

"God bless us," said Bracken. "You she won't let in, but he can hump her! Boy, oh boy! And for that he sends us a bill!"

"A fat one! You can depend on that," I said. (When I finally got the bill and saw just how fat it was, I had to sit down. A saint indeed, Dr. Lester Collins!)

"And now finish your breakfast," said Bracken.

"What's the hurry?"

"Sylvia's waiting. Her two free days are due anytime now. I've had the wildest scenes with her. She won't go on filming if we don't let her go. Can she see Babs now? At last?"

"Frau Doktor Reinhardt is against it. She has misgivings about it."

"But Sylvia won't go on filming!"

"I told Frau Doktor Reinhardt."

"And what did she say?"

"She said, 'Then let her stop filming.' You see, all she cares about is keeping up the halfway good condition Babs is in right now. She doesn't give a damn about our twenty-five million."

"I'll tell her a thing or two!"

"You'll tell her nothing."

"Why not?"

"Because she has thought of a way for Sylvia to see Babs."

Bracken slapped me on the shoulder. "Well then, everything's okay, man. Why look so grim. Sounds great."

"Because I'm afraid."

"For Sylvia?"

"No. For Babs."

28

And then it happened. October 6, 1972, on a Friday afternoon. Ruth and I were on the ground floor of the Sophienkrankenhaus in Nürnberg, looking out a window into the park behind the hospital. We could see old trees, bushes, a jungle gym, and other mechanical toys. Babs and psychotic little Sammy (Malechamawitz, the Angel of Death) were climbing on the jungle gym. A warming sun was shining. The loud voices of both children rang out in the clear air. I could see spiderlike silver threads floating in the breeze. Indian summer. Then I saw something else and could feel my stomach heave. Sylvia was walking out into the park!

Sylvia!

During my last visit in Madrid I had explained exactly how she was to behave when she came to Nürnberg. I had told her that Ruth, under protest, had agreed to take Babs away from Heroldsheid for a short period, and bring her to the clinic. But there was nothing very exceptional about that. Heroldsheid children were brought to Nürnberg when a test was necessary that couldn't be done at the school. Babs had come back here frequently. In Madrid I had come to an agreement with Sylvia as to the day and time of her arrival. She was to leave Paris on a Lufthansa plane, wearing a blond wig and dark glasses. At my request,—Chief of Police Sondersen had been so good as to see to it—Sylvia would not have to show her passport or identify herself in any way, either in Paris or in Nürnberg. Ruth and I would be waiting for Sylvia in this hallway, so that she could watch Babs playing in the park, as we were doing now. Anything more than that Ruth considered too risky. Sylvia had agreed to everything, and now . . .

"Dammit!" I cried. "Wait! I'll catch her!"

"No!" Ruth's tone was icy. "Stay here! If you interfere now it can only make matters worse. That woman is capable of anything!"

"She deceived us! She lied to us!"

"She is a mother," said Ruth. Her hands were fists as she pressed them against her chest.

I opened the window a crack and could see Sylvia approaching Babs slowly, from behind, so that Babs couldn't see her. Now she was quite close. I could hear her call out, "Babs!"

Babs, up on one of the rungs, looked around, surprised. She stared in obvious astonishment at the woman with the blond hair and dark glasses, dressed with exaggerated simplicity. Ruth had turned pale.

Babs slid down from the jungle gym and began to back away from Sylvia. Sammy stayed hunched where he was. Sylvia rushed up to Babs, fell down on her knees in front of her and burst into tears. She held Babs close, Babs struggling to free herself, and kissed and caressed her, and cried so loudly that we could hear it in the stillness of the afternoon, "Babs! Babs! My sweetheart! My darling Babs!"

- Babs was scared to death. She began to scream with fear. "Why are you screaming? Oh God, it's me, my darling, your Mommy."

"Not true!" screamed Babs.

"But it is, Babs, it is!"

"No! No! No!" Babs howled, and the Angel of Death remained crouched on the jungle gym like a big bird, motionless.

"But yes! You just don't recognize me! Look, Babs! Look!" And she tore off her wig. "Don't you recognize your Mommy now?"

"Not Mommy! Not Mommy! Go away!"

"But my darling, my treasure, what's the matter with you? Don't you recognize me?"

"Go away! Go away! Away!" Babs screamed, struggling out of her mother's embrace. But Sylvia clung to her child. Then, with an ear-piercing shriek, Babs tore herself free and kicked her mother, striking her so that Sylvia fell full length on the grass. Babs, completely out of control now, as in her worst days, kicked and stomped on her screaming mother, spat on her.

"Quick!" said Ruth. I vaulted out the window, Ruth followed, and we ran across the field to Babs and Sylvia. Ruth took hold of Babs and dragged her back to the house, Babs shrieking as if possessed. Sylvia was lying on the grass. "What . . . what . . . what . . ." she stammered.

"Why didn't you keep your promise?"

"My child . . . Pepito . . . it's . . . it's too terrible. Babs didn't recognize me! She is mad . . . mad . . ."

"*You* are mad!"

"Let me go!"

"You're coming with me!" As I picked up her wig, I looked back at the house. A lot of faces at the windows, curious, startled.

"I . . . I'm not going with you, you bastard!"

I jerked her to her feet and forced her to walk on ahead of me. We reached the open window. I lifted her up. She clung to the window frame, screaming hysterically. I slapped her hands, hard, and she let go of the frame and fell on the tiled floor in the hall. I climbed in after her, looked around, saw a utility closet and dragged her over to it. A walk-in closet full of junk. I pushed her into it, and she fell on a heap of rags and sacking, panting, sobbing.

"If you make one more sound I'll . . ." Yes, your honor, I would have struck her, my fist in her face. She saw the expression in my eyes and knew I would do it, and began to whimper softly.

"Smashed!" I said, the hatred in my voice threatening to choke me. "You've smashed everything, you realize that, don't you? You've scared a *healthy* child to death! Why in God's name did we ever let you come?"

Sylvia slipped from the junk heap to the dirty floor. I let her lie and went on upbraiding her. Then the door opened. Ruth. She closed it behind her. "What's going on here?"

"There." I pointed.

Sylvia recognized Ruth and stammered, "I'm sorry . . . I'm terribly, terribly sorry. I didn't know . . . I didn't realize . . ."

"Yes," said Ruth.

"What is the matter with Babs?"

"You must leave here at once, Frau Moran."

"What is the matter with my child?"

"Your child, Frau Moran, has suffered a serious relapse, and I have no idea what will happen next. We have had to give her a strong sedative. She is asleep."

"I must see her!"

"No!"

"Please, please, dear Dr. Reinhardt!"

Ruth said gently, "Frau Moran, that is impossible. Absolutely impossible. I just told you—you must leave. Quite apart from Babs, the whole clinic is in an uproar. You must leave Nürnberg, right away."

"How?" I asked.

"A helicopter will take Frau Moran to Munich. From there she can take the next plane to Paris."

410

"A helicopter? What helicopter?" asked Sylvia, confused.

"The emergency helicopter. On the other side of the park. You can't see it from here. I got in touch with Chief of Police Sondersen. He has notified the police in Munich. The crew of the helicopter know nothing. You must put your wig on again and your dark glasses. Nobody will ask questions."

"I won't do it!"

"You will have to do it, Frau Moran."

"I'm not leaving here!" She was screaming again.

"Take these," said Ruth, and gave her three white pills.

"What are they?"

"Tranquilizers."

"I won't take them! You . . . you lied to me. Babs didn't recognize me. Babs is insane! And always will be! Her face . . . those glasses! I want to die!"

A young doctor stuck his face in. "The helicopter, Frau Doktor."

"Thank you," said Ruth, and the doctor withdrew.

"Just sit quietly for five minutes, Frau Moran. You'll begin to feel calmer. Then you can leave. Mr. Norton will go with you. He will take you back to Madrid. And you will be given no more permission to see Babs until *I* say so. Have you understood me, Frau Moran?"

No reply.

"I asked—have you understood me?"

"I understood you. I . . . I'm sorry for what I've done."

"So am I," said Ruth. "But for Babs's sake."

"What is wrong with Babs? What will happen next? Have I done something that . . . that will retard her recovery?"

"I don't know, Frau Moran. What happened today has caused a severe relapse. I shall do everything in my power to restore Babs."

"Thank you . . . thank you, Frau Doktor."

Ruth said nothing. She looked out the window of the utility room, which also had a view of the park. I followed her gaze. Sammy, who called himself Malechamawitz, was still sitting, as if petrified, on the jungle gym.

29

The two women in the Rolls-Royce looked like identical twins. They both had the same big black eyes with the dark shadows of exhaustion; both had the same blue-black unkempt hair. Both the same high forehead, narrow nose, the same beautiful mouth with its bitter expression of deprivation and poverty, the same ocher-tinted skin, wrinkles, crow's feet around the eyes and on their faces, lines that only great suffering and anxiety can trace. Both were wearing the same gray kerchief that barely covered their hair, the same ragged gray blouse, dirty brown skirt. They both had the same ocher-tinted legs, and dusty feet in clumsy wooden clogs. They looked exactly alike, with one exception—one of the women was alive, the other was dying. Dying by her own hand because she wanted to die, in fact would die unless there was a miracle now, as the Rolls reached the Avenida Pio XII.

October 9, 1972, a Monday; 12:36 on the dashboard clock. The heavy car sped southward. I was at the wheel, and I never took my hand off the horn for a second. With its headlights on, the Rolls with the two women—the one alive, the other dying—raced down the streets.

"Babs . . ." Rattled breathing from the back seat. My lips tightened.

"Faster!" said Bracken. He was sitting in the back, Sylvia's head on his lap; Carmen Cruzeiro was sitting beside me. "Faster, you motherfucker!"

I pushed the gas pedal all the way down. The car surged forward as if it wanted to take off, up a hill and down the other side, past donkey carts, cars, trolley buses and taxis. A hundred, a hundred and five, a hundred and ten kilometers, and the needle never stopped moving up. Suddenly Carmen began to pray in Spanish. "Stop that!" I told her.

"But I'm so frightened!" Carmen stammered, in perfect English.

"So am I," I said. "Well . . . there we are!" The sound of

police sirens behind us. In the rearview mirror I could see two traffic cops on their heavy motor cycles, still quite some distance away but gaining. "The sons of bitches!" said Bracken, looking out of the back window. "God, are we ever lucky!"

A hundred and fifty kilometers . . .

Now the Rolls was heading for the skyscrapers on the Avenida America, the cold sunlight mirrored in their hundreds of windows. Beggars begging, vendors selling lottery tickets, bird men selling colorful birds, men and women on the curbs, looking horrified as we flew by. For a split second I saw them, then they were gone. Brakes screeched. A car almost ran into us. I'd driven through a red light.

"Pray!" Bracken yelled. "Tell the Mother of God to help us!"

And Carmen started to stammer her prayer again. "Holy Mary, Mother of God . . ."

The sirens were louder now and closer. The police were moving in on us fast. A lot of cars ahead of us were moving over to the side and stopping. "Babs . . . Babs . . ."

"It's all right, honey! Everything's all right," said Bracken, her head on his lap.

"Babs . . ."

"Yeah, baby. Don't talk now . . ."

Bracken stroked her head gently. The kerchief fell off. I could see everything in the rearview mirror. Sylvia looked ghastly. Spots all over her distorted features. Her body jerked up abruptly, fell down again heavily. Foam on the lips of Sylvia Moran, who was shooting the film she had dreamed of filming all her life, a life she had evidently decided to end a few minutes ago, at noon on this October 8, 1972, in her trailer on the vast lot of Estudios Sevilla Films. . . .

30

Grusha—Sylvia Moran—had appeared on the set at 7:30 A.M., on time. She looked exceptionally pale and nervous. I had brought her here from the Castellana Hilton, in her Rolls, directly behind us the four detectives from Seven Stars in two cars. It was very cold. A lot of people were already setting up what would be needed for the first scene. As I stopped the Rolls in front of a Caucasian peasant house, built four months ago, I saw Carmen. Sylvia and I got out.

Since the horrifying events in Nürnberg, Sylvia hadn't spoken to me. Not a single word had passed between us, not one word! Sylvia was pleasant and calm with the waiters, the other actors staying at the Hilton, with Bracken, da Cava, Steve, everybody. She spoke to them normally, as if nothing had happened. She only didn't speak to me. In our suite she locked her salon door right away, banishing me in my suite. It had been an eerie weekend. I had called Ruth and told her everything. She had said, "It will pass . . . I hope."

"How is Babs?"

"Not good."

"Bad?"

"Very bad. I don't want to talk about it. But call me again, yes?"

"Yes, Ruth, yes . . . I love you, Ruth."

"And I love you."

Sylvia was neither irritated nor angry with me, just calm, eerily calm and remote. Her attitude was friendly and polite, but mute. We ate in the restaurant. She didn't speak. We sat at the bar, drove out of the city on Sunday, took a walk. She didn't speak. She didn't even ask how Babs was. This morning she had been ready and waiting for me when I knocked on her door. I drove her to the studio. Not a word.

Now as we got out of the Rolls she staggered, just for a moment. I ran to steady her; she pushed me away. A bell rang; the rehearsal stopped. Bracken, Steve and da Cava hurried over and greeted us. Sylvia said good morning to them in a perfectly normal voice. The detectives remained scattered behind us.

Director da Cava, wrapped in a woolen blanket, looked at Sylvia, his expression concerned. All three men knew what had happened in Nürnberg. "Would you like me to call a doctor?" asked da Cava.

"Nonsense! What for? I'm all right. I just felt dizzy for a moment."

Bracken was wearing a thick overcoat. "What do you mean—dizzy? Were you going to fall?"

"Something went wrong with my eyes. In my head. But it's gone."

Steve turned up the collar of his tweed jacket. "I can see

you're not feeling well. Phil can take you back to the hotel. We can shoot the dance scene today, can't we, Julio?"

"No problem," said da Cava.

"I won't hear of it." Sylvia shook her head, her long blue-black hair flying. She was wearing a green pants suit and a leopard coat. She had on no makeup. "It's this damn wind!" she said. "It's driving everyone crazy. I'll take two pills and I'll be fine."

"It isn't the wind," said da Cava.

"Oh, do stop it, Julio!" She was getting angry. "Leave me alone! I'm getting my period, that's all. A good thing all the close-ups have been shot. It's just that I'm getting my period, so please calm down!"

Nobody said anything.

"So . . ." She shrugged. "Where are Katie and Joe?"

Katie and Joe were waiting in the makeup room. "All right, then," and she walked away from us to the studio building. We watched her go. She disappeared through the entrance. Now Katie and Joe and the wardrobe mistress would work on her. It would take an hour before she was ready for the most important scene of the entire picture—shot 512.

31

SHOT 512. THE COURTYARD OF THE PALACE. EXTERIOR. DAYTIME. Camera on dolly. Three-meter-high view of the entire scene. The noose that had been intended for Azdak dangling (not sharp) in forefront throughout the entire scene.

Azdak drinks for a long time, the fear of death in his eyes as he surveys the scene around him. The wine takes effect. More blood seeps out of his wounds as the miserable clothes he is wearing redden in various spots. Azdak wipes the blood off his face and belches before he starts to speak . . .

That was what I was reading in the shooting script lying on my knees. I was sitting on a prop in front of a floodlight, Carmen beside me.

I put the script aside and looked up at Azdak-Crown, at the whole scene: the actors, the stage crew, the technicians, the dolly with the cameraman, Roy Hadley Ching, the most famous cameraman in Hollywood, sitting on a small stool behind the heavy camera, saw his three assistants, technicians, prop men—at least three dozen people—saw Sylvia . . . and heard Azdak speaking Brecht's words:

"Plaintiff and defendant! The court has listened to your case but cannot see clearly enough to decide who the real mother is. Therefore I, as judge, am obliged to *choose* a mother for the child. I'll make a test. Shauwa, get a piece of chalk and draw a circle on the floor."

The actor playing Shauwa draws a circle on the floor.

"Now put the child in the center," Azdak cries.

Shauwa stands the boy, who is smiling at Grusha, in the center of the circle.

"Plaintiff and defendant! Stand beside the circle!"

The actress playing the governor's wife and Sylvia step up to the circle.

"Take the child by one hand, both of you. The true mother will have the strength to pull the child out of the circle."

Just as in the Brecht play, the Second Lawyer now steps forward and speaks: "High Court of Justice, I object. The fate of the great Abashwili estates to which the child is heir should not depend on such a doubtful duel. And what is more—my client is not as strong as this person, who is accustomed to physical work."

Azdak waves him aside. "She looks well fed enough to me. Pull!"

The governor's wife grabs the boy and draws him out of the circle. Sylvia has let go. She stands there, aghast. The First Lawyer congratulates the governor's wife. "What did I say? Ties of blood!"

Azdak says to Sylvia, "What's the matter with you? You didn't pull!"

Sylvia replies, and I can see Carmen's lips move as she speaks the words with her, "I didn't hold on to him." She runs up to Azdak. "Your honor, I take back everything I said against you! I beg to be forgiven! If only I could keep him until he can speak all the words! He only knows a few."

Oh God, I thought, what a woman she is! This wasn't acting, this was living experience! If only she can hold out!

While I am thinking this, Azdak is warning Sylvia not to

influence the court, and the test is repeated. Again Sylvia lets go of the boy. In despair she cries, "I brought him up! Shall I tear him apart? I can't!"

Azdak rises. "And in this manner the court has established who the true mother is." He turns to Sylvia. "Take your child and be off! I advise you not to stay in the city with him!" And to the governor's wife, "And you disappear before I fine you for fraud! Your estates are forfeited to the city. They'll be converted to a playground for the children. They need one, and I've decided it'll be named after me: Azdak's Garden!"

The governor's wife faints and is carried out by the lawyers and the adjutant. Grusha stands motionless. Shauwa leads the child to her as Azdak says, "For I'll take off this judge's gown now—it's got too hot for me. I'm not cut out to be a hero. But I'll invite you to some dancing on the field outside, as farewell."

The boy beams at Sylvia. She looks at him for quite a while very seriously, then she smiles at him, takes him by the hand and begins to walk slowly to the exit of the palace, the camera following her until she is out of range, then both stand still. The camera goes on shooting for a few seconds so that the cutter will have space for the next splicing. Then da Cava's voice: "Cut!"

Nobody moved. "How was it?" he asked.

"Great!" Roy Hadley Ching replied. "Better than the first time."

A voice over the loudspeaker. "Sound too! Better than the first time."

"Thanks, all of you," said da Cava.

And suddenly the extras and actors, the stage crew and technicians, approximately two hundred people, began to clap and cry in rhythm, "Sylvia! Sylvia! Sylvia!" And Carmen clapped and cheered.

Sylvia stood there, expressionless, bowed and left the set quickly, walked fast to her trailer. The door closed behind her.

32

I slid off the prop I'd been sitting on and lifted Carmen
down. The set was swarming with people. Da Cava was
giving directions with a bullhorn. The next take was being
prepared. I saw Bracken walk over to Sylvia's trailer and go
in, closing the door behind him. He evidently wanted to
discuss something with her. I walked over to the trailer too,
Carmen following me. We had never talked about that disastrous night again. Perhaps you can understand, your honor,
why Carmen had become so strongly attached to me ever
since—I can't. Behind us da Cava's assistants were yelling
directions; the camera, on its dolly, was being moved back;
everyone was busy. Carmen and I had got to within five
meters of Sylvia's trailer when the door flew open and Bracken
looked out, his face white, his lips trembling. "Phil!"

"What's the matter?"

"Come quick!"

I ran, he jumped out of the trailer, I looked in. Sylvia was
lying on the couch, gasping, choking, her eyes rolled up, her
lips parted, foam on her mouth. "She's taken poison," Bracken
whispered.

I tore over to the Rolls, and drove over to the trailer. Got
out, helped Bracken put Sylvia in the back, he getting in
after her. I ran around the car, stopped, ran back, grabbed
Carmen and forced her into the seat beside mine. "What—"

I didn't answer, got into the car, slid behind the wheel and
stepped on the gas. Nobody had noticed a thing, not one of the
many people busy in the distance. Not even the detectives! I
got to the exit, 12:36 according to the dashboard clock.

33

The Rolls raced through the streets. The two motorcycle policemen were driving ahead of us now, their sirens howling. When they had finally caught up with me, a few words and they had realized at once what was going on. The clock read 12:56, 12:57, 12:58 . . . "There!" screamed Bracken.

The two policemen signaled with their left arms. I stepped on the brake and turned left. A white corner building. The hospital! The police officers stopped at the entrance and ran into the San Rufo Hospital, Bracken behind them, yelling, "Stretcher! Stretcher!"

People on the street stopped and watched Sylvia being lifted out of the car by orderlies in white. Nobody said a word. A beggar woman, all in black, lifted a little boy who looked starved high over her head so that he might see better.

"Get going!" I told Carmen, and shoved her ahead of me. Before she had a chance to realize what was happening, she was in the hospital, in a long passage, in a large elevator in which the orderlies were taking Sylvia, lying motionless now on the stretcher, up to the first floor. I knelt down beside her. Spoke. Don't remember what. Senseless stuff. First floor. The orderlies rolled the stretcher out again and along another passage. A doctor came running, lean fellow, black hair. "I am Dr. Molendero," he said, in English.

"Philip Kaven. This is Miss Moran. She has taken poison."

"When?" asked the doctor, who was already leaning over Sylvia and starting to examine her.

"Ten minutes ago . . . fifteen!" Bracken handed the doctor a phial. "There. She took the whole thing."

"Good God!" exclaimed the doctor when he read the label. "Emergency! Move! Fast!"

The orderlies lifted the stretcher and hurried down the passage as fast as they could. The doctor wanted to follow them, but I grabbed his arm. "What did she take? Will she pull through?"

"I can't say."

"What are her chances?"

419

"Not good, with what she's taken. Please let me go!" Dr. Molendero pushed me away and ran off after the orderlies. Looking back, he said, "Go in there, Room 111."

"Yes, doctor." I turned to Bracken, who was trembling. "Go downstairs, talk to the policemen. This thing mustn't get out! Drive to police headquarters with them. To Lejeune's friend. If necessary get hold of Lejeune!"

"Okay, Phil!"

He ran down the stairs beside the elevator. I looked at Carmen. She was sobbing. I took her into Room 111 with me.

34

"Hello? ... Hello? ... Steven Stars? ... This is Philip Kaven, calling from Madrid. An emergency! Give me Mr. Gintzburger, on the double!"

Twenty minutes had passed. In Room 111, everything was white—the table, chairs, walls, the tiled floor, the telephone. Carmen was sitting beside the window, which looked out on a bare garden. I was sitting at a white desk. "Hello? Hello? Joe?"

"Hello, Phil," in his gentle Bible salesman's voice. "You seem to be in Madrid. Where in Madrid? What's happened?"

"Something terrible, Joe! I'm in the San Rufo Hospital." I noticed that I was trembling, just like Bracken. I stammered as I reported what had happened.

There was such a long silence that I asked, "Are you still there, Joe? Did you understand what I said?"

"I understood perfectly, Mr. Kaven." So now it was to be Mr. Kaven. No more Phil.

"So, what next, Joe?"

Again a long silence. Then, "Who knows about this beside Bracken?"

"Her stand-in."

"And where is she, Mr. Kaven?"

"Here. With me. I took her along because . . ."

"Who else, Mr. Kaven?" I could hear his heavy breathing.

"Two police officers. The doctors. Several doctors. The staff here . . ."

"Well now, there is such a thing as medical discretion," the honeyed voice said slowly, thoughtfully. "As for the police officers . . ."

"I sent Bracken out to them right away. He's driven to police headquarters with them. Just called. Lejeune's taking over. The whole thing will be hushed up."

"What are Sylvia's chances of pulling through, Mr. Kaven?" Deep breathing.

"Really, Joe . . ."

"What are her chances, Mr. Kaven? I want it in percentages."

"Joe! It's only just happened!" Carmen was watching me, shocked; she seemed to realize that I was at the end of my rope.

"I can't give you any percentages!" I shouted. "I haven't seen any of the doctors yet! I . . ."

"Don't," said the pious, gentle voice on the other side of the Atlantic and across a whole continent.

"Don't what?"

"Don't shout, Mr. Kaven. I don't like it. I'm not shouting at you. Would you say that the chances are great that Sylvia will die?"

"Very great. Yes, Joe. I'm afraid so."

"Hm. But as long as she's alive, the filming must go on. I'm sure that's quite clear to you, Mr. Kaven."

"Yes. That's quite clear to me. But . . ."

"No buts, Mr. Kaven. As long as Sylvia hasn't been pronounced dead, the shooting has to go on. Have you understood me, Mr. Kaven?"

"Understood you . . . yes . . ."

"I see that Sylvia did this insane thing after her experience in Nürnberg."

"Who told you about Nürnberg?"

"Bracken. He called me right away. Why didn't you call me, Mr. Kaven?"

"I . . . because . . . I . . ."

"Let's drop it." Deep breathing. "We'll talk about that later. You can be assured, Mr. Kaven, that if and when Sylvia pulls through, we'll talk about it."

"Joe, I'm only . . ."

"If Sylvia dies, the ABA insurance must pay. You know that, I am sure, Mr. Kaven."

"Yes, Joe."

"And who was it—after all we'd gone through with Sylvia—who insisted on a suicide clause, Mr. Kaven? And who finally succeeded, at an astronomical price, in finding an insurance company that would pay?"

"You, Joe . . . you were the one."

"Yes. I was the one. And who was against it because it would cost such a horrendous amount? Who made a fuss and said it wasn't necessary, Mr. Kaven?"

"I did, Joe. I'm sorry, Joe. You're a great man, you really are!"

"Unfortunately surrounded by too many idiots. No, no . . . the ABA must pay if Sylvia dies. The twenty-five million is safe. But the film—what happens to the film if Sylvia . . . passes on?"

"I . . . I don't know, Joe."

"How much has been filmed?" Can you at least give me *that* in percentages?"

"Joe! Sylvia may be dying at this very moment, and you . . ."

"In percentages . . . how much?"

And all the time Carmen was staring at me. The receiver slipped out of my hand. I picked it up again.

"Pull yourself together, Mr. Kaven. How much have you filmed? More than half?"

"Yes . . . no . . . yes, of course . . ."

"So . . . how much? The percentage?"

"Fifty-five. Perhaps sixty."

"How much with Sylvia?"

"I don't know. I really don't know. I'd have to see the material. It's at the processor's or in the cutting room. *You* must know that!"

"But I'm asking *you*. I'm shooting a few other films, you know, Mr. Kaven."

"A lot with Sylvia, of course. We began with the exterior scenes . . . the crowd scenes . . . the scenes in the palace. Nothing in the mountains yet, but all the location shooting around Saragossa. We were going up into the Pyrenees on Tuesday . . ."

"The crowd scenes . . . Sylvia is in them, naturally?"

"Of course. In practically all of them."

"Up front?"

"Naturally."

"Facing the camera?"

"Of course."

"So we can ditch the most expensive scenes if Sylvia dies. Great! Really great!" Deep breathing.

"Listen, Joe ... just a minute!" I looked at Carmen and told her, "Please wait outside for a minute, yes?"

She nodded and left the room.

"Joe? ... Joe? ... I just sent Sylvia's stand-in out of the room."

"You did, Mr. Kaven? How interesting!"

"And now you listen to me for a change, Joe!"

And Joe Gintzburger listened to me.

35

The same day, 5:35 P.M.

I drove the Rolls up to the entrance of the Castellana Hilton. Bracken helped Sylvia out. The garage man took the Rolls down into the garage after I got out. The staff greeted us cordially, smiling, as polite as ever; they were all great admirers of Sylvia and loved her. We were given the keys to our suites and went first to Sylvia's apartment. She was wearing her green pants suit and leopard coat. She threw the coat nonchalantly on one of the tables in the salon. Bracken was grinning.

"So how about it, baby?" he said. "Didn't everything go off first rate?"

Carmen Cruzeiro sat down on one of the chairs. Her hands were trembling. She couldn't speak. "Courage!" said Bracken, still beaming. "You'll make it! No doubt about that."

"Rod's right, Carmen."

"Of course I'm right! This is your big chance. You won't get anything like it again!"

He patted her cheek. She looked up at him silently. She was still speechless. There she was, in a super-elegant salon, the little foreign-language secretary, dressed in Sylvia's pants suit, sitting beside Sylvia's leopard coat, wearing Sylvia's shoes, all of which we had fetched from the lot or brought back with us from the clinic. She looked at me, then at Bracken, then at me again, her gaze unsteady. Her eyes took in the silk wall covering, the pictures on the wall, the marble mantelpiece, gilded and silvered, the exquisite furnishings, the desk beside the window; and there was the bedroom, and a bathroom, and a dressing room! Carmen was struck dumb.

Bracken laughed. He walked into the dressing room, where every built-in closet had its own mirror, and opened all the doors. Dresses, furs, gala gowns, lingerie, shoes . . . shoes . . . Bracken opened the wall safe—we'd taken the key with us—and a small part of Sylvia's jewelry glittered. Carmen stammered, "No . . . please, no! I've never been in a suite like this in my life! I'll do the wrong thing! I know I will! And it will all come out!"

Bracken walked over to her, sat down on an arm of her chair, put his arm around her. "Nonsense! I'll be with you all the time! We're going on location now, for three weeks. First up into the Pyrenees. It's very lonely up there. From now on *you'll* be in front of the cameras, acting as Sylvia Moran!"

"But I can't do that!"

"Sure you can! Why not? Phil and I have talked about it often, haven't we, Phil?"

"Yes, indeed," I said.

"What have you talked about?"

"That you're loaded with talent, girl! We were there during all the lighting rehearsals, whenever you had to stand-in."

"You *were*?" Carmen couldn't believe it, wanted to believe it.

"Really," I said, and thought, Yes, we watched you, you poor devil, and it was pitiful how untalented you were! Oh damn damn damn . . . I'll have to let da Cava in on this, the actors, the technicians, but they'll keep their mouths shut. Why? For money. On the chance that we'll be able to finish the picture if, by a miracle, Sylvia pulls through. And if she does, Joe will think of something, the old bastard. He was crazy about my idea, thank God. That Mr. Kaven bit had had me feeling queasy, but now he was eating out of my hand. Now I could threaten and blackmail everyody: Either you do as I say, or you'll never make another picture with Seven Stars! Meanwhile Bracken to Carmen, "You've just gotten into pictures, baby. No doubt about that!"

"Yes . . . but not as a second Sylvia Moran! Not as her . . . her successor if . . . if she . . . oh God!"

"Maybe she'll pull through. Doesn't matter. Of course not as her successor," said Bracken. "As a star all on your own! With me as your agent, if you like—you won't find a better one! Let's look at the worst that can happen—Sylvia dies. Who knows—maybe you go on playing Moran. Or you play

424

Sylvia in a picture about her life. Sensational, baby, simply sensational! And gold! Pure gold!"

"I could never do that!"

"Of course you could. And now just try to imagine what a sensation it could be when this picture is released! Something that's never happened before! During the filming the star died and her stand-in went in for her and nobody noticed the difference!"

At which point I tuned in enthusiastically, "I'd like to see the person who wouldn't come running to see that picture!"

And Bracken; "Suddenly you'll be famous! People will be thinking: Is that still Sylvia or is it Carmen? And now let's look at the other side: Sylvia survives and can finish the picture. By that time, though, they'll have seen the rushes with you, and they're no fools—they'll say: Get this Carmen Cruzeiro over here! We've got to have her! I swear, baby, whichever way the cookie crumbles, you're with Seven Stars right now, and I'm your agent! And in a few years I'll have made a big star of you, in a few years you'll be on top!"

The phone rang. "I'll take it," said Bracken. "I told them at the studio that I was in conference with Sylvia." He lifted the receiver. "Bracken . . . yes, doctor?"

I could scarcely breathe. I ripped off my tie, opened the top button of my shirt. Bracken was listening. Then he signed off and put the receiver down. Looked at us. Said, "It's still a matter of life or death. They're doing the best they can. They'll be glad if they can pull her through the night." Suddenly he began to laugh and looked at Carmen. "How about that, doll? Good news, wouldn't you say?"

Carmen stared at him, wide-eyed, and I hoped to God she wasn't going to fall flat on her face. I walked over to the bar and quickly filled a glass. "No! I don't want to!"

"Please, sweetie." I pressed the glass to her lips.

"I . . . I must ask you something, Mr. Kaven."

"Ask away!"

"What happened in Nürnberg?"

"In Nürnberg?"

"Yes. During your call to Mr. Gintzburger he said that she did this insane thing after what happened in Nürnberg. It was so quiet, I could hear what he said. Forgive me, but what happened in Nürnberg?"

"No idea!"

"But Mr. Gintzburger spoke about it, so did you."

"You must have misunderstood, Carmen."

"No I didn't! Why did Señora Moran want to commit suicide after that?"

"I've told you—I have no idea. But *I'll* commit suicide any minute now. This is a madhouse! I don't know, Carmen, I really don't know, so help me God!" I said, filled my glass and drank the contents down and thought: I hope I don't choke on the miserable lie!

36

Seven-twenty P.M. I was knocking on the door of Rod's suite. I was wearing a tuxedo.

"Come in!"

There he was, sitting at the desk in his salon, in his shirt sleeves, the jacket of his tux slung over the back of a chair, writing, and crushed pieces of paper lay on the floor all around him. "Hi, Phil."

"Good evening, Rod. What are you doing?"

"What do you think? Writing the obituary."

"What obituary?"

"Sylvia's obituary! The minute she croaks it's gotta go out." Beside him a silver tray and a bottle of whiskey, an ice bucket, soda, and a glass half full. He finished his drink and poured himself another. "What have you been doing?"

"I was with da Cava and the people on our list. They've all promised not to say a word about the whole thing. Nobody on the lot saw anything, not a soul. They were happily shooting the dance scene. The detectives are in the know too."

"Great!"

"I've notified AP and UP and AFP and a few other agencies that Sylvia's stand-in has had a heart attack and is in the San Rufo Hospital. The people working on the lot also think that's what happened."

"Good boy!"

"Any more news about Sylvia?"

"Not yet."

There was a konck on the door. "Yes!" yelled Bracken.

Enter Carmen Cruzeiro in a mauve evening dress, the shoulders bare, made up exactly like Sylvia, wearing Sylvia's jewelry. She closed the door and stood there looking embarrassed. Bracken had risen; now he whistled through his teeth. "Boy, oh boy! What a dish!"

"You said I was to get all dressed up for the gala."

"I'm ravished! You're absolutely stunning! Better than Moran! A lot better!"

"But I'm scared to death! If anybody speaks to me or asks me to dance, or asks me anything . . ."

"Phil will be there, and da Cava, I'll be there, the detectives too, if necessary. We have a table reserved just for us. In the meantime, Phil has notified all agencies that you're in the hospital. Heart attack. Fortunately you have no relatives. So everything's okay. Nobody'll come near our table. Just let them photograph us! Lots and lots of photos! We'll go back upstairs the minute we've eaten and have a drink or two here . . ."

"In her dress . . . I'm wearing her clothes, her lingerie, her jewelry . . ." Carmen shivered.

"Sure you are! And why not? It's what you've got to do," said Bracken. "Try to grasp it at last—you *are* Sylvia Moran. From now on you're staying at the Hilton with Phil next door and me on the other side. Nothing can happen to you, sweetie!" He went up to her, sniffed. "You're even using her perfume!"

"You said I should use it!"

"I'm enchanted!" Bracken threw his arms around her and kissed her on the mouth, quite a long kiss. It wasn't a friendly kiss.

"Please . . . let me go!" She pushed him away.

"Look here, you little bitch, if you think . . ." this child of the Bronx began to say, when there was another knock at the door.

"Yes!" yelled Bracken.

No answer.

"I said yes!"

Not a sound.

Bracken walked over to the door and swung it open. A boy, a page, couldn't have been more than sixteen, stood outside, a silver tray in his hand, an envelope on it. "Excuse me, please, Señor Bracken. Telegram for Señor Kaven. But he isn't in his suite. I thought he might be here. I'm sorrv . . . oh, good evening, Senor Kaven."

I walked over to the boy, who was holding out a pen to me. I looked at him, surprised. "What's that for?"

"You're to sign for it, please."

"What on earth do you mean?"

"You're please to sign that you've received it."

"What sort of nonsense is this? I've never had to sign for a telegram before!"

"But you have to sign for this one, please, Señor Kaven, or I'm not to give it to you."

"Says who?"

"The office. They received their instructions in a second telegram. You'll understand when you read this one, they told me. It asks for confirmation by signature. Please, Señor Kaven—it's not my fault."

"Of course not." I patted the boy on the head, signed, found some change in my trouser pocket and gave it to him.

"Gracias, Señor, muchas gracias!" He withdrew, looking relieved.

I went back into the salon, opened the envelope, took out the telegram—a cable, actually—and sat down at Bracken's desk. Bracken stood behind me and read right along with me. I didn't notice it at first.

SEVEN STARS HOLLYWOOD 9 + 10 + 0950
FROM: JOE GINTZBURGER
TO: PHILLIP KAVEN HILTON HOTEL MADRID
RALPH LORDER VICE PRESIDENT SEVEN STARS FOR EUROPE AND MIDDLE EAST ARRIVING 10 + 10 + PM IN MADRID + FILMING MUST NOT BE STOPPED ACCORDING TO PARAGRAPH XV111/3 ABA INSURANCE UNLESS ZERO REACHED + LORDER HAS FULL POWER OF ATTORNEY TO SUBSTANTIATE OUR TELEPHONE CONVERSATION + UNTIL LORDERS ARRIVAL FOLLOW THESE DIRECTIONS IMPLICITLY + WITH DA CAVA MUST GO THROUGH ALL MATERIAL SHOT TO DATE AND DECIDE WHAT CAN BE USED IN CASE OF ZERO IF ZERO NOT ALREADY REACHED + REPRESENTATIVE OF ABA ARRIVING 10 + 10 AIR FRANCE VIA PARIS INSTRUCT BOOKKEEPING TO HAVE ALL RECORDS READY FOR INSPECTION + IN CASE OF ZERO STOP ALL WORK + REPEAT + STOP ALL WORK + FLYING TO NEW YORK IN AN HOUR + ANABELLE ATKINS BROADWAY PLAY WEAK RECEPTION + ATKINS AVAILABLE WITH CONVENTIONAL DAMAGES FROM NOVEMBER ONE IN CASE OF ZERO + SEVEN STARS STATES AS PRECAUTIONARY MEASURE THAT THEY WILL DECLARE SYRAN PRODUCTIONS RETROACTIVELY LIABLE IN CASE OF ZERO + YOUR ACCEPTANCE OF THIS CABLE COUNTS IN COURT AS PROOF THAT YOU HAVE RECEIVED IT + GINTZBURGER + STOP + + STOP + + +

I stared at the cable. "The pig!" said Bracken, standing behind me. "*Best* was too much for him!"

The telephone rang again. Bracken took the call. I put my ear beside the receiver and heard, "Dr. Molendero speaking. Mr. Bracken?"

"Yes, doctor, yes!"

"Your patient regained consciousness five minutes ago."

"Wonderful!"

"Not so wonderful," said Dr. Molendero. "In cases like this the patient often regains consciousness before the end. She has asked for a priest."

37

"I can't go on."

I find this sentence in my diary. I have to resort to it again, things happened so fast at the time. I mustn't confuse you, your honor, so I'll tell what happened chonologically.

Between October 9, the day of Sylvia's suicide attempt, and October 27, 1972, the following events took place. Summary from my diary:

October 10, 1972. Ralph Lorder for Seven Stars and John Steeple for the ABA Insurance Company arrive. I start discussions with them immediately. Don't understand what it's all about. Without da Cava, Steve and Rod I'd be lost. But have to play the boss. Everybody helps me.

John Steeple is an aggressive rat, Ralph Lorder could be Joe's younger brother. Big disagreements right away. All Lorder wants is to put the entire blame on Syran Productions, that is to say on *me,* to get Syran Productions *out* and hand over the entire production to Seven Stars (a fat profit!). The man from ABA is determined to pay nothing. Much shouting and swearing. Endless transatlantic phone calls. Discussions last until 4:00 A.M., until all of us are ready to drop. Results: nothing. All this interspersed by calls to the clinic. Dr. Molendero: Sylvia still hovering between life and death. Call Ruth secretly. Tell her everything. She is horrified. How is Babs? After long hesitation: very bad. More aggressive than ever. Destructive. Raving. Can't be subdued. Newspapers in Madrid and other countries report the heart attack of Sylvia Moran's stand-in, Carmen Cruzeiro. Print pictures of Carmen as Sylvia at the gala. Nobody suspects anything.

October 11 to October 15, 1972. Still Madrid. My departure delayed. More hassling with Seven Stars and ABA. Transatlantic calls with Joe. Disagreements and insults . . . with $25 million involved, not surprising. On the Estudios Sevilla Films lot they're filming as if nothing had happened. Sylvia still critical. Ruth: Babs's condition gets worse and worse, almost as serious as when she was first brought in. All progress wiped out. I have to stay in Spain.

October 16 to October 23, 1972. Still filming. We have finally managed to come to an agreement with Lorder and Steeple. Off to the Pyrenees. Location in the central massif. Here the snow already lies deep. Way up near the glaciers, a miserable little village consisting of twelve peasant houses— that's our set. For days on end we freeze. By now Carmen is positive that she is to be the Sylvia Moran of tomorrow. Acts until exhausted. Terrible! No talent! But of course we praise and applaud her at every opportunity. Bracken has already told her what salary she can command when she gets to Hollywood. The cameras freeze up frequently. Snowstorms. We have to use mules. Every morning and evening I drive a jeep across icy roads to the nearest town where there are telephones. Sylvia's condition is improving, then her life is in danger again. Ruth: no improvement in Babs's condition. A new alarming symptom: She keeps trying to run away. Ruth and I love each other. We tell each other that over and over again. When I report to Bracken and Carmen how serious Sylvia's condition is, Carmen starts to scream. We have to hold her mouth shut. Bracken slaps her. By the way, he's sleeping with her.

Sylvia: out of danger. Babs: a little calmer, condition slightly improved. Still trying to run away.

Carmen greatly changed. Behaves like a hysterical diva. Believes every word Bracken tells her. Has no idea that we're really filming without her! When she is on, there's no film in the camera, ever since the first takes with her reached Hollywood and Joe instructed me on the phone not to waste another foot of film on her. Scenes with Grusha will have to be reshot as soon as Sylvia is equal to it. He calls me Phil again. Of course we tell Carmen that they're crazy about her in Hollywood. Her "star" behavior becomes increasingly hard to take, but it doesn't bother Bracken with his tough hide. He goes on sleeping with her; she worships him. On October 19, Dr. Molendero reports Sylvia is up and about again. Only one more day in the hospital necessary for observation. On October 21 I get Sylvia out of the hospital late at night. We drive up into the mountains. How is Babs? Fine again, I tell her. Find out that she called Ruth before asking me. Ruth told her the same thing, thank God! Sylvia loves me and nobody but me, her Pepito. . . .

Call Rod and arrange for the switch Carmen-Sylvia. Everything goes smoothly. On the night of October 23 I drive Sylvia up to the little village with the twelve houses beside the glacier. She moves into an empty room until the one Carmen is using is free. Because on the following morning we are going to stage Carmen's return. I drive her down to the village the same night, only to bring her back up to our location the next morning as returning from Madrid, completely recovered from her heart attack.

October 24, 1972. First shooting day for Sylvia since her suicide attempt. Carmen is her stand-in again. Doesn't like it. Tears. Bracken consoles her. A lot of whispering. I can imagine what he's promising her. All the scenes we "shot" while Sylvia was away have to be shot again. Sylvia insists. Bracken explains to Carmen: We have to let her film them for contractual reasons, even if time is lost, even if—this to Carmen—the takes with her were enchanting! Carmen now hates Sylvia. Doesn't dare to show it. Is the impatient stand-in again. Lives in the absolute certainty that now the way to Hollywood lies open to her.

I'm not needed any more, so—off to Nürnberg. Babs's condition so far improved that I can take her back to Heroldsheid.

38

On Friday, October 27, toward evening, I drove Babs from Nürnberg to Heroldsheid with the little bus. On my arrival at the Sophienkrankenhaus she had greeted me with no sign of pleasure. She seemed indifferent to everything, as if still under the influence of medication. Perhaps she was, and Ruth hadn't wanted to tell me. I tried to draw Babs into a conversation. Impossible. I turned on the radio to some music to see if that would cheer her up, but she beat on the radio with her hands and I turned it off. Just as I was about to leave the main highway and take the narrow dirt road that led to the school, Babs gave me a push. "What is it?"

"Peepee."

"But we're almost there!"

"Peepee! Now! Now!" She began to hit the dashboard with her fists, her expression furious.

"Surely you can wait a few more minutes!"

She bit my right hand. I swore and stopped. "Out! Out!" she cried. In the next moment she had jumped out of the bus and stumbled into the woods. It was raining very hard and was almost dark. The wiper tick-tocked monotonously. I waited. Five minutes. Ten. Babs didn't come back. I sat there staring out at the rain and watched the windshield wipers swish back and forth. It was very cold, I noticed, when I let down the window on my side and called out to Babs.

No answer.

I tried again.

No answer.

Condemn me, your honor, but this is what I thought: Friday evening. Nobody at the school any more. The staff left long ago. And Babs has run away again. And I'm supposed to look for her, in the dark woods, in the rain, in the cold. After all I've gone through these last days! I yelled her name again. It rained into the bus. There was no answer. I went on shouting her name, and the more I shouted, the angrier I got. In the end I was in a towering rage. I couldn't take any more,

432

it was just too much. I'd had it! Suddenly I understood all the people I'd despised because of their negative attitude toward handicapped children. They were right. My friend Hitler! Let these idiots die, the sooner the better!

I thought suddenly: And what if you stop shouting for Babs? What if you go to bed now—God knows you're tired and have gone through more than enough—and don't wake up again until tomorrow morning? And open a window in Babs's bedroom so that people will believe you when you say she ran away during the night? She kept trying to run away from the clinic. If I do it . . . she'll never find her way back to the school alone. She'll flounder around out there in the woods, fall, get up, fall, stay down. Exhausted. And, God willing, die in the night.

I rolled the window up again, put the bus in gear and drove on to the locked gate. I had the key. I parked the bus where it was always parked, then I locked the gate again and walked in the rain to our little house. First I opened all the windows, because the air was stale, then I closed them again, except for the one in Babs's bedroom, and went to the kitchen and made some tea and drank it with a lot of rum. Then I got up, undressed, washed, put on my pajamas and lay down on the living-room couch. The rain beat on the roof. And Ruth was in Nürnberg, in the Sophienkrankenhaus, and Sylvia was in the central massif of the Pyrenees, working in the snow, and I was here, and Babs was somewhere out in the woods and would soon be dead. . . .

39

I stood it for an hour, not quite an hour. Then I got up, dressed again, found the raincoat and heavy rubber boots that the houseman had left behind, along with his lantern, and left the house. At first I walked, then I began to run. A fence that ran from the iron gate, was flattened in places, so I was able to get directly to the woods. I shouted, "Babs!" Ten times. Twenty times. Fifty times. I was getting hoarse. There was only one thing on my mind—to find Babs. I had to find her! I was responsible for her! I was not a murderer. I didn't want to be a murderer. "Baaabs!"

I went on calling her name and cursing her and praying that I might find her. The trees were old, the woods dense. First I looked along the side of the road where Babs had gotten out of the bus. But I didn't find her there. She must have run deeper into the woods, into the goddamn woods! "Baaabs!"

I went on shouting, slipped, fell, ran my hands and face bloody against the branches of trees and shrubs. Staggered on. Fell. Got up again. Reeled onward. And then, suddenly, as if in a dream, I heard Ruth's voice. "Babs! Babs!" And decided I was going mad. "Baaabs!" And "Babs! Babs!" Ruth's voice answered.

About twenty minutes later I came to an open field. In the dark between the tree trunks I thought I could see a light. It wavered up and down, disappeared, was there again. And then Ruth was standing in front of me in a cloth coat that was wet through. No hat. Her hair was dripping wet. She was carrying a lantern on a pole. "You?" I stammered.

"Yes."

"What are you doing here?"

"I wanted to visit you tonight. A surprise." She sneezed. "And as I was driving down the road I could suddenly hear you shouting. I thought Babs must have run away again and you were looking for her. So I got out, and—Phil . . ."

"What is it?"

She raised her lantern and pointed, and I could see a rotten old feed trough and Babs asleep in it, so fast asleep that she didn't wake up when we called her name and I lifted her out of the trough.

"Get her into the house fast," said Ruth. "Thank God! If we hadn't found her she might have frozen to death!"

Yes . . . she might have frozen to death in the night. . . .

40

"Ruth?"

"Yes, Phil?"

"I lied to you."

"I know."

"What do you know?"

She had given Babs, who was half awake, a hot bath and rubbed her down, now she was putting her to bed. I had given Ruth a pair of my pajamas and socks and slippers, and a robe. It was warm in the house. I stood there, watching Ruth covering Babs, who was fast asleep again. She took Babs's training glasses out of her robe pocket and laid them on the little table beside Babs's bed.

"What do you know, Ruth?"

"I know that you're at the end of your strength, Phil."

"I can't go on!" I said.

She nodded, and turned to face me. "On the way home you let Babs get out . . ."

"She insisted on getting out. She wanted to peepee."

"Or she wanted to get out and run away again, and you thought, The hell with it, let her go, and drove on."

"Yes," I said. "Yes."

"I know," she said. "I know, beloved."

"I wanted to kill her."

She nodded and walked up to me.

"I really did. Because I couldn't take it any more. My hand—look—she bit me."

Ruth looked at me without saying a word.

"I left her in the woods and drove here. I wanted to go to bed and sleep. I left the window in her room open. In the morning I'd have said that she ran away during the night."

"I know."

"You know?"

"Everything. Also that you couldn't bear it and got up again and went to look for Babs."

"How . . . how did you know?"

"Come," said Ruth, and took my hand, the one Babs hadn't

bitten. We left the room, leaving the door open a crack, and walked into the little living room.

"But Ruth! A potential murderer!"

"Yes, Phil."

"So?"

"So I love you. "You didn't kill, Phil. You can't kill. You are a decent human being. . . ."

41

After that we were quiet for some time. The night wind blew around the house. Babs was fast asleep. Finally Ruth said, "What you are doing is such a comfort to me, beloved. Everything you have done since I met you. Just because you are you. We love each other; we deceive Sylvia, but I can't seem to feel guilty about it. I must be amoral."

"You are wonderful!" I said.

"I am going to stay with you tonight, because I know everything you've been through. But I'm not staying for your sake alone, but because I need you just as much as you need me. I have hesitated for a long time; now I see clearly. You and I, who are looking after Babs, have the right to do something for ourselves too. . . ."

As my lips touched hers, the bell in the living room rang. You see, your honor, I could only phone from the director's office. In the case of calls at night—and they were usually emergencies—there was a bell in our little house that rang when there was a call in the director's office. It had never rung since I had been here. "I must go and see what it is," I said.

Ruth and I quickly put on the heavy raincoats and boots again. The office telephone never stopped ringing, and the bell in the living room didn't either. We ran to the school through the wind and the rain. In Hallein's office, I picked up the receiver, said, "Norton," then handed Ruth the phone. "The hospital."

She listened, said a few words, nodded, spoke again, her face expressionless. Finally she said, "I'll be there in half an hour," and hung up. "I must leave, Phil."

"What?"

"A child—just brought in. Critical."

"But . . ."

"Please, Phil . . ."

"Yes," I said, "of course."

We left the school, Ruth dressed, then we were standing in front of the house. She wanted to go to her VW, which was parked on the right. Of course she turned left. I ran after her, took her arm and led her to her car. She looked at me sadly. "You're angry."

"No."

"But disappointed."

"I'm not. You have to go to this child. I'm not disappointed." That was a lie.

"Thank you," she said. "Thank you for being so understanding. I was really going to . . ."

"I know."

I ran and opened the gate for her VW. Ruth was looking straight ahead. I hoped she'd wave or at least glance in my direction, but she didn't. I realized that in her thoughts she was already with the child in Nürnberg. Suddenly I felt dreadfully tired. Ruth loved me, yes, but she probably loved her sick children more. It was a sad recognition, because I could see what our future was going to be like. To love your fellowmen . . .

42

According to my diary:

As long as Sylvia was filming in the Pyrenees, I couldn't contact her. Not until November 9, a Thursday, when Sylvia and the whole crew were shooting in the vicinity of Saragossa, was I able to reach her at her hotel. I told her that Babs was much better, which happened to be true. Her medication had been changed, and she was calm, friendly and patient. Frau Bernstein and Frau Pohl gave her a lot of attention, and she was close to the condition she had reached before this last relapse. She was being given music therapy, she was modeling in clay, strange figures in a special sort of clay that didn't harden fast. She never mentioned Sylvia.

But Sylvia talked about herself whenever I called. She told me how strenuous the work was. They really were the most difficult scenes, fortunately the last. Then Sylvia and all the actors would have to proceed at once to Hollywood to record the final sound track in the studio.

Ruth came to Heroldsheid almost daily to see Babs. She never stayed very long. We never mentioned that night again. Sometimes we kissed.

I was kept very busy, visiting rich industrialists, tax offices, government offices, the mayors of various cities. Dr. Hallein loaned me his car for these trips. Frequently I came across people with understanding and returned to Heroldsheid with donations, large and small, but just as often I got into heated arguments and was rudely turned down. Twice I flew to Saragossa.

Sylvia had recovered completely and was acting better than ever. We had a double suite in Saragossa too, and Sylvia always locked her door. She was friendly and grateful, but she wouldn't let me touch her. And the city was in an uproar with us around. The police had to protect Sylvia from her fans, and there were framed photos of the two of us in shop windows, amid lingerie and pig's knuckles! Carmen was ever present too. We chatted like good old friends. She was very optimistic. Bracken was still assuring her that she had a great future in films. She was still sleeping with him.

Friday, November 24, 1972, my second visit to Saragossa. The film was finished. Some members of the American staff had already flown on ahead with the cameras and other equipment. That Friday I said goodbye to Sylvia. With tears in her eyes she thanked me for everything I had done for Babs and was still going to do. That was at the Madrid airport, late evening. She and Bracken were flying to Los Angeles, nonstop. Sylvia stuck something in my pocket. Later I saw that it was a check, a very large sum. For the telephone calls, which would now cost a lot more. I got into Sylvia's Super-One-Eleven with her because a gaggle of reporters and photographers had turned up as usual, and the impression had to be given that we were flying to the States together. I left just before takeoff via an emergency exit.

Far out on the airfield, in total darkness, stood the four detectives Joe had sent over to protect Sylvia from herself.

One of them said to me, "Mr. Bracken gave instructions to drive you to Barcelona. At night. So that no one gets wind of . . . of what's going on here. Is that all right with you?"

"Certainly."

"Thank you, sir," said the detective.

43

"Sylvia!"

"Who is it?"

"My beloved Sylvia . . ."

"Who are you?"

"My God, when I hear your voice, I shiver. I love you, Sylvia, I love you more than ever . . . you and our child." It was a man's voice.

Sylvia, in her house in Mandeville Canyon in Beverly Hills, sank down on the couch. She whispered, "You . . . you . . . you're Romero Rettland . . ."

Rod told me about this telephone conversation on January 21, 1973, a Sunday, in the salon of "our" old Suite 419 at Le Monde. A snowstorm was sweeping across the city. It had been snowing for days, in Heroldsheid too. That's where Bracken had reached me and told me he'd meet me at Le Monde. So much had happened. And there we were, sitting opposite each other. I had spent all the intervening time, since Babs's return to the school in January, in Heroldsheid. I had noted further, mostly tiny, improvements, and I had grown ever closer to those who live in the dark. I shall not go into any great detail about those weeks, your honor. What I have to tell now is much more important.

"Rettland?" I said to Bracken. "The man she made her first film with in Berlin, who was so popular? He called Sylvia?"

"Yes. He called Sylvia. I was there. I heard the whole conversation on the dining-room phone. It was on the evening of November twenty-eighth."

"That long ago! But why didn't Sylvia tell me about it?"

"You've got enough on your hands. And she hoped there wouldn't be another call."

"But there was."

"Godammit, let me tell the story, Phil! We're in a fucking mess up to our necks again." And he went on.

"Yes, this is Romero Rettland," said the voice on the phone. "I managed to get your number. Welcome home, darling. I was so happy when I read that your film was such a fantastic success. I—"

"Mr. Rettland, what do you want from me?" Suddenly Sylvia was screaming. Bracken signaled to her to keep calm.

"You can call me Mister as long as you like, Sylvia. Both of us know why you're doing it."

"I asked you, what do you want from me?"

"I love you more than ever. We have a child. I want to marry you."

Sylvia gasped. Bracken left the phone and hastily made two drinks. She needed it; so did he.

Meanwhile Sylvia had managed to say, "You are out of your mind, Mr. Rettland. I don't love you. I never loved you. But above all—we don't have a child!" After which she drank, and her hands were trembling so that the whiskey trickled down her chin.

"Darling, you have a long hard day at the studio behind you. I don't want to make you hysterical. I love you much too much for that. But what's all this nonsense? Of course you loved me until . . . until I got all fouled up and you felt you had to drop me. I don't hold it against you. I never stopped loving you, and I forgive you. But there's one thing we can't avoid any more."

"What?"

"The fact that I am Babs's father."

"You are *not* Babs's father! You are not!"

"Don't get excited, darling. Remember how excited you got years ago when I finally picked up the courage to ask you for money? Do you think it was easy for me to come begging to you?"

"I gave you money!"

"Yes. You did. But I have my pride too. I didn't come again, not even later when I was in big trouble."

"Because I told you I wasn't going to give you another cent and that I'd have you thrown out!"

Bracken put down the receiver, went to another phone and called the police. "Rod Bracken speaking. Sylvia Moran's agent. She has just received a call from a certain Romero

440

Rettland. Is still speaking. He is apparently blackmailing her. Can you find out where he'd speaking from and go there and arrest him?"

"We can hold him, yes, if charges are brought against him."

"I'm bringing charges."

"All right, then. Now—she must go on talking to the man as long as she can."

"Okay. I'll write her a note."

"And leave this line open. I'll get back to you as soon as I have any news."

"Right."

Rod scribbled a note and handed it to Sylvia. She nodded. Rod picked up the receiver connected with the phone she was talking on and the receiver of the other phone, one for each ear. Meanwhile the dialogue continued.

"You had me thrown out!" Teary voice. "And that was rotten—you on top and me in big trouble. But I never came back, not until now."

"What's the matter now?"

"Sylvia . . . I'm old. I'm lonely. Terribly lonely. You don't know, you'll never know, you can't imagine how much I love you."

"Oh, stop it, you bastard!"

"No, I'm not going to stop it. Let me talk, Sylvia, my beloved Sylvia."

"Keep talking," Rod wrote on the pad. Sylvia nodded and drank again. "So what *is* the matter now?"

"You have no idea how much I loved you, how much I've longed for our child . . . for years . . . for so many years."

"She is *not* your child, and you know it."

"She *is* my child, and I know it!"

"I have a doctor's report—"

"False! Is that the thanks I get for bringing you to Hollywood! So you could play your first leading role with me!" The teary voice again. "I was in trouble, in a lot of trouble, and that's when you got rid of me!"

"Keep talking," wrote Bracken.

"That's not the way it was," said Sylvia, nodding to Bracken. "You know better than that. I'd never have thrown you over if you hadn't . . ."

"That was a joke, a harmless joke!"

"You call *that* a joke?"

441

"And it happened years ago. Now listen to me, Sylvia—I love you and I love my child. I shall always love you both. You are the greatest film actress in the world. Your picture will be a sensation. I can imagine that right now you want no part of a wreck like me." The teary voice changed, became vicious. "But things can't go on like this. You leave me no choice—either you marry me and the three of us take up life together—yes, the three of us, because Babs *is* my child, I *am* her father! Will you finally grasp that?—or . . ."

"Or what?"

"Or there will be a scandal that will ruin you, you can bet on it!"

"What do you mean?"

"I mean . . ." A pause. "Oh, I see."

"You see what?"

"You're dragging this conversation out so that the cops can find out where I'm talking from. I get it. That's a pretty obvious trick, Sylvia."

"I am not dragging anything out! There aren't any cops . . ."

"Of course not. You'll hear from me again soon." Click. Rettland had hung up. Bracken swore.

"It's not my fault. I did what I could."

"Hush!" The police officer was on the other wire.

"The Mandeville relay station says the call was interrupted."

"Was there enough time?"

"No. They couldn't trace the call."

Bracken swore and yelled, "And you can't arrest the bastard?"

"On what charges?"

"He's lying! He says he's Babs's father!"

"Please, Mr. Bracken. He declared that quite openly when Babs was born. I can't get out a warrant for that."

"What about blackmail? He just said if Sylvia doesn't marry him he'll create a scandal that will ruin her!"

"I can understand you very well when you speak normally, Mr. Bracken."

"Okay, okay!"

"You've got the wrong department, Mr. Bracken. You'll have to bring criminal charges. Do you want me to connect you?"

"Of course!" Bracken told me now in Le Monde, so many weeks later. "And they listened to everything I had to say. Then—"

"Skip the suspense," I told him. "Make it short. I imagine quite a few more things have happened since November."

He made it short; I'll make it short too.

The police said that they certainly would arrest a blackmailer, but for that they had to have proof of blackmail. They could arrest him now but might have to release him twenty-four hours later. In any case, a recorder was attached to Sylvia's phone and a tracer was set up at her local telephone exchange. The police also tried to locate Romero Rettland. They didn't find him. And for five weeks nothing more was heard from him.

"You can imagine how it hit Sylvia," said Bracken. "Overworked, a nervous wreck because of Babs, and this on top of everything else. Joe put his detectives on the job again, but detectives can only look after your security, they can't do anything for your nerves."

"So what did you do?"

"We consulted a doctor. Not an asshole like Collins. A real psychiatrist. Dr. Elliot Kassner, chief of staff of the psychiatric clinic at Santa Monica Hospital. He treated Sylvia. He's still treating her. Great man! Were you aware of the fact that she is going through the greatest crisis of her life?"

"No!"

"That's what I said. A great doctor. Especially when one takes into consideration everything else that happened."

"What else?"

"Professionally, to begin with, in April, as you know, there are the Oscars. It's a sure thing: *The Chalk Circle* will be nominated. And Sylvia, naturally."

"When is this happening?"

"April sixth."

"And I take it Rettland knows."

"He must have known it, or took it for granted. This is the moment he's been waiting for. Now or never! That's why he never called again. He thought of something better."

"What?"

"He went to one of those movie magazines. Did it right after Babs was born too. These magazines—you know them—quite a few of them are okay, most of them are not. The rags have the higher circulation."

"That figures."

Bracken took an article with a photograph out of his inside jacket pocket and gave it to me. "Published two weeks ago."

I looked at the article. Pictures of Sylvia, glamorous pictures of Rettland in his heyday, and beside them pictures that showed him as he looked now, poor, old, white-haired, an expression of grief in his eyes. And—my heart began to beat fast—at least five pictures of Babs when she was well. Big headline running across two pages. *"Romero Rettland; 'I can't be silent any longer!' "*

The article was written in the first person, certainly not by Rettland. An expert had worked on it, and the magazine was expecting a sensation, three months before the Oscar presentations.

"When you read it," I said, "you could say it was good publicity for Sylvia."

"Yes, you could, if you didn't know that Babs was a brain-damaged child now, hidden away in a school for the retarded in Germany. And if you didn't know about Sylvia's little outburst in Monte Carlo. And if you didn't know that she'd been blackmailed for that for years. And if—"

"That's enough," I said. I felt sick. Now *I* needed a drink. I went over to the bar and fixed two double whiskeys. Bracken downed his drink and I fixed another whiskey for him.

"Dr. Kassner is looking after Sylvia," said Bracken. "I asked him if he thought she could hold out till April."

"And what did he say?"

"He said yes."

"If nothing more happens," I said.

"Yes," said Bracken. "That's just it. Now Rettland's making it big, in other magazines, better ones, serious ones. Every word checked by lawyers, I'll bet. And we can't touch him. That's what Joe's lawyers say. That's what everybody says. Invulnerable! And think how it looks: A man—poor, old, abandoned—fights for his daughter. A woman—beautiful, successful, much too successful—won't let him have or even see his child. Won't even acknowledge that it's his! And all this just before the Oscars!"

"And one really can't do a thing about Rettland?"

"Not a thing. We have the best advisers, the best lawyers." He shook his head and went on. "We don't know if Rettland knows the truth about Babs. We think not. But no one can find out that you're in Heroldsheid, and who else is there. Until now everything's worked out all right. We've told the reporters that you're traveling in Europe, preparing our next picture. You know, you three, Sylvia, you and Babs, are very popular with the reporters."

"Yes. But for how long, if any of them gets a hint of what's really going on?"

"Exactly. Then you're finished. We can't produce Babs, but you—you've got to show your face in Hollywood, and certainly at the Oscar presentations. You've got to be there with Sylvia, that's quite clear, isn't it?"

I nodded.

"God, are we ever in a fucking mess!" Bracken sounded lost. "And all this has to happen now, of all times, just when Sylvia is really going to triumph!"

"If you were Rettland, would you have chosen a different time?"

He gave me a strange look. "That's right," he said. "I'd have behaved just like Rettland."

Something suddenly occurred to me. "By the way, what did you do about Carmen? What's become of her?"

"What should have become of her? She's back with the export-import firm in Madrid, cursing all of us. Although she should be grateful. We gave her five thousand bucks extra."

"What for?"

"To shut her up. Lejeune saw to everything. When we left she thought we'd send for her right away. When we didn't, she began to write letters. First to me—she doesn't know your address. Then to Sylvia, and Joe. Was a real pest. Threatened to tell the truth about Sylvia's suicide attempt, etcetera."

"And?"

"So Lejeune went to see her. She made a real production of it at first, but ended up this big." He granted Carmen a half inch between thumb and forefinger. "At the clinic, Dr. Molendero, the police—they'll all say nothing. Says Lejeune. And you can believe what Lejeune says. He listened to Carmen's story right up to the wonderful rushes that had created such a furor in Hollywood."

"But there weren't any rushes with Carmen! We shot without film during her takes."

"But *I* told her Hollywood was crazy about the rushes. Lejeune explained to her that according to me I'd never told her anything of the sort. Her word against mine. Who are they going to believe? She wept. Wept through the entire interview, Lejeune told me on the phone."

"Just a minute! It was *we* who told her she had to go to the hospital with a heart attack. If she consults a doctor and can prove we were lying, if she quotes da Cava and the camera crew and everybody else who was in on it—what then?"

"Da Cava has just signed up for two more pictures with Seven Stars. Ching and his crew are already working on a new picture. Every one of them's dependent on Seven Stars. They're not interested in a little Spanish whore."

"And you?"

"What about me?"

"You slept with her."

"What's that got to do with it?"

"Oh, I see. Sorry."

"The photographers and the new girl should be here any minute now."

"What photographers? What girl?"

"We need photos. You and I are conferring in Paris about the next picture, and we've found a stand-in for Sylvia. You never saw such a darling creature! Picked her out yesterday. Our scout came up with two dozen little pussies. One cuter than the other. But Chantal was the pick of the crop. Man, what a figure!" He demonstrated with his hands. "Twenty-one. And she thinks I'm Mr. Miracle Man! I'm staying over an extra two days. Chantal Clesson. She's fantastic!"

"What if she puts on the same act as Carmen?"

"First interview. You know what that means. Nothing'll come of it in the end. Happens all the time."

44

The Swedish actress Liv Ullman, standing beside Rock Hudson, opened the envelope and announced, "The Oscar for the best male actor, in *The Godfather*—Marlon Brando!"

Applause in the audience assembled in the Music Center of Los Angeles for the forty-fifth Oscar Presentations. Nothing else had been expected. The applause grew as everyone waited for Brando to go up on stage. In his place, however— and the applause waned—there appeared a dainty little Indian girl, still very young, wearing the tribal dress of the

Apaches. With a determined gesture she rejected the statuette. Hudson and Ullman, startled, didn't know what to do.

The young Indian girl stepped up to the rostrum and spoke. She was holding what was obviously the script of a speech in her hand. "My name is Sacheen Little Feather . . ."

"What bullshit are they going to dish out now?" muttered Joe Gintzburger, breathing heavily. "That Brando! Nuts! Keep calm, Sylvia darling, keep calm!"

"I am perfectly calm," Sylvia said amiably. She was sitting beside me.

I turned halfway around. Bracken was sitting on Joe's right, Dr. Elliot Kassner, the psychiatrist from Santa Monica Hospital, on his left. Joe and Bracken looked at the doctor . . . he nodded confidently. Meanwhile, Little Feather had gone on speaking.

"Ladies and gentlemen! Mr. Brando has honored me with the task of telling you that he rejects the Oscar you have presented him, for the following reasons. With this short declaration he wants to demonstrate worldwide against the unjust, discriminatory treatment of the Indian in America and especially in the motion picture industry." The rest of her words were lost in outbursts of indignation and the applause of the three thousand guests.

Approximately six million people were watching the Oscar presentations, about the same number as had seen Sylvia's telecast from Monte Carlo, and had just witnessed Marlon Brando's refusal to accept the most coveted prize in the film industry. Until now there had been one mishap after the other in this forty-fifth gala presentation. Charlton Heston, who was supposed to be one of the hosts, had been detained on the freeway with a flat tire. Clint Eastwood, who wasn't prepared and therefore didn't exactly cut a good figure, had had to take his place. Bob Hope hadn't been well enough to attend, the second year in a row. So much was going wrong, resulting in a tense atmosphere that now, after Brando's dramatic rejection through his little Indian princess, seemed to come to a head. I looked at Sylvia. She smiled back.

I had arrived three days before. Sylvia was in a good mood, or seemed to be. She was still under Dr. Kassner's care, and she was on medication. Romero Rettland's private war against her was still going on. Six more newspapers and magazines had published his plaintive accusations, and he had been interviewed twice on radio. Joe had managed to prevent a telecast that had been planned for the day of the Oscars.

Quite a few awards had already been given—Francis Ford Coppola and Mario Puzo for best script, Luis Buñuel for best foreign film, and then—Joe snorting—a shower of Oscars for *The Chalk Circle:* for best supporting actress, best supporting actor, best cinematographer, best score, best script, best director . . . Joe had every reason to snort. Music started up again, Diana Ross, leading lady in *Lady Sings the Blues,* still in the works, sang "My Man" as overture to the announcement of best actress. It was Rock Hudson's turn. He pulled the card out of the envelope. "Ladies and gentlemen! The Oscar for best actress, in *The Chalk Circle . . .*" and the applause began . . . "Sylvia Moran!"

Thunderous applause. Sylvia remained seated, calm, relaxed. I said, "You've got to go get it."

"What did I say?!" Joe, behind us, triumphant. "Didn't I say all the time . . ."

Sylvia rose. "You've got to come with me," she said.

"No!"

"Yes you do."

Sylvia walked ahead of me toward the enormous stage with its orchestra, a backdrop of man-high Oscars, amid a sea of flowers. The applause was overpowering. By now Sylvia had reached the short, red-carpeted staircase, then we were on the brilliantly lit stage, and a spotlight picked us up and followed us all the way to the center. Embraces, kisses, handshakes. Raquel Welch was presenting the Oscar. She kissed Sylvia again. More applause. I kissed Sylvia. *Voilà,* the Great Lovers of the Century. Gradually the applause died down.

Forty-one men of the NBC television crew had nothing else to do at this moment but record Sylvia's picture and words on the television screen for approximately six million people. She was standing in front of the microphones.

"Ladies and . . ." She stopped, smiled happily, I smiled happily. "Ladies and gentlemen, and my dear friends. I thank you with all my heart for the great honor you have bestowed on me . . ." The Oscar slipped from her hands, fell on the floor, rolled to one side, as she collapsed. I was just able to prevent her from falling on the floor. Shrieks in the audience!

I held Sylvia in my arms. I was convinced, your honor, that I was holding a dead woman. Men came rushing on stage, Dr. Kassner first. "Slowly . . . very slowly," he said calmly. I had never seen him anything but calm. "That's it." And to the Seven Stars detectives, "Get an ambulance."

"On its way."

Sylvia was lying on her back, her eyes open wide, unseeing. Her dress was torn at the shoulder.

45

Dr. Kassner said, "We must be quite clear about one thing, gentlemen. Until now I have treated Miss Moran in a way that would make a complete breakdown unlikely. That would make it possible for her to appear in public, accept her Oscar . . ."

"And she did all right," mumbled Bracken.

We were seated in Joe's office on the Seven Stars lot, Joe behind an enormous desk, Dr. Kassner, Bracken and I in front of it.

"Be quiet, Rod," Joe said pleasantly. "Her breakdown was the best thing that could have happened to us. Haven't you been reading the papers? With her collapse, we're in for another million, or two, or three. Excuse me, Dr. Kassner. You were saying?"

The heavy man with the wise face said, "Everything I have done for Miss Moran to date was a stopgap measure, unfortunately not the treatment that was necessary. Because I realized that Miss Moran had to remain in the public eye for some time. How long a rest can she take now?"

"We want to start shooting her next picture—*Mission in Berlin*—in the fall," said Bracken.

"Want to?" Have to!" said Joe.

"The picture is going to be filmed in Berlin?"

"Berlin, Paris and New York," I said. "A espionage story."

"But not the run-of-the-mill espionage story!" said Joe. "This one will top every one of them! There'll never be another like it!"

"I presume you want to keep Miss Moran on top as long as possible," said Dr. Kassner.

"Not only I—all of us! Sylvia does! You've got to strike while the iron's hot!"

"I understand what you want, Mr. Gintzburger," said Dr. Kassner. "But if things are to turn out right, you'll need a truly healthy Sylvia Moran."

"You mean—then you've got to get her well for us first."

"Exactly. Miss Moran is in Santa Monica Hospital, and she is going to stay there."

"For how long?"

"For months. At least four. You want to earn a lot of money with her, Mr. Gintzburger, don't you?" Dr. Kassner's face was expressionless.

"I don't want you to misunderstand me, doctor," said Joe, his voice plaintive. "Please treat our Sylvia just as long as you feel is necessary. Money?" He made a derogatory gesture. "Means nothing to me. All I care about is . . ."

"That Miss Moran should be a healthy, fit, happy member of your big happy family. I know."

"That's right, doctor. That's absolutely right."

Not a muscle in his face betrayed what Dr. Kassner might have been thinking. "I think we understand each other perfectly."

"Of course if your great experience in tragic cases like this could make it possible for you to restore our dear, courageous Sylvia in time for the fall schedule, it would . . ."

"Yes, yes. I shall do my best, Mr. Gintzburger. It won't be easy. Babs . . ." Dr. Kassner was informed. "But I'll do what I can."

"What are you going to do with Sylvia?" I asked. "Just briefly, doctor, and understandably for the layman."

"For the layman?" Dr. Kassner looked around at all of us. "Well, as you know, I have managed to keep Miss Moran ambulatory until now with drugs. That is what I meant by stopgap measures. Now she must remain in the hospital, and all the drugs will be stopped."

"But she'll be in terrible shape!" cried Joe, the loving, worried father.

"She certainly will be, Mr. Gintzburger. For a while she's not going to be at all well. But that's nothing to worry about. She will be with us; we'll be in charge. This period will take weeks, no doubt about that. During these weeks it would be best if none of you visit Miss Moran—I mean, best for her. I think it would be advisable if you returned to Germany, Mr. Kaven." I nodded.

"When we have succeeded in getting her off the medication

and she can manage without it, we will do two things: First of all, we'll put her on quite different medication; secondly—and this is much more important—we'll be able to start therapy."

"Good God!" said Bracken. "Not again!"

"Again? Oh . . . you mean . . . no," said Dr. Kassner. "No couch, no narco-analysis. Nothing like that. I shall talk to Miss Moran and listen to her. We'll discuss her problems. What she needs is a period of behavior therapy. In some respects similar to what Babs is getting."

"What do you mean by that?"

"I mean," said Dr. Kassner, "that we must transform Miss Moran into a woman with an active, positive attitude toward life, to the extent that she rejects destructive behavior."

"And you think you can do that?"

"Yes, Mr. Kaven. Such things can be achieved, again as in Babs's case. Through affirmation and rejection."

"And what does that mean?"

"When the patient's behavior is correct, the doctor rewards her—and for the patient it really is a reward—by a very obvious personal appreciation. When there is negative or destructive behavior, the response on the psychiatrist's part is rejection. He seems to be neglecting the patient; it looks as if he no longer cares for her. All this is very difficult and requires great patience from all concerned. But it is the only way. Do you want me to proceed?"

I said, "Yes." Bracken said, "Yes." Joe said nothing. We watched him as he got up and walked over to a portrait of Sylvia hanging on the wall, shook his head, then bowed it.

Bracken nudged me. "What is it?" I whispered.

Bracken pointed with his chin, and I could see that Joe was crying. Big tears were rolling down his cheeks. His cigar had gone out.

"Poor, dear Sylvia," he said, choking on the words. "Yes, doctor, do whatever you think is right. I see everything clearly. You will do the right thing. You will give us back a healthy Sylvia."

46

According to my diary—a short account of what took place in Heroldsheid after my departure to the States and my return, and later, during spring, summer and early autumn, until shortly before the final catastrophe.

While I was away, the weather turned warm, and the children could play outdoors. Babs was having one of her "good" times. No aggression. Her writing was improving, barely noticeably but improving, and so were her reading and counting. She had at last passed the number-three hurdle. In a kitchen designed for the children she was learning how to prepare simple things: bread and butter, chocolate milk and so on. The muscular weakness on her left side was considerably less. She was anxious to take part in the rhythm and calisthenics classes. Fräulein Gellert, the speech therapist, was happy. Babs's speech was much clearer, her sentences longer. And she had become increasingly interested in clay—she made plates, cups and little figures, which she liked to paint. She could go to the toilet alone and wash herself. A good period, as I just said. She often danced for me and Ruth when Ruth came to the school or visited our little house. Ruth and I behaved like a happy married couple. We hadn't slept with each other, not once. Sometimes we kissed, but not often. I . . . I, your honor—hadn't slept with a woman in months, didn't sleep with a woman for months to come, and didn't miss it. And all this time I went on working.

During the first two and a half months after my return to Heroldsheid I spoke only to Bracken. Dr. Kassner had requested that Sylvia be left in peace. She found out through Dr. Kassner how Babs was getting along. She asked about her often. Throughout this period Dr. Kassner reported only positive developments in Babs's condition.

During the summer the children visited a nearby pony farm, a nursery and a department store. We went to a supermarket, observed work at a construction site and visited the Heroldsheid fair. We never experienced anything like the scene in the post office again, but there were always people who didn't know how to behave with the children. They paid no obvious attention to them because that "wasn't done."

Toward the end of August I was allowed to talk to Sylvia. She was still in Santa Monica Hospital. She gave every indication of being completely transformed—calm, nothing hectic about her, no signs of egocentricity, equal to coping even with reports of Babs's relapses. Dr. Kassner was a very good doctor. He told me once that Sylvia was also a very good patient.

"She has responded so well to the therapy, she is basically so sound. I hope she will be able to make the picture."

Mission to Berlin started off with me again as producer. The preparations in Paris and Berlin began in September. In New York, Steve represented me; he naturally also had to do my work in Europe. All I had to do was a lot of flying. As for *The Chalk Circle*—you know that it was a worldwide sensation, your honor. Up to the catastrophe it had grossed $80 million in a few months, with showings in many large countries still to come. During all this time, not a word from Romero Rettland. As far as we were concerned he might have died.

On September 15, Sylvia left Santa Monica Hospital. She was in good spirits, and the drug she was on now was so effective that Dr. Kassner happily gave his permission for her to work in the new film.

On September 23, Sylvia arrived in Berlin. She had to be present a week before the shooting began. I flew with her— Joe insisted on that, and so did Bracken and the lawyers— and we put on the usual show of meeting and greeting.

Three days before I left Heroldsheid, leaving Babs with Frau Grösser for what I knew would be quite a long time, Babs took me aside and said she had a wish. "Yes, Babs. What is it?"

"I ... Phil ... I'd like to have a Nounours again. I promise I won't harm him. I just want to love him."

"And what do you want him to look like?"

"Black, please, with blue eyes."

So I drove to Nürnberg and bought a little black teddy bear with blue eyes. There was a button in his ear, which especially delighted Babs.

47

What extraordinarily small feet for such a big man, thought Chief of Police Vigbert Sondersen. He was standing in the middle of the room and for quite some time now had been staring motionlessly at the place where the big man had collapsed. The dim light of a weak bulb made everything in the wretched room look even more wretched. The peeling wallpaper with its faded stripes and flower pattern, blistered, like huge boils, damp spots gleaming darkly, was encrusted with dirt and tough, hardened slime. A dresser. A bureau with a big broken mirror. Beer caps under a heavy stand. Opposite it, an iron bedstead, rusty struts, the linen stained and torn. A muggy, sour smell. Short dirty-green curtains hung like damp rags on either side of a small window. The window frame, once white, now showed only dark rotten wood.

I can report all this, your honor, because Chief Sondersen told me about it later.

In a corner by the window there was a washbowl, cracked in three places, stained yellow and brown. Two folded towels with red stripes at the edge and a dried piece of soap in a soap dish. A hazy mirror above the washbowl. The bare light over it didn't work; neither did the hot-water faucet. Sondersen had tried them both. A movable wooden bidet and a tin pail behind a dilapidated screen, its material probably once pink, now browned and blackened, shot, thin, torn. Between pail and bidet, a can of disinfectant spray, shocking yellow.

All this and more in the dim light of a weak bulb with a green porcelain shade, hanging from the middle of the ceiling in this foul room, in this sleazy hotel called Zum Weissen Rad—the White Wheel. Every now and then street noises and the sound of voices from the narrow alley below could be heard through the open window, and the sound of cars from a nearby parking lot. A dead-end street in Nürnberg's Old City. The sound of church bells. Has to be St. Lorenz Church, thought Sondersen. Already nine o'clock. The autumnal night was cold; black clouds sailed by, low, but it wasn't raining, not yet. Sondersen heard the sound of a radio from another room, probably just like this one.

At first all the people in the hotel were out in the hall, thought Sondersen, crowding in front of the door to this room, senile, lascivious, lewd in their horror, shivering sensuously; they tried to get inside, but an old pimp who had found a place here as janitor held them back, with the help of some cops and two housemen—a Yugoslav and a Turk. They screeched, gasped, hectic red spots on their gray cheeks, whispering senseless things to me, malicious suspicions into my face, spitting as they spoke, their breath foul—eight whores and their clients, then six old couples, dirty robes, stockings slipped down, suspenders hanging, slippers, one man with only his upper dentures in his mouth, his wife with breasts sagging like empty sacks under her open dressing gown, running, stumbling, quick, quick, right after the shot, anxious not to miss the unbelievable. And then, pale and hollow-cheeked, with teary, inflamed or dull eyes, unkempt hair, runny noses or noses dry from sniffing cocaine, twitching constantly, with age-old faces, stupidly bold or just plain stupefied, so young yet no longer of this world, a few boys and girls in discarded American army jackets, pullovers with holes, dirty jeans, ragged corduroy pants, sleazy T-shirts with the names of big-time newspapers printed on them, all those who like the old people lived year round in this house, the last stop in their lives.

Then, one after the other, they shuffled, limped, staggered, crept back to their rooms, silent suddenly, no longer lewd but horrified. Enough of lascivious shivering, tearful, afraid of becoming involved, of being drawn into the terrible thing that had happened. All gone now, the hall empty, nothing left but the stench of disinfectant and urine.

And the man still has his shoes on, thought Sondersen. Impossible to tell, therefore, how really too small his small feet are. I'll have to look when they've taken his shoes off and he lies there naked, on a stone slab.

Everything about him is well proportioned, thought Sondersen, even at his age, in his miserable condition. Only the feet are too small. Sondersen felt a bad taste in his mouth and a feeling of helpless bitterness. Such little feet, that's bad, he thought. I don't know why I think it's bad, but it is. And of course I'm shocked, profoundly shocked, because the other person, the one they found staring down at the man lying on the floor, whom I found still standing there, stunned, was Sylvia Moran.

Sylvia Moran . . .

"I shot him . . . I shot him . . ."

"Why, Frau Moran?"

"I shot him . . . I shot him . . ."

When she had arrived at the hotel she had been wearing a scarf tied around blond hair. Sondersen had found that out in the meantime. And a raincoat and dark glasses. She carried a dark shoulder bag. Sondersen had taken the scarf and glasses from her, her blond hair too—a wig. Sylvia Moran's blue-black hair had tumbled loose from under it, her fixed, staring eyes dark and huge.

"Frau Moran . . . Frau Moran . . . why did you shoot this man?"

Steadily and simply she had replied, always the same thing; "I don't know . . . I don't know . . ."

By that time the room had been full of men. Beside Sondersen there were his deputy, a man from the Bureau of Investigation, a photographer, two investigators, the medical examiner. In front of the house and inside the house were police from the nearest headquarters, which janitor Kunzinger had notified right away. And the police officer who had called Sondersen. Sylvia Moran . . . world-famous Sylvia Moran, whose film *The Chalk Circle* had been running for weeks in Nürnberg to sold-out houses, the most famous film actress in the world, here, in this filthy room, in a filthy hotel, an unknown man dead at her feet, whom she admitted over and over again she had killed.

"I shot him . . . I shot him . . ."

"But *why,* Frau Moran?"

"I don't know . . . I don't know . . ."

The medical examiner waved everybody away, told Sondersen, "Stop, Vigbert. It's no use. She's in shock. We have to get her to a hospital."

So they had taken her to the hospital, in custody, of course, in an ambulance, with her coat, her scarf, her bag, wig and glasses. Two police officers with her.

The curious people watching had to be practically beaten back. They didn't leave voluntarily. Photographers arrived. A barrage of flashes. The howling of police sirens. The ambulance drew up with total disregard for the gaping crowd. That had scattered them.

Sondersen and his men had remained behind and worked for hours. Sylvia Moran ... Sylvia Moran ... I can't grasp it, thought Sondersen. Good God! Sylvia Moran! The world has its sensation now, he thought.

The man hadn't had a single bit of identification on him. They would have to find out through investigation who he was. All that he had in his pockets was three keys on a ring, eighty-five dollars and thirty cents in American currency, and two traveler's checks, each for a hundred dollars. Sylvia Moran didn't say who he was. She was out of her mind, stunned, her face gray. She was holding a pistol in her hand. Vogel, the police officer in charge, finally took it from her. A 6.35mm Walther pistol, model TPH, Serial Number 128467 ...

Cautiously Sondersen walked around the outline of the body, as close as possible, careful not to erase any of the chalk line by treading on it. From the head, alongside the right shoulder, then along the outside of the bent right arm, walking the bend precisely, arriving at the right hand; on tiptoe along and up the inside of the arm. Three short steps, and about-face. Now down the right side of the body, chest, stomach, thigh. The right leg was twisted unnaturally, not broken, although one might think so. Sondersen kept changing direction around this leg, his steps getting smaller. The right calf ... along the outside. Around the right foot, still on tiptoe, and up the inside of the right calf, the inside of the right thigh. Stop. About-face. Now all the way down the inside of the left thigh, the left foot, and up the left side of the body again. The man had fallen on his back.

Sondersen couldn't explain why he took this macabre walk. Something forced him to—instinct acquired in decades of investigative work. He stopped on the left side of the chest, bent down and looked at the blood.

He straightened up and went on walking. Now he was standing at the head of the man who wasn't there, only his blood, only a chalk outline, the man with the bent right arm and the grotesquely twisted right leg, the chalk outline of a man with no ears, eyes, nose, mouth or hair, a man consisting of nothing but empty space and foul air. A man who was a man no longer but who had been here, in this room, on this spot, made of flesh and warm blood, breathing, talking, thinking, listening, behaving—alive! Until his hour had come. *Vulnerant omnes, ultima necat* ... that's what they used to write on sundials, thought Sondersen. "All things wound, the last thing kills."

The last hour that had killed this man, when his time had come, was 5:13 P.M. plus forty-four seconds on Monday, October 8, 1973. Black clouds hung low over Nürnberg, but it didn't rain, hadn't rained at 5:13 plus forty-four seconds, the moment when this man had sunk to the floor, and the glass on his wristwatch had shattered and the watch had stopped *Ultima necat.*

Sondersen glanced at his own watch—5:55 P.M. The call reporting a murder had come into police headquarters at 5:32.

Just before the telephone rang, this tall, lean chief of police, with the steely-gray hair that lay like a pelt around his skull, had been about to cross out the date October 8, 1973, on the calendar inside his file drawer, just as he had crossed out so many dates before this October 8. He had crossed out the date before answering the phone. But with that this day wasn't really crossed out, it was by no means over, but was a day that would prevent Chief of Police Sondersen from retiring on December 31, 1973. Such a short time before the retirement he had been longing for, this man, grown sad and hopeless in his struggle against evil, because there was no hope when faced with evil, was forced to face evil once more in Room 39 of the sleazy Hotel Zum Weissen Rad.

48

The investigation took its routine course. The police questioned everyone in the house and took down their personal data. The Yugoslav houseman fortunately spoke German and Turkish and could translate for his colleague. The photographer came, the man from the Bureau of Investigation; the body was examined by the coroner. Death had been instantaneous. Meanwhile Sondersen had done a lot of telephoning. The man in the lab couln't get anything out of the fingerprints of the murdered man. The highest echelons would

have to be notified. After all, the case involved Sylvia Moran!
So all available information concerning the dead man went
out to police headquarters in several countries. The janitor
had declared the man was an American, and Sondersen had
called in Interpol. An inquiry was therefore going on in 120
countries for the identity of the unknown man. Through a
happy circumstance the famous ballistics expert Dr. Walter
Langenhorst was in Munich on a case. Telephone calls.
Langenhorst promised to come to Nürnberg right away. In
the meantime the district judge had been called in and was
giving his instructions. A psychiatric expert would be needed
later, at the trial. Sylvia Moran declared she had shot the
man, but she couldn't remember anything. Sondersen called
Professor Eschenbach in the Psychiatric University Clinic
near Erlangen. He was already on his way to Nürnberg. The
press was clamoring for information. Sondersen made a public statement, as brief as possible—Sylvia Moran's name had
of course to be mentioned. A press conference had already
been held at police headquarters. Police remained in the
hotel. Sondersen could have left, should have left, he was
surely needed in the hospital to which they had taken Sylvia,
and at headquarters, but he chose to stay at the Hotel Zum
Weissen Rad. He was still stunned. Sylvia Moran . . .

Standing motionless in the room where the crime had been
committed, just where the chalk line ran around the head of
the body that was no longer there, Sondersen stared down at
the blood—there was quite a lot of it—some of which had
already seeped into the wooden floor. It was still wet and
glittered. He stepped across the chalk line around the head to
the pool of blood. He crouched down, leaned forward, his face
very close to the blood now. Then he saw clearly what he had
seen vaguely from a distance. In the middle of the pool of
blood there were two strange lines imprinted on the floor, as
if drawn by some sharp object. If you completed them, you
would come up with the outline of two small ovals, attached
to each other, like two eggs. So something had lain there,
that was certain. And was no longer there. Where was it?
Why had none of his men found it?

Still on his haunches, Sondersen looked around the room,
from door to window and back to the door again, pondering.
Where was it? Taken away secretly? Hidden in a desperate
hurry? Sondersen looked at the old bureau. It stood against
the wall next to the door, flat on the floor, no legs.

Sondersen stood up. He walked up to the bureau and tried to move it. It was lighter than he had expected. There was no wallpaper behind it, only gray plaster. Sondersen knelt again. With his pocket knife he tried to pry up one of the floorboards. It didn't move. The second one didn't either. The third one did. It was broken at the front edge of the bureau. Sondersen pried it up and found what he was looking for, lying on the damp, rotten wood underneath. Well, there you are, he thought.

He went back to the chalk man, crouched again, holding what he had found with the tweezers with which he had picked it up, lowered the tweezers carefully. The thing he had found hovered over the two oval impressions in the wood. Sondersen continued to lower it until it touched the blood on the floor. The outline fitted the impression on the floor exactly.

Sondersen stood up. He put what he had found into a plastic bag—a locket, its edges sharp. It must have fallen on the floor, face down, then the man had fallen on it, heavily. Thus, thought Sondersen, the outlines of the locket must have been lying there *before* the man had fallen on it, and somebody who had seen it fall had pulled it out from under the dead man. Not easy. The locket was smeared with blood on the outside, clean on the inside. The man had bled on it. After the removal of the locket, his blood had continued to seep onto the floor.

Whoever had done this had been in a great hurry. You could see where the floor plank was broken, even when the bureau was back in position. Somebody before him must have noticed this and hidden the locket where Sondersen had just found it.

He stood motionless, the open locket in the little plastic bag. Nothing on one side; on the other, under celluloid, the photo of the smiling, happy face of a little girl. And Sondersen knew this face.

49

Sondersen left the room and walked out into the stench of the hall. He saw two of his men, both still very young. He nodded to them. "Won't be long now," said Sondersen. "Everybody in the place checked and questioned?"

"Yes, sir. Jollow and Heilig have already left. They took two kids with them."

"Dope?"

"Heroin. Two-bit pushers. Addicts themselves."

Sondersen nodded absently and walked down the narrow, dirty wooden staircase to the entrance of the hotel. Through the opaque glass door he could see the silhouettes of two policemen.

"You goddam son of a bitch!"

"You can kiss my ass!"

Sondersen stepped into the little office. Two people looked up at him—the janitor, Josef Kunzinger, short, thin, about fifty, with a flattened boxer's nose, the inflamed eyes of a drinker and thin lips, and a young woman wearing high-heeled black boots, her bright-red plastic coat leaving her bare thighs free. Pretty, coarse face, wearing her blond hair high, a red plastic bag dangling from her left arm. She smiled at Sondersen.

"Terrible, terrible, what's happened, isn't it, Herr Hauptkommissar? And Sylvia Moran . . . I worship her! I've seen *The Chalk Circle* twice! Cried my eyes out every time! God, what a wonderful picture!" And as a non sequitur. "Do I have to let myself be insulted by this pig, Herr Hauptkommissar? I'm registered. I pay taxes. Everybody at headquarters knows I'm honest! Oh . . . Krake, that's my name. Elfie Krake, Herr Hauptkommissar. I swear I don't owe this pig a thing, not a cent!" She turned around and yelled at Kunzinger, "And I'm going to talk now, I'm going to tell everything, and you'll end up in the can. You've picked on us long enough, you asshole!"

"Adi," said Kunzinger. "All I'll do is tell Adi you . . ."

The girl screamed, swung her bag wildly and tried to hit

Kunzinger with it. Kunzinger, looking bored with the whole thing, kneed her in the groin. Elfie Krake turned white and fell on the sofa. She pressed one hand between her legs and groaned. Sondersen strode up to the janitor; the latter backed away.

"Shut up, both of you," said Sondersen. "And you, Kunzinger, watch your step! Quiet now. I have to make a call."

He walked over to the wall phone and dialed the medical examiner's office, asked for Professor Prinner. Sondersen had worked for many years with Hans Prinner. A good friend. Not a tall man, well-rounded potbelly, thick short neck, thick lips, big nose, protruding eyes, sparse hair. He also had a hip deformity that had shortened one leg, and walked awkwardly. But he had exceptionally beautiful hands, beautiful eloquent eyes and a melodious, warm voice. Chain smoker, always a cigarette in his mouth, even during postmortem examinations. If it got in his way, he clamped it between the toes of the corpse.

"Prinner."

"Hello, Hans. Just wanted to know how things were going."

"Working at it. With Langenhorst. He's been to the hospital and examined Frau Moran's hands. He'll tell you about it. Three of your men are here. We've opened him up."

Sondersen could see Prinner. Corpses were his passion. He probably had on his rubber apron, shirt sleeves rolled up; he always worked without gloves. "A fine gentleman. Everything grossly neglected. Sixty if he's a day. Can you tell me why Moran murders a sixty-year-old man?"

"No." Sondersen sighed. "Let me speak to Langenhorst, if he's not too busy."

"Just a minute . . . Herr Langenhorst! Here he comes." Prinner handed over the receiver.

The ballistics expert sounded arrogant. "Have you come to any conclusions, Herr Doktor?"

"Not yet, Herr Hauptkommissar. Had to examine the clothing first, then the body before the autopsy, then after. The shot penetrated the breast one hundred and thirty-three centimeters above the heel of the foot; two centimeters beside the sternum, left, on a direct line between the nipples; a circular hole, two point five millimeters. We removed the bullet from the muscular flesh between the second and third rib, five centimeters left of the spine, one hundred and thirty-eight centimeters above the heel of the foot."

"Conclusion?"

"Not so fast! With a rising trajectory like this, the person firing the shot could have been standing directly in front of the victim, at the most two centimeters twenty away. But I can tell you right now that I'm ruling out a close shot with the pistol held against the body."

"Yes?"

"Yes. The shot was fired, I'd say, from a distance of approximately one meter. But for a final decision you're going to have to wait a while, my good man. My report . . ."

"Of course, of course. I hear you went to see Frau Moran."

"Yes, I did."

"And?"

"She's still in shock. Examined her hands for gunpowder residue."

"Go on."

"Sylvia Moran's hand gave positive evidence of gunpowder residue."

"So there's no doubt about it—she shot."

"No doubt whatsoever."

"Thank you, doctor, I'll come by later."

A distance shot. Fired at a sixty-year-old man. Insane! I must go to the hospital and arrest her, he thought. No two ways about it. Oh God, three months from now all this would have been no concern of mine!

Kunzinger and the Krake woman were still arguing with each other. "You goddam little whore!"

"Shut your fucking mouth!"

Sondersen pounded on the keypanel. "Quiet! I want to ask you once more, Kunzinger, and if you lie, I'll find out and you're finished. What happened? Which of the two came here first?"

"Sylvia Moran," Kunzinger replied like a well-behaved schoolboy.

"When?"

"Just before five."

"Were you alone?"

"Yes, Herr Hauptkommissar." Kunzinger humble.

"So—no witnesses."

"No witnesses. But I'm telling the truth! I swear I'm telling the truth! I . . . I . . . wait!" He brought over a big ledger that was lying open on a desk, spotted, dirty, greasy. "You see, Herr Hauptkommissar, here . . ." Then something seemed to occur to him. "Krake was there! She was here, Herr Hauptkommissar!"

"When?"

"When the lady called. Krake heard it all! She can swear that I'm telling the truth!"

"You were really here?" To Krake.

"Yes, Herr Hauptkommissar. That's when this pig and I had our first quarrel, because I told the fucking bastard . . . he's always shitting on me . . . it was the day before yesterday."

Krake wasn't going to lie for the janitor. Never. If she says she was there, she was there, thought Sondersen. A witness I can believe. . . .

50

"Here . . . here . . . Herr Hauptkommissar!" Kunzinger was underscoring a line in the ledger with his finger. "Here it is! Saturday. That was when the lady called. But I've already shown it to your men."

"You didn't tell them that Frau Krake was present when the call came in?"

"No."

"Why not?"

"Nobody asked me."

"All right. So?"

"Saturday afternoon. There, you can see for yourself. Vera Klein. That's who it was."

Sondersen looked at the shaky handwriting. "October 6, 1973. 4:20 P.M. Frau Vera Klein. A room for October 8, 5:00 P.M."

"And *she* reserved the room?"

"Yes, Herr Hauptkommissar," said Krake. "For once the pig's not lying. I was standing right here, and I heard him speaking to the lady and repeating what she said, word for word."

"How do you know it was Sylvia Moran and not some other woman?"

"She spoke very loud. I could hear her voice. We talked

about it afterward, Kunzinger and I did. Such a beautiful voice. Must be an actress, I said."

"Yes, that's what Krake said."

"Where did she call from?"

"I don't know. Maybe from out of town."

"Perhaps from Berlin?"

"Possible."

"How did she happen to know about this hotel?"

"I don't know. I don't ask that sort of thing."

"Does this happen often?"

"Does what happen often?"

"That a woman calls up and reserves a room."

"Oh, Herr Hauptkommissar! You have no idea who calls up and reserves a room! I don't talk about it, ever, but you'd be surprised what ladies they sometimes are."

"And they're the ones who ruin our business!" Krake said bitterly, then stopped abruptly. "Of course, not Sylvia Moran! I didn't mean her. I really didn't!"

"Let's go on. So Frau Moran ... this woman reserved a room on Saturday and arrived here shortly before five ... allegedly."

"Not allegedly, Herr Hauptkommissar! She really did! At five I have to take my medicine. Something wrong with my lungs. I was just going to take it when there she was—raincoat, shoulder bag, scarf around her hair, dark glasses. I knew at once—somebody special."

"How did you know that?"

"Well, the way she was got up. A Mercedes and a chauffeur would have been right for her but ... but not this place! Not Zum Weissen Rad! But *just* a lady like that would have to come disguised, if you get what I mean."

"Go on."

"She said her name was Vera Klein, and I gave her the key to 39. Wanted to take her up, but she didn't want that."

"Go on."

"Well, she went up. Before that she said a gentleman would come and ask for her. A Herr Rand. Herr Werner Rand. She described him, and that was just the way he looked when he came."

"And when was that?"

"Fifteen minutes later. Not more than that. I'd just taken my medicine. An American, Herr Hauptkommissar. I'm positive."

"How can you be so positive about it?"

"I worked as a bartender after the war, after I got out of prison camp. In Garmisch. For the Amis. I can tell one right away, however much he disguises himself."

"All right then. An Ami. And?"

"And the old goat . . . excuse me, Herr Hauptkommissar—and the poor old man asked, is Frau Klein here, and I said yes. And he asked, in what room, and I told him, and wanted to take him up but he said he'd find it all right himself. After that I was kept very busy . . ."

"Doing what?"

"Other guests. We're always full up on Monday afternoon. Funny, isn't it? And it's the worst day for the theaters and movie houses. But we . . . well, anyway, then I heard the shot and rushed upstairs."

"Where to?"

"To Room 39."

"Why to Room 39?"

"I don't know. I had a feeling . . . the false name, the beautiful woman, the old guy . . . Anyway, I dashed upstairs, opened the door, and there she was, standing, he lying at her feet, and she pointing the gun straight at me! I still feel sick when I think about it. But I've told all this three times already."

Suddenly the entrance door flew open. The two policemen were holding a man who was struggling to get in. "You can't go in there!"

"I have to! I have to!"

"No!"

"Let the man go," said Chief of Police Sondersen.

They let me go. I staggered over to Sondersen. "What . . . what . . . where is . . ."

"Where is who, Mr. Norton?" Sondersen asked, and I noticed that there were two other people in the room and that they were backing away from me, eyes open wide.

"Sylvia! Where is Sylvia? For God's sake, has she . . ."

"Has she what?"

"Has she met Rettland?"

"Rettland?"

"Yes. Romero Rettland. What's happened here? Has she . . . has she shot Rettland?"

"What makes you think that?"

"Answer me!" I cried.

"*You* answer *me!*" said Sondersen. "What makes you think she shot Rettland?"

"She arranged to meet him here at five," I said. I was still panting. I had run quite a way before finding the hotel.

"How do you know that?"

"She called from Berlin, from the studio. One of the dressers was curious and listened in. But I wasn't told right away."

"Told what?"

"The name of ... of this hotel, the date, the reservation. That Sylvia gave a false name ... and the other false name ... Werner Rand. She said she was going to meet him."

"And?"

"And what?"

"You're Philip Kaven!" the girl cried suddenly. "Philip Kaven! That's who you are, aren't you?"

"Yes, I am." Nothing mattered any more. Nothing. I had come too late.

"Where is Sylvia?"

"Not here any more."

"Where is she?"

"Why are you here?"

"Because I wanted to prevent a murder!"

"*What* did you want to prevent?"

"A murder!" I was shouting now. "I knew that Sylvia had to meet Rettland ... that he had forced her to ... that he had followed us to Europe and was blackmailing her ..."

"Blackmailing her?"

"Yes. No. Yes ... but that's it, that must be it, or she wouldn't have come here! She has a gun, ever since she came to Germany."

"Does she have a permit?"

"No."

"Where did she get the gun?"

"I bought it for her from ... from a man."

"What man?"

"I don't know. I bought it in a bar in Meineckestrasse. Men who go in for such transactions don't give their names and addresses."

"But perhaps you know what kind of a gun you bought for Frau Moran?"

"Of course. A Walther pistol ... 6.35mm."

Sondersen looked at me sadly.

"Did she ... did she shoot Rettland with it?"

Sondersen nodded.

"Where is she? I must go to her at once!"

"That's impossible."

I felt dizzy. Everything was revolving around me. Sylvia had shot Rettland. Here in Nürnberg. With Babs in Heroldsheid. Now it will all come out . . .

"Aren't you going to answer me, Herr Kaven?"

"What . . . I didn't hear what you said . . ."

"I said: Why did you buy the pistol for Frau Moran?"

"So that she could defend herself if necessary."

"Was she afraid?"

"Terribly afraid."

"Of whom?"

"Of Rettland."

"How do you know?"

"She told me."

"And you bought her the weapon. Then you flew here because you were afraid she might use it."

"Yes."

"How did you know Frau Moran was in Nürnberg?"

"I told you. The dresser called me. She says she fought with herself for a long time whether she should tell me or not."

"She did, did she? When did she call you?"

"Tonight. At around six."

"But you knew—the dresser must have told you that Frau Moran's meeting with this man was at five o'clock."

"Yes . . . yes . . . certainly, Herr Sondersen. I wanted to save her if there was still anything to save . . . stand by her . . . I had to . . . I flew here on her plane."

"Did you tell anyone in Berlin about it?"

"Certainly not!"

"And you didn't come here as an alibi for yourself?"

"An alibi?"

"It's possible, isn't it? That you planned the murder together with Frau Moran. After all, you did buy the gun for her. And now you tell your story as if you had followed her here, horrified, after having persuaded her to do it."

"Herr Sondersen!"

I stepped back. Now I was standing beside the girl in the red plastic coat. She handed me a pad and a pen and said breathlessly, "An autograph, please, Herr Kaven!"

I looked at Sondersen. He said, "Give her your autograph," and I hastily scribbled my name on the pad. The girl thanked me. "And now," said Sondersen, "I'm sorry, but you're going to have to come to headquarters with me."

I nodded. I had nothing to say.

51

"What will become of Babs now?"

"I'll look after her, Phil. I'll take care of everything."

"I can't come out any more. I've got to stay in Nürnberg now. In the Fränkische Hof. I hope to God nobody from the Bristol or anyone else recognizes me!"

"Everything's going to be all right," said Ruth.

"It's not going to be all right! Take a look at Nürnberg! Two days after it happened—a circus! A three-ring circus! Reporters, photographers, television crews from all over the world! I got a small single room at the Fränkische Hof, that's all they had left. The city's bursting at the seams, Ruth! It's a madhouse! And getting worse all the time! We're going to have to meet in secret too, not in your clinic any more. Nor in Heroldsheid. Oh dear God—Heroldsheid! If anyone ever gets suspicious about Babs . . ."

"Nobody will! Please calm down, Phil, please!"

"But this leaves Babs alone, and she's going to be alone for a long time. She's not going to make it so long without me."

"Frau Grösser is going to look after her. We're telling everybody that you've gone to America on a funding trip for the school."

"But *I* won't be able to make it without Babs!"

Ruth got up and came over to me, sat down on the couch beside me and kissed me. "You . . . who used to hate her, who found her repulsive, who wanted to kill her once . . ."

"Oh . . ."

She traced the contours of my lips with her finger. "I know," she said. "I know. But that was in another country . . . isn't that what Marlowe says?"

I nodded.

For the first time since I had met her, I was in Ruth's apartment. We had to be so careful, take so many precautions, avoid so many dangers. What a life!

Joe Gintzburger had arrived from Berlin, and Julio da Cava. Rod Bracken had come in Sylvia's Rolls. He had

469

brought my things. Katie and Joe Patterson, Steve Comming, and others had arrived in Nürnberg. Cameraman Roy Hadley Ching; the author, Mike Toran; the architect, Joel Burns; the cutter, Allen Lang; almost the same team that had filmed *The Chalk Circle,* and all of us were staying at the Fränkische Hof.

". . . Sylvia Moran, who received an Oscar for her film *The Chalk Circle,* still refuses to give any information as to why she shot sixty-one-year-old former popular film actor Romero Rettland . . ."

Telecast, 8:05 P.M. ARD news report. An announcer, behind him stills of Sylvia, of Rettland. I was sitting facing the set, in Ruth's apartment.

"As has already been reported, after the shooting and treatment for shock by Professor Eschenbach from the Erlangen Psychiatric University Clinic, Sylvia Moran was taken to police headquarters and interrogated by Chief of Police Vigbert Sondersen. This was followed by her arrest, and the actress was taken to the county jail in Nürnberg-Fürth, pending trial. She is being defended by the famous Bundesrepublik lawyer Dr. Otto Nielsen . . .

". . . According to Chief of Police Sondersen it is becoming increasingly difficult to find any explanation for the apparently senseless and unmotivated crime. The police are asking for your cooperation. We are looking for anyone who may have seen or spoken to Romero Rettland"—a picture of him appeared on the screen—"on or before October 8, 1973. This could be anywhere in the Bundesrepublik or outside Germany . . ."

Newspapers were lying on a low table in front of me. I read the headlines. "Sylvia Moran insists: I killed him!" "Why did film star Sylvia Moran commit murder?" 'I can't remember anything,' says Sylvia Moran!"

". . . All European radio and television stations are broadcasting this appeal . . ." Followed by more stills of Rettland—full-length, profile and full-face.

". . . Romero Rettland was born August 9, 1912, in Myrtle Creek, Oregon, U.S.A. It had been ascertained that at the time of his death he was practically penniless. He was wearing old clothes and gave an impression of total neglect. Rettland was an American citizen, spoke German fluently with a slight accent, but no foreign language besides German. He was one point seventy-five meters tall, slim, had

470

gray hair, bushy gray eyebrows and a sallow, unhealthy complexion . . ."

Ruth turned off the set. "I know you're sick of hearing it. So am I. But it has to be if Sylvia is to be helped."

"She can't be helped. She killed Rettland, you know that as well as I do."

"I'm not so sure."

"Who else could have done it? She had the gun in her hand when the police came. And she had every reason to kill the bastard. She didn't tell me—she didn't tell anybody—but I have the feeling that he found out what was wrong with Babs and was trying to blackmail her."

"How?"

"Oh, by demanding a huge sum of money, for instance. You know that somebody has been trying to blackmail her for years. Or he wanted to force her to marry him. Or . . ." I looked at her helplessly.

"The truth will come out," she said. "It always does."

"Yes," I said. "But when?" I slammed my hand down hard on the papers. "And what's driving me crazy is the fact that with this deah, with Sylvia's arrest and all the misery that still lies ahead for Babs, millions are being made! Hundreds of millions!"

"What do you mean?"

"*The Chalk Circle*—that's what I mean! It cost twenty-five million to make. Since the murder, the picture and Sylvia are headline news everywhere. Gintzburger thinks that after this murder and after the trial—and it will be sensational, whether Sylvia is convicted or not—*The Chalk Circle* is going to gross three hundred and fifty million! Ruth, there isn't a film in the world that's done that! Joe is ecstatic! *It is repulsive!*"

"Have some more wine," said Ruth, and filled my glass again. We had eaten a little something at her place. The glasses and bottle were still on the table.

"Let me talk!" I said. "Do you know how many sick and starving children there are in the world?"

"Oh yes, Phil," said Ruth.

"And do you know how much money will be allocated next year to these children by world health organizations?"

"According to what I've read—two hundred million."

"That's right. Two hundred million, for *all* the children in the world who are sick and hungry and dying of starvation.

In the world, Ruth! *If* the children are lucky. Because I'm not at all sure that the two hundred million will be forthcoming! Cobalt bombs have become cheaper, but they still cost a lot. But all right—let's say two hundred million. That means that every tenth unfortunate child . . . every tenth one, Ruth . . . can *perhaps* be helped! Nine out of these are doomed to die!"

"But it's so useless, Phil! Why are you torturing yourself?"

"Let me talk! Yesterday I watched a documentary. More statistics. Have you any idea how magazine and newspaper circulations will increase all over the world, because of this thing with Sylvia? It's fantastic! Absolutely fantastic! A *low* estimate, Ruth, comes up with eighty million dollars! On top of that the insane prices charged by the agencies for photos! And the horrendous fees being paid by German television alone for interviews with me or Joe or anybody anywhere who has a word to say about it! And Sylvia's old pictures. According to Joe they'll be resurrected and shown now in thousands of movie houses all over the world! And the gross on them? Do you realize what it all adds up to? Minimum? *Nine hundred million dollars!* And that would be something even for the bosses of multinational corporations! Why don't you say anything, Ruth?"

"Because there's nothing to say! Stop talking about money, please! Do you think this has never happened before? This has been going on since time began, only this time, for the first time, it affects you! What about this Dr. Nielsen?"

"What about him?"

"Well, he's really a very famous lawyer. Have you met him?"

"Yes. At the hotel. He made a good impression on me."

"Did he say anything?"

"What do you mean?"

"Well, he must have spoken to Sylvia."

"He has. She sticks to her story. She shot Rettland, she doesn't know why, she can't remember anything."

"How is he going to defend her?"

"He isn't sure yet. I think he intends to lean heavily on the psychiatric expert from Erlangen, Professor Eschenbach. He's supposed to have mentioned a dissociative reaction while she was in shock, with a pathological affect. What is all that?"

"Dissociative reaction may reach a degree in cases like this," said Ruth, "where the mental processes come temporarily to a standstill; or the influence of one obsessive idea

472

results in explosive behavior, with the blotting out of all restraints. The important thing is that during the time of this cessation of consciousness, there is amnesia, in this case due to shock. Did Eschenbach mention amnesia?"

"Yes."

"Then there's nothing Nielsen can do with a client who can't help him in any way but invoke Paragraph 51 of the penal code."

"Not responsible for her actions at the time of the act?"

"Yes. Not responsible."

"And what's to become of Babs?"

"I told you—I'll take care of everything. I'll arrange things with Hallein and the staff."

"But what if it takes months to prepare this case . . . and it will . . . what if it lasts weeks? And everybody will know where Babs is!"

"Not necessarily. Didn't you tell me once that your motion picture company has a healthy Babs somewhere that they can show? I imagine a child that looks like Babs."

"That's right. But what if things go wrong? Oh, what am I saying? Even if things don't go wrong, even if Sylvia is found not guilty, Gintzburger and his lawyers are adamant about the fact that the truth about Babs and Heroldsheid must never be told! Never! It would . . . it would be ruinous for business! But how can we prevent it from getting out?"

"By all sticking together. Nielsen is a good man."

"You don't understand! Even if it can be kept secret, it means that I can never see Babs again now that I am here officially as Philip Kaven!"

52

". . . And here, ladies and gentlemen, let me introduce Joe Gintzburger, President of Seven Stars, on whose authorization Sylvia Moran's company, Syran Productions, filmed *The Chalk Circle*. The five gentlemen with him in the booth are Seven Stars lawyers. Did you all come to Nürnberg together, Mr. Gintzburger?" asked the reporter for German

Television I. There was a spotlight on the booth in the bar of the Fränkische Hof where the proceedings were being reported for ARD—*live!* The reporter had already interviewed some of the others, including me. I leaned my back against the counter and listened.

"No," Joe was saying, "the gentlemen came from Los Angeles. I've come from Berlin, where we are getting ready for Sylvia Moran's next picture." Hie Bible salesman's voice, gentle eyes cast heavenward, his white hair, his expression of benevolence . . .

"I take it, Mr. Gintzburger . . . by the way, you speak German wonderfully well . . ."

"Thank you."

"I take it you gentlemen are here to give all your support to Dr. Nielsen, to help him get to the bottom of this dreadful thing in which Sylvia Moran is involved."

"Naturally. Everything that can possibly be done will be done to help Sylvia. You see, my friend, at Seven Stars all of us are somehow related to each other, one big happy family, from the biggest star to the smallest clapper boy. It's the only way to make first-rate international films."

The lawyers looked solemn. The reporter cleared his throat. "I presume you are convinced that Sylvia Moran is innocent."

"Absolutely! Anything else doesn't come into question, my friend. You don't know her personally. Sylvia is . . . Sylvia is an angel! Purity and kindness personified! She couldn't possibly have committed such a crime!"

"But she insists that she did."

One of the lawyers leaned forward and whispered something in Joe's ear. He nodded and said, "Sylvia is still in a state of shock."

"Professor Eschenbach says she came out of that quite some time ago."

"Professor Eschenbach!" Joe wrung his little pink hands. "And what does that mean? At the time when it happened, she *was* in shock, and not responsible for what she was doing. Or does he dispute that too?"

"Not as far as I know."

"There you are! Everything's proceeding according to plan. A famous American psychiatrist will be here soon, a Dr. Kassner, and when he's had his say, everything's going to look very different, you can be sure of that! Poor, poor Sylvia! Dr. Nielsen is one of the best defense lawyers in the country. He will have Sylvia out on bail in no time!"

One of the lawyers whispered something. "And Dr. Nielsen will see to it," Joe went on, "that justice is done. You can't accuse a woman who has recently had a nervous breakdown of what she accuses herself! The very idea is ridiculous!"

"But Romero Rettland is dead, Mr. Gintzburger."

"Yes. But who knows how he lost his life? He was an evil person, my friend."

"Once big box office for you, Mr. Gintzburger."

"When? When? Years ago! And then—women, alcohol, drugs and worse. Yes, that story's got to be told at last, and I'm going to tell it in court. Romero Rettland ... once I looked upon him as a son, my son. I built him up, made a star of him. And he?" Again one of the lawyers leaned forward, whispered to Joe, who nodded, and waved him away disgustedly.

The reporter asked, "Is it possible that Rettland was blackmailing Sylvia Moran?"

"Why? Whatever for?"

"I don't know. I'm asking you, Mr. Gintzburger."

"Look here, my young friend, your question is absurd! Have you seen *The Chalk Circle?* Then *I'd* like to know if you'd dare to ask again who could possibly have any reason whatsoever to blackmail this wonderful woman? The greatest personality the film industry has ever produced? I am grateful to you for giving me the opportunity to say this on television, in front of an audience that surely runs into the millions! Sylvia Moran does *not* belong in jail! She belongs in a sanatorium! Do you remember Judy Garland? Was *she* a star? Well, there you are! And remember the condition she was in because she was overworked, and the tranquilizers and stimulants she had to take to be able to work."

"Are you saying that Sylvia Moran was on drugs?"

"Stop!" One of the lawyers rose. "Mr. Gintzburger is saying nothing of the sort!" He poked his finger at the reporter.

"But," the reporter insisted, "after her collapse during the Oscars, Sylvia Moran was in the Santa Monica Hospital for a long time."

"She was overworked. That's why Mr. Gintzburger drew the parallel with Judy Garland. Miss Moran was overworked and went to the hospital to rest. Of course she has never been on drugs of any kind, tranquilizers or stimulants! She was overworked! How often must we tell you that?"

"I don't need to hear it again." The reporter sounded aggressive.

Joe shook his head sadly. "Young man, has your generation lost all compassion?"

This made the reporter furious. "I am interviewing *you*, Mr. Gintzburger. We agreed beforehand that I was to ask the questions!"

"So ask your questions!" cried the lawyer. "But skip the conclusions and conjectures!"

The reporter changed the subject. "Just as the whole world knows Sylvia Moran, they also know her little daughter, Babs. Does Babs know what has happened?"

I broke out in a sweat and had to put my glass on the counter, my hand was trembling so.

"She has no idea of what has happened."

"No idea?"

"During all this time," said Joe, "we have managed to keep where Babs is a secret, so that the child isn't bothered constantly by reporters and photographers—no offense intended. So that she may lead a peaceful, normal life. Now you can see how right we were to protect Babs as we did, to send her to a private school because she was exhausted from traveling constantly with her mother, just as exhausted as her mother was from overwork. Babs needs peace." I had to close my eyes, which made me feel dizzy. I clung to the counter. "And Babs won't find out now what her mother has done. We'll see to that. The child is safe, and no reporter can reach her."

I felt for my glass and drank. Whiskey ran down my chin. "But . . ."

"Yes, yes." Joe was smiling. "The court will want to know where Babs is. Well, my young friend, we have already told the district judge where she is, and he has no objection to our revealing it to you now, and with you the millions who are watching."

I felt weak in the knees.

"Because the first thing Sylvia will do when she is free again is go to see Babs, and then the press and all photographers and television crews in the world may be there." Dramatic pause. Joe leaned back, closed his eyes, folded his hands and said slowly and eloquently, "Babs is in a private school in Norristown, Pennsylvania, a small city northwest of Philadelphia. This is one of the most exclusive private schools in the United States."

"Another whiskey," I told the bartender. "Triple. Neat. And fast!"

53

Seven hours later I was in Madrid, sitting opposite Carmen Cruzeiro. "Pigs! That's what you are," she was saying. "All of you! Pigs! You too. But Bracken is the biggest pig of all!"

"We're only employees," I said. "We're not the bosses. It's not our fault that things turned out as they did, darling."

"Don't 'darling' me!" cried Carmen, and began to weep again.

We were in the living room of her small apartment in the Hotel Cervantes. She was sitting in front of me. I hadn't taken off my coat; she had on a robe over her dress. I tried to stroke her hand, but she withdrew it quickly. "Don't touch me!"

"Dear, dear Carmen—it is *not* my fault."

"It's your fault just as much as any of the others! Have you any idea what sort of a life I'm leading now? An object of ridicule for all my colleagues! 'Going to be a star! Like fun she is! Sits there and types the way she always did.' Have you any idea what women can be like?"

"Oh yes!"

"Oh no! Every morning when I go to the office, I start crying. I don't want to cry. I'm ashamed in front of all those people. But I have to cry. Because I dread every day I spend at Spanex. And now you come along; you who got me into this mess! Don't say you didn't! You, for whom I did everything! Everything! You and your film company! And you ask me not to tell a soul what happened here when she tried to commit suicide, and the trick when I took her place!"

"Carmen, be reasonable! Have a little compassion! Sylvia has been arrested. She's going to be charged with murder!"

"I know," said Carmen. "I've received a summons."

"You've received a summons?"

"Yes. I'm to testify. It came a few days ago. The letter from the court. In Nürnberg, isn't it?"

"Yes." I began to feel uneasy.

"You don't believe me? Wait . . . I'll go get the letter."

"You don't have to. I believe you. It's perfectly natural that you should be called as a witness." They're no idiots, I thought, those investigators.

"Carmen! I just explained. Sylvia has been indicted for murder. She may get life!"

"That suits me fine!" said Carmen.

"You don't mean that! It's not like you, Carmen, not as I know you."

"You know me?" She laughed bitterly. "You don't know anything about me."

"Carmen . . . I've come to make you an offer."

"If it's that Seven Stars is going to ask me to come to Hollywood if I don't say a word about what happened here, then you can get out right now! I believed your filthy lies the first time around, because I'm an idiot! But I'm not enough of an idiot to believe them a second time!"

"I didn't come to promise you a Hollywood career," I said.

I had flown to Madrid on a commercial plane after Joe and his lawyers had told me it was absolutely necessary. If Carmen told the court what had happened in Madrid, Sylvia's position would be considerably worse. Because then the question would come up: Why had she tried to commit suicide? And from there it didn't take much to think of Babs. And Babs had to be kept out of this, if it cost millions. Sylvia's outburst in Monte Carlo and what had happened to Babs subsequently should on no account be made public, or business was ruined. Only one thing counted: business! They had insisted that I fly to Madrid, and in a way I understood their argument. So I took my orders. . . .

"I didn't come to promise you a Hollywood career."

"I'm to shut up for nothing? Perhaps for love of Bracken, the pig?" Carmen laughed. "You must have gone out of your minds over there in Nürnberg!"

"I'll make you a different offer."

"What do you mean—a different offer? At last I have a chance to get even! Now you're going to see a thing or two!"

"Carmen, at least hear me out! You say your work at Spanex has become hell because of your colleagues. You told me once that it had always been a dream of yours to have your own secretarial and translation bureau. You speak such a lot of languages. And you'd like to be on your own. Didn't you say that?"

She looked at me irritably. "You know I don't have any

money, certainly not enough for that! Have you any idea what an apartment in Madrid costs? And I'd need an apartment. Do you realize how many new buildings are standing empty because nobody can afford the rent? And how many people don't have an apartment because of it?"

"I know," I said, and saw my chance. "Carmen. A proposition. And this time I'm not going to play a dirty trick on you like Bracken. Seven Stars will pay you however much you need to open your own office. Buy an apartment, the typewriters, copy machines, tape recorders—whatever you need. You can hire help, do whatever you like, if you promise to keep quiet."

"And I'm supposed to believe that?"

I took two pieces of paper out of my pocket, Seven Stars heading, signed by me, substituting officially for Joe. It promised Carmen everything I had just mentioned. Provision: that she keep quiet.

She read it slowly. I had signed the original and copy. It took Carmen quite a while to say all right.

"You see, we really mean well by you."

"Yes, yes. A hundred thousand dollars!"

"What?"

"Or forget it."

"No, no! If you think you need that much."

"I need that much."

"Very well. I'm glad we can help you."

"I can see that. And in cash. No check."

"I don't have that much cash with me."

"Then fly to Nürnberg and get it. Since your bosses are agreed, that shouldn't be difficult. Come back with it and I'll sign."

"You don't trust me?"

"No. Of course I don't trust you. I don't trust anybody any more. Fly to Nürnberg and come back with the money and I'll sign." She was smiling. Now she got up and gave me a kiss. "There. And now we're friends again."

I took a taxi to the Barajas airport and caught a flight to Munich. When I left the plane to change for a flight to Nürnberg, I saw Chief Vigbert Sondersen standing at the foot of the ramp. "Hello! What a surprise! What are you doing here?"

Sondersen's cheeks were sunken; he looked ill. He said, "I am here to arrest you, Herr Kaven."

"What?"

"To arrest you," he repeated, and held out a paper. "This is the warrant."

"For *my* arrest?"

"Yes, Herr Kaven."

"But why? You let me go because I had nothing to do with Rettland's murder."

"This concerns something else, Herr Kaven."

"What?"

"Compounding a felony, if not for perjury, then for the giving of false testimony, or at least attempting to . . ."

"I don't understand! This is madness!"

"No, it isn't, Herr Kaven. You have no legal domicile. There is a possibility of obstructing justice, also the possibility of flight. That is why you are being arrested."

"But whom am I supposed to have influenced to perjure himself?"

"You know very well, Herr Kaven. I want to say how sorry I am. You have been in Madrid?"

"Is there anything wrong with that?"

"A Señorita Carmen Cruzeiro informed us on the phone that you tried to influence her to give false testimony. You know, I am sure, what she's talking about. You have the papers you took to Señorita Cruzeiro on you. Please give them to me."

Suddenly I was terribly tired. I gave Sondersen the papers. He nodded.

"I have a patrol car here. We're driving to Nürnberg."

"How long will I be under arrest?"

"Your trial can take place only after Frau Moran's. You will certainly be in jail until the end of the Moran trial, Herr Kaven. And now please follow me."

I followed him.

54

—I followed him to you, your honor, to this jail in which everything is in the best order. As it so happened you became my *and* Sylvia's examining magistrate. That has simplified things a lot. For instance, getting me to write this report, which has kept me busy for months. I have been given a lawyer, a friend of the famous Dr. Otto Nielsen, a Dr. Karl Oranow. Dr. Oranow was hired to defend me against the charge of soliciting the commission of perjury, which I could scarcely deny, nor could I supply a motive that could mitigate or reduce my sentence. Dr. Oranow needed my whole story.

I am writing these lines at a time when the sensational trial of Sylvia Moran is in full swing. It is being held in front of the eyes and ears of a sensation-hungry people, mercilessly, inexorably. May 22, 1974, and it is already very warm in Nürnberg.

Dr. Karl Oranow is a tall, heavy man with a kindly face, a quiet voice and endless patience. We are alone when he comes to see me. You, your honor, have instructed him not to tell me anything that is not directly concerned with the charge against me. You have forbidden, and justly so, that I find out anything about what is going on "outside" through newspapers or any other source. You have, to date, given no one permission to visit me, except Dr. Oranow. For months, therefore, I have been cut off from the outside world, and it serves me right when one thing tortures me, almost unbearably: I don't know how Babs is! Often I wake up bathed in sweat, out of a horrible nightmare in which something dreadful has happened to Babs!

In an effort to prepare myself for what lies ahead, I asked Dr. Oranow what the basic procedure of the trial would be, before telling him the whole truth.

"Well now," he said, "the procedure is somewhat like this: First the proclamation of the case, in the case that interests you: 'The Court verses Sylvia Moran.'" My lawyer speaks precisely. "The judge establishes that the accused and her defense lawyer are present, also all witnesses and experts, and the exhibits. In a long case, which this one will certainly be, witnesses and experts may be heard on different days. The presiding judge is in charge of the trial, of the examination of the defendant, the witnesses and experts. The prosecutor has the right to question, and so has the defendant and counsel for the defense. There may be a cross-examination, in which case the witnesses are interrogated by either counsel for the defense or prosecutor. The judge may interrupt the cross-examination with his questions. You will be a witness for the prosecution, that is clear."

Fine, I thought, but before I asked my next question he continued, "The judge informs all witnesses of their duties, especially that they must tell the truth and hide nothing. He goes on to explain the meaning of perjury and giving false testimony, without stating the penalties. All he says is that such acts may be punished with a considerable loss of liberty."

"How considerable may that be, Herr Doktor?"

"Perjury . . . lying under oath . . . imprisonment for not less than one year; with extenuating circumstances, six months to five years."

"To five years with extenuating circumstances?" I said, astounded.

"Exactly, Herr Kaven." I was Philip Kaven now. My "protective" passport had been taken away immediately. "False testimony," my lawyer went on amiably, "but not under oath—a sentence of three months to five years in extreme cases. And finally the so-called accidental false statement— prison to one year. If corrected in time, you may count on acquittal."

Naturally I stuck obstinately to this last point. "Please explain the procedure for witneses to me, Herr Doktor. When I am a witness, do I *have* to testify?"

"Herr Kaven!" he said, shaking his head.

"Yes?" I blinked innocently. "Have I said anything wrong? I just want to be informed, that's all."

"Certainly, Herr Kaven. You just want to be informed, that's all. So . . . there are several grounds for refusing to testify. First: Every witness may refuse to testify if the answer to a question could incriminate him or a close relative, who could then be prosecuted for a crime or misdemeanor. The witness is informed of this right." If the witness doesn't know already, I thought. Because Gintzburger and Company had certainly worked out some sort of evasive plan by now. They will not lie—that would be perjury; they will refuse to answer many—a great many—questions. So will I.

"Such a refusal to answer the question," I said, "can that have a negative effect on the defendant?"

"Certainly. That can happen. But not necessarily. It can have the opposite effect and harm the witness. But, to continue: secondly, the right of relatives to refuse to testify on the basis of the relationship."

That doesn't concern me, I thought, and asked, "Third?"

"Third, Herr Kaven . . . those who are committed to professional secrecy."

Well, at last, I thought. There we have it!

55

"These people who are committed to professional secrecy," Dr. Oranow went on, "cannot refuse to testify if they have been released from their obligation to remain silent"—Dammit, I thought—"but the court cannot release them." Well now, that was better! "Only the person who is protected by the silence can do that, a lawyer's client, for instance, or a doctor's patient. I must also draw your attention to the fact that since Babs is a minor, only her legal guardian can release any of the witnesses from their right to refuse to testify on anything concerning her, and that would be Frau Moran," whereupon I felt a lot better.

"Well, naturally, it won't come to that," I said.

"I'm not so sure. Professional discretion affects only the area of the confidential relationship—for instance, in the case of a doctor, his diagnosis and treatment. It is not concerned with any other aspects of life the medical witness may know about—in your case, for instance, the whereabouts of Babs."

"But dammit!" I cried. "What sense is there to it if doctors who testify have the right to remain silent about Babs's illness and the treatment she's getting but have to reveal that she's in a remedial school? That's just as damaging!"

He looked at me like a friendly Santa Claus. "Not so fast, Herr Kaven! If it is in the medical interest, for instance a possible endangerment of health if where Babs is staying were revealed, then the witness has the right to refuse to answer the question."

"Aha!" I said, and thought: So Ruth, Dr. Sigrand and other doctors involved could refuse to testify. The scandal, the publicity, the reporters, the media, would endanger Babs's life. She was safe! And if Carmen Cruzeiro did appear as a vengeful witness, Dr. Molendero from the clinic in Madrid, Dr. Collins who "suffered" from too strong transferences, and Dr. Kassner from the Santa Monica Hospital could all refuse to testify against Sylvia. That she had been at the Santa Monica Hospital for a long rest cure was common knowledge. So . . . things didn't look quite as bad as I had thought. But Dr. Oranow squelched my burgeoning optimism.

"However," he said, "the medical and ballistic experts who were authorized to do the autopsy or participate in any way with the inquiry do not have the right to refuse to testify."

"Does this also apply to Chief Sondersen?"

"Yes."

Not good! Not at all good!

"You wanted to know what the procedure was in a case like this, Herr Kaven. I'm afraid we've . . . hm . . . strayed away from the subject a little."

"Yes."

"Well, to continue. After the opening statement, the witnesses leave the courtroom, the experts remain. The presiding judge examines the defendant; the prosecutor reads the charges. He then instructs the defendant that he is free to speak or remain silent. I take it Frau Moran will choose to remain silent."

"She won't be able to talk about it," I said.

"Won't be able to . . . yes. Especially where Herr Rettland's death is concerned. And the experts will say why she can't testify in her own defense. Amnesia. She can't remember anything about it. She *thinks* she did it, but . . . and so on. The defendant, having nothing to say, will be useless for the prosecutor, but not for you, right? And now the hearings will start. The questioning of the witnesses and experts takes place according to the choice of the judge. The experts who have remained in the courtroom witness the whole procedure. They hear the examination of all witnesses, whereas the witnesses are called in singly, one after the other. Experts and witnesses may be warned when, for instance, it is necessary to refresh their memory in accordance with earlier testimony, or when contradictions come up. If a witness refuses to answer the question—if he has the right to do so—then his testimony on earlier records may not be read."

"That can go one way or another."

"Right. After the hearings it is the prosecutor's turn to sum up; after him, the defense lawyer. Each has the right to rebuttal. The defendant has the last word."

"And then?"

"Then the court withdraws to deliberate. If the presiding judge hasn't set a date for the sentencing, sentence is passed in open court immediately after the deliberations. If the defendant is acquitted, the court must state why the defendant is not convicted or if and for what reason the crime, which has been accepted as proved, is not considered punishable. If the defendant did not commit the crime, he or she is acquitted, and in the verdict it is stated that he or she did not commit the crime. All this has to be proved. Prosecutor, defense lawyer and the defendant have the right to appeal the sentence ... but I don't think this interests you any more, if I know what you're thinking."

"You do, Herr Doktor."

"I want to give you a piece of advice, as your lawyer and in your best interest, but just as much, perhaps more, in the interest of Frau Moran. This after giving her case a great deal of thought."

"Yes?" I sounded shaky and felt it.

"Yes," he said. "I think we can foresee pretty well what line of defense Dr. Nielsen is going to take. The psychiatric experts will support him. If he can get the court to accept Paragraph 51, it will be an achievement. But I'm very much afraid he won't be able to."

"Why not?"

"Because of what I was able to gather from your questions, from your expression when you heard my answers, etcetera. I get the feeling that all witnesses, whenever possible, will refuse to answer the questions, and that will make a highly unfavorable impression. We must therefore, I regret to say, count on a very stiff jail sentence for Frau Moran. For premeditated murder."

"And there's nothing we can do about it?"

"There is one thing."

"What?"

"To take the bull by the horns."

"And who is to do that?"

"You."

"Me?"

"Yes, Herr Kaven—you. You are the man who knows everything. If from now until the day of the trial—and this will give you plenty of time—if you were to write a detailed report for the trial judge, who for you and Frau Moran happens to be the same man, a detailed account of what *really* happened, then I can see a much greater chance for Frau Moran, for Babs, for you, for everyone concerned. Don't forget one thing—Carmen Cruzeiro will testify with venom, testimony that will certainly be extremely damaging to Frau Moran. Her position will be damaged further by the testimony of the experts, even if the police, especially Chief Sondersen, keep silent about Babs's whereabouts. Nobody is going to be in any doubt whatsoever that everything that happened centered around the child."

"All right. So?"

"Write your testimony in the form of a precisely detailed, absolutely truthful description of the events. The examining magistrate will inform the prosecutor and the defense lawyer of your written report. You refer to this report when you testify. Do *not* refuse to testify but, on the contrary, tell the truth. Then, Herr Kaven, I can imagine—beside the sensation it would cause—that it might turn the whole trial around and be of infinitely greater benefit to Frau Moran than stubborn silence or the refusal to testify. And that is my opinion as a lawyer and as a human being who admires Frau Moran. This is not a trap, this is the best advice I can give you if you want to help Frau Moran."

I was silent, but not because I felt defiant. I was very impressed by what he had said.

"If you like, I'll discuss this with the judge and he'll talk to you about it. Would you like that, Herr Kaven?"

"Yes."

Dr. Oronow spoke to you about it, your honor, and you discussed it with me. And I promised you that in this report I would never lie. I can't lie any more anyway, not after what I have experienced with those who live in the dark, the nameless, the weak; and, in the final analysis, what I have experienced with their integrity and infinite humaneness. They are the strongest of the strong. With this report I have borne witness, your honor, by telling the truth.

It is Monday, May 22, 1974, 4:00 P.M. The report has been in your hands now, many days before the trial. You have passed it on to the prosecutor, the defense lawyer and the court. Cut off as I am from the outside world, I don't know what effect it has had on those who have read it.

Tomorrow, May 23, 1974, at 10:30 A.M., I am at last to appear as a witness in the trial of Sylvia Moran. It was my intention to help her in the way just described, but again everything turned out differently because I had no idea of what had happened in the meantime, in the course of the trial. When I finally found out, it was too late. For a better understanding of the events to come, I shall tell what I found out too late. It conerns three very decisive events.

56

On the day after Joe Gintzburger had announced, on a live television broadcast, where Babs allegedly was, the conference room of the Clarion Hotel was so crowded that those who hadn't been able to get in stood assembled in the halls, the dining room and outside the hotel. The Clarion was the largest hotel in the small city of Norristown, not far from Philadelphia. The men were reporters and photographers from all over the world. A white-haired, distinguished-looking gentleman, Dr. Clemens Holloway, director of the exclusive private school, was the speaker. "Gentlemen . . . gentlemen . . ." But the noise all around him was deafening and he stopped speaking. Cameras hummed and clicked as he wiped the perspiration off his forehead and finally went on. "I am going to read to you a statement prepared by the chief of police of our city, our court-appointed physician and myself. 'Babs Moran is a pupil in my school. She knows nothing about what is going on in Nürnberg. She would be in great danger of suffering an emotional collapse if she were to find out from one or more of you gentlemen what happened in Nürnberg, news for which she is in no way prepared. To prevent this we have given permission to the security people of the Seven Stars Film Company, who flew in a few days ago, to protect the child from meeting any strangers whatsoever, and, with the cooperation of our local police force, to protect our grounds from being invaded.' "

Loud cries of protest.

"Gentlemen!" Dr. Clemens Holloway was hanging on to the microphone, his voice was imploring. "This can't go on! You're turning our city into a madhouse!"

"So what!" "Shut up!" *"Mon Dieu, quel con!"*

"Silence!" The loud voice of a policeman using a bullhorn. It worked. Temporarily.

Dr. Holloway's speech was labored. "We must come to some sort of agreement. After all, you are human beings. I know your profession isn't an easy one, but do you want to accept the responsibility for the harm that the child Babs might suffer, the endangerment of her physical and psychological well-being, if she were to find out what happened in Nürnberg?"

At last there was silence, but the atmosphere remained tense.

Dr. Holloway went on reading his statement. " 'No one is permitted to enter the grounds of the school or to speak to the child.' Please, gentlemen, I implore you—be reasonable! *Don't* insist on a confrontation with Babs!" Dr. Holloway wrung his bony hands and tugged nervously at his shirt collar.

"In an effort to meet you halfway," he went on, "we propose the following: This afternoon at four P.M., Babs will be playing in the park with other children. On the condition that none of you endangers the proceedings by making a noise or calling out to her or creating any other form of disturbance, our chief of police, our court-appointed physician, Sylvia Moran's defense lawyer, Dr. Nielsen, Mr. Gintzburger of Seven Stars, and myself have given permission for pictures to be taken of the child *from behind the playground fence.*"

Applause!

"If there is the smallest incident contrary to the rules just laid down . . ."

Furious outcries!

". . . then I regret to say, your cameras and films will be taken from you, also any tape recorders, and you can thank your unfair colleagues for that!"

Same day, same place, 4:00 P.M. The school was situated in a large park and was protected by a high iron fence. On one side of it—reporters, photographers, tripods. Now the children emerged from the building, which was some distance away, a green lawn and groups of trees between it and the fence. Five, ten, twenty, thirty children. They began to play—ball, tag, hide and seek. Dr. Holloway was standing near them; he gestured with his chin to one child in particular. This was unnecessary, because anyone who had ever seen Babs would have recognized her. She was wearing a red dress with white shoes and socks. The children were singing and laughing. A light wind carried their words beyond the fence. "Doctor, doctor, must I die?—Yes, my child, and so must I."

While pictures of Babs, happy, laughing, dancing and singing could be seen in every newspaper and magazine in the world, you, your honor, were putting Dr. Clemens Holloway on the list of witnesses which you presented to the public prosecutor, together with the indictment. Dr. Holloway was subpoenaed and came to Nürnberg. On May 7, 1974, he was put on the stand. He was informed of the penalty for perjury, after which the following dialogue took place.

Judge: You speak German, Dr. Holloway? You understand everything being said?

Holloway: Yes, your honor.

Judge: Is the child in your school really Babs Moran, daughter of the defendant? I remind you again of the penalty if you give false testimony.

Holloway: Would you repeat the question, please?"

The question is repeated.

Holloway: I regret to have to say that the child living in my school under the name of Babs Moran is *not* the daughter of the defendant, and her name was not Babs Moran before she came to us.

Judge: Please explain.

Holloway: It is . . . it is a very bad business, I'm afraid. When I let myself in for it I had no idea that one day . . . I was told it was an absolutely harmless arrangement . . .

Judge: By whom?

Holloway: By the Seven Stars lawyers. They turned up one day with this little girl, who might have been Babs Moran's twin, and asked me to accept her in my school. The reason they gave was that Babs Moran had grown too old to travel constantly with her mother. They said they had taken the real Babs Moran to a school in the States, which was being kept secret, so that no reporters or photographers could find her. To be on the safe side, I was to take this child and pass her off as Babs Moran, in case anything happened that might disturb the peace of mind and the healthy development of the real Babs."

Judge: And where is that school?"

Holloway: They didn't tell me.

Judge: And who is the child you took in really?

Holloway: Her name is Margaret Cleugh. The lawyers explained that she had been discovered by Seven Stars talent scouts who had been looking everywhere for a child that resembled Babs.

Judge: And why were they doing that?"

Holloway: I can only report what the lawyers told me.

Judge: Naturally. Please go on.

Holloway: The lawyers said that in the case of such a famous actress as Miss Moran, and her equally famous and popular daughter, they felt they had to take precautionary measures, in case they anything were ever to happen to the real Babs—illness, an accident, but what was to be feared most was kidnapping. I could see their point.

Judge: And how could a kidnapping be prevented?"

Holloway: Well, through the presence of this second Babs. They had worked out a complicated plan. They had found a child who looked exactly like Babs—in Wisconsin, I think. Her parents were poor. They saw it as a blessing that from now on their child would have the best care and education imaginable.

Judge: But the decision to give the child away . . .

Holloway: Your honor, they were very poor people. There were four more children. Margaret Cleugh was four years old when the scouts found her, and Seven Stars took over the care of the child. She was told over and over again that her name was Babs Moran and that she was the daughter of the famous film star Sylvia Moran. They kept on telling her this until, as the years went by, the poor child really believed it, and forgot her real parents. Everything possible was done to provide the little girl with a wonderful life.

Judge: Did Frau Moran know about this?

Holloway: No. Nobody knew except those directly concerned with the search.

Judge: You therefore thought you were dealing in good faith and for the protection of the real Babs when you took in Margaret Cleugh.

Holloway: I certainly did. Excuse me please, your honor, but by now Margaret has completely forgotten her real name. Her parents died over a year ago in an automobile accident. Margaret thinks she *is* Babs Moran. She is a lovable child and has always been a good student. And yet . . . I would never have let myself in for anything like this if I had had any idea of what was going to happen here in Nürnberg.

Judge: Dr. Holloway, do you know where the real Babs Moran is?

Holloway: No, your honor. I don't.

And this, Your Honor, was the first decisive event that took place during the trial, about which I knew nothing.

And now—the second event.

The examination of Chief Sondersen was just completed. He had refused to tell where Babs was, which was very unusual but was accepted by the court, although, as a police officer, he had no right to refuse to answer the question. He had given the following reason for his refusal: "After serious discussions with specialists, I am convinced that to reveal where Babs Moran is at this time would have an unforeseeably negative effect on the child's health." After which statement, Chief Sondersen was dismissed.

It was Bracken's turn next. His personal data were just being checked when a court officer appeared with a sealed envelope. He handed it to the presiding judge, who opened the envelope, took some papers out of it, read them cursorily, then handed them to the other judges *en banc.* It had grown very quiet in the courtroom. Finally the judge said, "Herr Bracken. The Court has just received some very important information. It concerns you."

A stir in the courtroom. Bracken looked slightly nonplussed.

"I consider it absolutely necessary," the judge went on, "to inform the court of this deposition before interrogating you." The prosecutor objected; the objection was denied. "This deposition," the judge continued, "comes from the American consulate in Munich and was brought by courier so that it might be in the hands of the Court as soon as possible. The deposition is from the chief of staff of the Mount Hebron psychiatric clinic in Los Angeles. It is a statement made under oath by a patient in that clinic, transcribed, and witnessed by the chief of staff, two police officers and a notary. All of them have sworn that this statement is exactly

491

what the patient said. The court considers this deposition legally valid and will treat it accordingly. Herr Bracken, do you know a certain Roger Marne?"

"No, your honor."

"You are sure?"

"Quite sure, your honor. Oh ... just a minute ... yes, I know him by name. That was the man who tried to blackmail my friend Philip Kaven, here in Nürnberg, if I'm not mistaken."

"Yes, Herr Bracken. That's the man."

"I think the Americans flew him back to the States right away."

"Yes, Herr Bracken."

"Because this man Marne had escaped from several psychiatric clinics in the States, where he had been arrested for some offense or other and found not competent to stand trial. Am I right?"

"You are right, Herr Bracken. But personally you don't know this man?"

"I've already said so—I don't know him!"

"That's very strange."

"Why is it strange, your honor?"

"Because Roger Marne declares that he knew you very well."

"That's a lie! What do you mean—'knew' me very well?"

"Roger Marne is dead. What I have here, Herr Bracken, is a confession dictated a few days before his death, while still in possession of all his faculties. He had read about this trial, and there was something he wanted the Court to know, something that concerns you, Herr Bracken."

"Me? Ridiculous! I don't know the man."

The public prosecutor rose; the judge waved him back to his seat. "I shall now read Roger Marne's statement. I want absolute quiet, please!" And he got it. You could have heard a pin drop in the courtroom as the judge started to read.

" 'I, Roger Marne, born July 2, 1928, in Los Angeles, presently in Mount Hebron Hospital, want the following to be known.

" 'I met the agent, Rod Bracken, in 1968 in Los Angeles at the nightclub the Red Angel.' "

"That's a lie!" Bracken's tone was icy.

"Please don't interrupt, Herr Bracken. I shall continue. 'We conversed all that evening, then Bracken told me I could make good money if I would work for him occasionally.' "

Restlessness in the courtroom.

"Quiet!" And it was quiet again. "Please bring a chair for Herr Bracken. He seems to feel ill."

A chair was taken to Bracken, who sank down on it. He asked for a glass of water and spilled half of it as he drank with trembling hands.

" 'I did several jobs for Bracken,' " the judge read on. " 'Most of them are not connected with this case, except for two. The first started in July 1969. What resulted from it has not stopped. It began in Monte Carlo . . .' "

Loud murmurs. The judge had difficulty keeping order. Bracken sat motionless.

" 'On July 25, 1969, Sylvia Moran made a speech on Television Monte Carlo, on the occasion of a benefit for handicapped children sponsored by Princess Grace of Monaco. The telecast was broadcast worldwide. The text of Sylvia Moran's speech had been written by Bracken. He said to me at the time: "She's going to hate every word she has to say; I find it just as nauseating, but she'll go through with it because it's first-rate publicity for her. But I know the dame, and I have the feeling that when it's over and she realizes what she's said, she'll be furious and make a scene. I know her fine character. So you come along to Monte Carlo with us, Roger. This is your next job and the biggest thing I've ever fed you, and you'll pocket a bundle." I asked what he expected me to do and he explained it to me.

" 'I flew to Nice on TWA two days before the telecast, drove on to Monte Carlo and stayed in a little town nearby—Eze. Bracken had a lot of technical know-how, especially when it came to electronics. He'd worked once in that field. So he installed bugs in Sylvia Moran's apartment at the Hotel de Paris and in her dressing room at the television station. It was my job to take care of the bugs after the telecast as quickly as possible. I was to remove everything fast and find out if anything Miss Moran had said on the tapes could be used against her.' "

"Rod!" It was Sylvia's outcry, choked and weak. She was deathly pale. Rod didn't move. The judge read on.

" 'Right after the broadcast I removed the bug in the dressing room, after that the one in the Hotel de Paris. The details of how I did this don't matter. The tape from the Hotel de Paris was worthless, because what Sylvia Moran said there she had already said in the dressing room. There

Bracken had rigged the two-way paging system for the actors. By pressing a button they could talk to the people in the studio. Bracken had stuck a tiny match chip in the talk button so that he was able to hear and record everything that was said in the dressing room. And Sylvia Moran had a lot to say. I listened to it as I played the tape. With which my job in Monte Carlo was done.

" 'I flew to Vienna and waited there in a small hotel, then I sent part of the tape, which I had copied—I have Bracken to thank for my knowledge of tape recording—together with the blackmail threat, also on tape. I distorted my voice electronically. I sent all this off from the main post office in Vienna to Miss Moran's private address. I asked for fifty thousand dollars. If I didn't receive it I promised to make the tape public. Bracken had thought up a way to have the money sent so that nobody could find out who was receiving it. Everything I did, I did on Bracken's orders. He paid me well. What Sylvia Moran said in the dressing room was so horrifying, it would have destroyed her career. Bracken was therefore able to blackmail her. To this day she makes payments of ten thousand dollars monthly. Bracken will deny all this, but Sylvia Moran can corroborate the blackmail. Now she knows who the blackmailer is. That is the one instance.' "

The judge turned the page. " 'The second instance: In November 1971, Bracken called me from Paris and told me to come at once. He wired me the necessary money. In Paris I stayed in a small rooming house. On December fourth, Bracken finally got in touch with me and sent me to Nürnberg. This happened shortly after the brawl in the yard of the Hôpital Sainte-Bernadette in which Philip Kaven was involved. I don't know to this day what happened there. I was to fly to Nürnberg and take pictures of Kaven and Dr. Ruth Reinhardt. Bracken showed me pictures of them. I was to photograph them in as dramatic a setting as possible. I found such a setting when Kaven and Dr. Reinhardt attended a funeral at the West Cemetery. Bracken had told me to take pictures of them with a Minox, and to try to blackmail Kaven with the photos, but without actually selling them to him. He and Sylvia Moran, and others, I presume, were only to know that the pictures existed. I did as I was told, in the course of which I was trapped by the German and American police. I was deported, sent back to the States and ended up in Mount Hebron Hospital, from where I am dictating this statement. I would like to add that Bracken said to me once: "Sylvia Moran belongs to me because she can't leave me or fire me—that's why!" Fully realizing that I am near death, I swear that everything in this statement is true.' "

The judge scanned the paper and said, "There follow his signature, date, place, and the signatures of the witnesses." He put the paper down. "Herr Bracken, what do you have to say to this?"

No reaction. Bracken seemed lost in thought.

"Herr Bracken!" Louder.

Suddenly Bracken leaped to his feet, his features distorted, and cried out, "Yes! Yes, your honor! That's how it was! That's exactly how it was! Everything the fucking son of a bitch says is true!"

"But why?" Sylvia's voice, barely above a whisper. "Rod . . . why?"

He whirled around to face her. "Because I had to be sure of you. Sure that you'd never fire me!"

"But I'd never have done that!"

"That's what you say! That's what you think! Have you any idea what people can do? You don't! But I do! I know!" cried Bracken, the most famous and highest paid agent in the world, onetime shoeshine boy, dishwasher, car washer, embalmer, hustler, pimp . . . Bracken, whose hobby was exotic fish, millionaire, son of a drunkard and a whore, raised in orphanages and the misery of New York slums, which is a very special misery. "I had to know I controlled you, Sylvia. Especially after Kaven turned up, the fucking bastard! You could have thrown me out any day . . ."

"Never! I would never have fired you!"

"Talk! Just talk! I couldn't depend on it. I'll tell you why I did it! Because I never, never, never wanted to be poor again!"

His voice broke. He was silent, panting as he sank down on his chair again.

"So what Roger Marne deposed is true?" asked the judge.

"Yes." Bracken's voice was toneless.

The prosecutor rose. "This being the case," he said, "I ask the Court to arrest the witness."

"Sergeant!"

"Yes, your honor."

"Herr Bracken, you are under arrest."

"Come with me, sir," said the sergeant, taking Bracken by the arm, and Bracken went with him silently, offering no resistance. As he left the courtroom, he looked at no one.

And this, your honor, is the second decisive event about which I knew nothing.

And now, finally, the third.

A quiet, modest-looking man is standing in front of the judge, but he speaks firmly. "Your honor. Immediately after the examination of the dead man by the firearms expert, Herr Doktor Langenhorst, I ascertained that he had concluded that the defendant fired the shot from a distance of at least one meter. His substantiation for this conclusion didn't seem right to me. I therefore asked to see the lawyer for the defendant, Dr. Nielsen, and told him of my doubts and misgivings. Dr. Nielsen contacted the public prosecutor, and I was called in as second firearms expert. All this took place fortunately within two days so that I found the cadaver in a condition that made the second examination possible."

Judge: And what is your opinion, Dr. Feddersen?
Feddersen: I was given an opportunity to examine the clothing of the dead man and the cadaver. My colleague determined that the shot was fired from a distance because of the absence of powder marking on both clothing and the entry wound. However, I was not completely satisfied and was given permission to speak to the defendant. In spite of being able to remember nothing, she still stuck to the fact that she had killed the man, Romero Rettland, and so there were certainly certain areas of her memory that had remained intact.
Judge: What areas?
Feddersen: Her clothing. She was quite positive that she had been carrying a flat shoulder bag. And where was this bag? She couldn't find it among the exhibits. The bag was not presented to my colleague.
Judge: And you were able to locate it?
Feddersen: Yes, your honor. I made inquiries at the hospital where the defendant was taken after Rettland's death, still in a state of shock. They found her shoulder bag. In the excitement it had been overlooked and a nurse had laid it aside.

(He opened an attaché case and took the bag out of it.)
Feddersen: This is the bag. The defendant recognized it at once as hers. As you can see, a shot passed through the bag. Here, too, is a gold compact. Also shot through. Here, please

... the bag and the compact ... all of which leads to the conclusion, your honor, that the shot was fired during a struggle. Using spectrography, I was able to ascertain the distance of the shot fired in the case of the bag, and arrived at a range of three, at most five, centimeters, a shot at close range therefore. Moving on from this premise, I came to the conclusion that with such a short distance between the bag and Rettland's chest, a metal chip from the powder compact might very well have entered the entry wound. I X-rayed the skin around the entry wound in an expanse of ten by ten centimeters and found tiny metal particles at a distance of up to two centimeters from point of entry. It was possible to analyze the metal chips. The proof that they were gold was reached spectrographically. By making comparison shots I was able to conclude that the splintering of the gold chips took place, at most, at a distance of fifteen to twenty centimeters between body and bag. The distance between the mouth of the gun barrel and the bag was three to five centimeters. That gives us a distance between chest and gun barrel of eighteen to twenty-five centimeters."

Judge: Please express yourself less technically, Herr Doktor.

Feddersen: Certainly, your honor. I found gunshot residue on the left cuff of Rettland's shirt. This could indicate a struggle. But it could also indicate that Rettland was trying to get hold of the gun without a struggle. The same holds good for the ejected shell lying on the wrong side, that is to say to the left of the defendant. The position of the shell indicates that at the time of the shot, the pistol could have been in a position making the ejection of the shell to the left possible. Or the shell might have been diverted, for instance from the firing position of the defendant. Both conclusions indicate a struggle in the course of which Rettland got hold of the defendant's bag and held it in front of his chest. The position of the shell, however, can be presented as evidence only conditionally, since the place where it was found does not necessarily have to conform with its original position. The position of the shell could have changed for various reasons and under various circumstances just after the shot was fired.

Judge: That is perfectly clear.

Feddersen: And now, your honor, I have been able to close the chain of evidence by something my colleague also failed to do, namely by a precise examination of grip or handhold evidence in the form of tiny hemorrhages and scratches on the wrist of the defendant. All these factors, your honor, indicate without a doubt that there was a struggle, in the course of which Rettland twisted the hand that held the gun and with it the weapon, and fired the shot that killed him.

Judge: With that are you saying that this is not a case of murder but that Rettland shot himself?

Feddersen: That is exactly what I am trying to say. In my opinion the defendant did not shoot Rettland but the latter—unintentionally, of course—shot himself.

That, your honor, is the third decisive event in the course of the trial about which I knew nothing. I have reported these three events, of which I learned later, in order that what follows may read more comprehensibly. And now I shall continue my chronological report. It is Monday, May 22, 1974, by now almost 6:00 P.M. Tomorrow, May 23, 1974, at 10:30 A.M., I shall at last be called upon as a witness in the trial of Sylvia Moran.

57

Tuesday, May 23, 1974, 10:50 A.M.

A police sergeant accompanied me, and as I entered the courtroom I could see that it was full to overflowing. All strange faces. The men sitting on another bench were the experts, I decided, who had to be present throughout the entire trial. Sylvia was sitting beside her lawyer, Dr. Nielsen. She looked dreadful, exhausted, as if filled with a profound sadness. I could see: This woman is at the end of her strength. I smiled at her. She smiled back, a distorted grimace. I stood before the bench.

"Herr Kaven," said the judge, "during your time in jail awaiting trial, you wrote a detailed account for the Court of everything that happened. I thank you for it, and so do all concerned—the Court, the defense and the prosecution. They are all familiar with your report. Still, it is necessary to examine you. I feel sure you will answer all questions truthfully."

"I will, your honor."

"Even if they incriminate you."

"Even if they incriminate me. Because I am testifying to help the defendant with the truth, because nothing but the truth can help her . . ."

"Phil!" A scream!

I turned around. Sylvia was standing, swaying slightly. "I don't want you to incriminate yourself!" Her voice was broken, hoarse. She spoke fast. "I don't want others to be punished for what I did! I don't want . . ."

The prosecutor, a small man with a sharp voice, wearing glasses, interrupted her. "Your honor! I object! The defendant stated at the beginning of the trial that she would refuse to testify, and until now she has remained stubbornly silent. I object to her interrupting the testimony of this witness . . ."

Meanwhile, Sylvia had gone right on speaking. "I don't want more tragedies! I am guilty! I am guilty! And I want this torment to end! I will tell what I did! I will tell what happened!"

"But not now!" cried the prosecutor. "The witness Kaven is testifying!"

"Your honor! I am a murderess!"

Disorder in the courtroom.

"And I am more than that, I am . . ."

"Your honor, I object!"

"Let her talk! Let her talk!" Cries from the courtroom.

"Quiet!" The judge. And to the prosecutor: "Please calm down, Herr Staatsanwalt. If Frau Moran wants to speak, let her speak."

"I want to speak! I want to speak!"

All this and what followed happened fast and amid turmoil. Sometimes several people spoke at once. But there was no stopping Sylvia, although her lawyer tried several times. Each time she pushed him aside. Sylvia spoke in spite of shouts of protest and outcries, all of which were soon silenced. The expression on her face was wild; every now and then she had to stop to draw a deep breath. She spoke with every ounce of strength she had left.

"I am a murderess, yes! The second firearms expert, Dr. Feddersen, testified that I did not shoot Romero Rettland, that he shot himself, accidentally! But I intended to shoot him, so I *am* a murderess. I came to Nürnberg with the intention of killing Romero if he threatened me again . . ."

"Threatened you with what?"

"He called me in Berlin, and he said . . . he said . . . no, he commanded where we should meet, the time, the place . . . he blackmailed me . . ."

"Slowly, slowly," said the judge. "With what could he blackmail you?"

"With Babs!" Now Sylvia was screaming. "He threatened . . . he is her father. Yes, he is her father!"

Tumultuous commotion in the courtroom.

"Quiet! Quiet! But Frau Moran, you always denied that he was the father."

"And I was always lying."

"Why? Why did you lie, Frau Moran?"

Sylvia was panting. "Because I refused to recognize him as her father . . . because he . . . while we were filming in Berlin, he raped me! He did things to me . . . I have hated him ever since. And I swore, if there was a child, I would never admit that it was his!"

"But the statement of the doctor in Berlin, that you were pregnant before you met Rettland!" The prosecutor interrupted again. "The doctor's statement that Rettland couldn't be the father. The statement you have used so successfully since the birth of your child!"

"It was a fabrication! The doctor in Berlin was a kind man. In my misery I turned to him. We invented the dates . . . he helped me . . ."

"By lying and falsifying willfully?"

"Yes, yes! Make him responsible for it, Herr Staatsanwalt! Try him! Convict him! He's been dead for years!" She became more and more excited, frantic now. "Romero was evil! A miserable, filthy dog! That is why I refused to have anything to do with him in the States!"

"But you accepted his help to get to the States. Why did you go?"

"I am an actress, Herr Staatsanwalt. I wanted to act. I wanted to show what I could do! I wanted to be famous! I knew, I was convinced, that I was a great actress!"

"And you accepted the help of a man you hated."

"Yes."

"A curious moral sense, Frau Moran."

"Herr Staatsanwalt! What do you know about morality and the conscience of an actor? There is nothing, nothing on this earth that would be immoral or unscrupulous enough to stop an actor if it gives him a chance to act! Yes, I had no integrity, I was immoral, unscrupulous! I am telling you, all of you—I am guilty! I was guilty right from the start! So convict me, for God's sake! That's what you're here for!"

"Sylvia, please . . ."

"Be quiet, Phil! You're a good man, but be quiet. Everybody here knows, the whole world knows how Romero pursued me, how he went on and on about being Babs's father, right after she was born, all these years! All of you know it! But Babs is not his child! Babs is *my* child! Mine!"

The judge said, "Frau Moran, you must calm down!"

Sylvia didn't hear him. She went on talking fast, almost incoherently. "He tried to blackmail me! He gave interviews! He wanted to force me to marry him! All of you know it! And all of you know that I broke down under the pressure and was in the hospital for months! All of you know what happened at the Oscar presentations. But after that, when I came to Berlin, to work on my next picture, feeling fairly well again, he called me up! And ordered me to meet him here. He had followed me! He knew everything!"

"Knew what?"

"And demanded to speak to me in Nürnberg, in that dreadful hotel! He was the one who named the place, the hotel, the date.He! He! He! He! But *I* had to order the room under a false name! I had to fulfill his demands, because he had me cornered. Or so he thought. Because he had found out the truth about Babs by following Philip Kaven one day . . ."

"What?" I cried.

"Yes. I didn't tell you, Phil. There was no time. He only told me during that last call. He knew where Babs was! He knew what was wrong with her! And he told me on the phone that if we didn't come to some sort of agreement in Nürnberg, in that hotel, if I didn't marry him now, if I didn't finally admit that he was Babs's father, then he would make the truth about Babs public! Then he would see to it that . . ."

"What truth about Babs?" asked the judge.

"The truth . . ." There was an insane expression on Sylvia's face now. "The truth . . . my child, my Babs, my beloved Babs, is suffering from serious brain damage!"

Cries, disorder in the courtroom. It took the judge several minutes to restore quiet. I had closed my eyes when Sylvia had said "brain damage." I kept them closed and heard Sylvia cry, "Brain-damaged! After meningoencephalitis! An idiot now, if you prefer it that way. In a school for brain-damaged children! And she'll never be well again! Never! Babs, my beloved child, the most precious thing I have—an idiot!"

58

"A doctor!"

The judge had risen after Sylvia had fallen back on the bench. "A doctor, fast!"

Sylvia sat up abruptly. "I won't let a doctor touch me!" she cried.

"But you need a doctor, Frau Moran. Please!"

I could see that one of the experts, probably a doctor, had risen. "Sit down!" Sylvia screamed at him. "There's nothing wrong with me! I want to speak! I have to speak!"

The man sat down again.

"Then," Sylvia went on, "Romero said he would see to it that the whole world found out what we—my company and I—had taken so much trouble to keep quiet, and that would write finis to my career! So I ordered the room in the hotel. I flew to Nürnberg. I met Romero. Of course we quarreled and there was a struggle, just as the expert said. A locket fell out of my bag. It had a picture of Babs in it. Then . . . then . . . I don't know what happened next, but there was a shot. But *I* pulled the trigger! *I* did! And it was my gun. If he hadn't shot himself, I would have shot him!" She was gasping for breath. "Then . . . then the locket . . . this I can remember . . . it had fallen on the floor and was lying under him . . . I was afraid it would be found. So I lifted him . . . and hid the locket so that no one should find it."

"Why shouldn't you be carrying a locket with a picture of your daughter?"

"Herr Staatsanwalt, you . . . you don't understand. I don't understand it either. I behaved absolutely irrationally at the time. I was out of my mind. I stood there with the gun in my hand . . . I can't explain it, but that's what happened . . ."

"Sylvia! Please! Please stop!"

She didn't seem to hear me. "So now you know," she said softly.

"You say that Rettland was blackmailing you," said the prosecutor. "How could he blackmail you? With a brain-damaged child? That isn't *your* fault."

"It is God's punishment!"

"God's punishment? For what?"

"You . . . all of you saw how Bracken was arrested because he had recorded what I said after the telecast for handicapped children in Monte Carlo. I said dreadful things . . ."

Bracken arrested? Bracken the blackmailer with the tapes? Right then I knew nothing about it. I sat there stunned. Impossible to follow further. All of it beyond me! All of it! Bracken . . .

"Your honor, Herr Staatsanwalt! All of you present. I am guilty. In any case, in every case—guilty! At the time, in Monte Carlo, as I made that eloquent speech, I felt that brain-damaged and crippled children were repulsive! Among other things I said that Hitler was right when he wanted to do away with them. And I said worse things. I used foul language. As far as I was concerned, children like that weren't human beings. They should be put to sleep. Killed! I only gave the talk because they told me it would be fantastic publicity. And Babs was sitting beside me. She was healthy then. My beloved Babs . . . So God punished me. Today I feel differently about it. But to get me to think differently, Babs had to become an idiot child. Since Babs was ill, they don't revolt me any more. Today I no longer feel that they should be put to sleep. Today, when it is too late . . . too late for everything, I love Babs more than ever. But all my love is no help, no help at all . . . love must . . ." She drew a deep whistling breath and fell to the floor.

The expert whom I had presumed to be a doctor rushed over to her. All hell broke loose in the courtroom. I ran to Sylvia. She was lying on her back, her eyes wide open. The doctor was kneeling beside her, examining her. Now there was absolute silence.

The expert looked up at the judge and shook his head. The judge said, "We'll take a short recess. The defendant has to be examined by a physician." And Sylvia was carried out of the courtroom.

503

59

Two hours later the judges came back from the presiding judge's chambers. Everybody in the courtroom rose. Strangely enough, the judges remained standing. Why didn't they sit down? I wondered. Would Sylvia have to be taken to the hospital? Would the trial be postponed?

The judge said, "Frau Moran is dead. The doctor who examined her has ruled that death was due to heart failure. After reviewing all the testimony, the Court is convinced that the defendant was not guilty and the case is dismissed."

60

That afternoon I received a visitor for the first time. Ruth suddenly stepped out of a door into the yard where I was taking a walk. The grass in the yard was green again, and there was fresh green on the trees. The sun was still shining above the prison wall. I was walking slowly, in a big circle, along the prison wall with its barred windows. And suddenly there was Ruth, standing in a doorway.

She raised one hand—I could see that she was carrying a small package—then she came toward me, and I walked to meet her. When we reached each other we embraced silently and kissed, a long kiss. And then we walked slowly on the gravel path.

After a while Ruth said, "The trial judge had his secretary call the hospital half an hour ago. She said I might visit you. I have asked for permission to visit you over and over again— I'm sure your lawyer must have told you—but it was always denied."

"Yes. My lawyer told me." I stopped walking. "Do you remember when we saw each other last?"

"Of course." She turned to me. She was very pale. "That evening in my apartment, after they'd let you go. Before you flew to Madrid."

"Yes. On October tenth. Today is May twenty-third. We haven't seen each other in seven months, Ruth. Seven months! And before that I was accustomed to seeing you daily. I couldn't imagine a day without you!"

"And I couldn't imagine a day without you, beloved," Ruth said softly. We couldn't stop looking at each other. "It's been a bad time."

"The worst time of my entire life."

"Of my life too. Worse than when my brother committed suicide."

The birds were singing in the trees. "I thought of you," I said. "Day and night. I wrote down everything I experienced with you."

"The magistrate told me. And I thought of you too, beloved. Waking and sleeping. I was with you all the time."

"Yes," I said. "Sometimes I could feel it. But it was dreadful just the same."

"For me too," she said, and passed her fingers across my cheek.

"You look all right, Phil . . ."

"I know what I look like. But you, Ruth . . ."

She put her finger against my lips. "Don't. I also know what I look like. I feel just as miserable as you do. Let's not talk about it, because it isn't over yet."

"But you'll be able to visit me oftener since Sylvia is dead and the trial is over."

"Yes," said Ruth. "Poor Sylvia."

"She is at peace," I said. "I hope. I wish we were."

"All people wish they were at peace."

"And you can reach that state only when you're dead. At best."

She looked at me for quite a long time, then she asked, "Do you still have the little medallion?"

I nodded and put my hand in my jacket pocket. There it was, the little medallion she had given me such a long time ago. "Peace to all men."

"And you?" I asked. "Do you still have the little lamb?" She drew the worn little toy out of a pocket of her dress, then both of us smiled, but I could see that her lips were trembling and could feel mine trembling, and I said, "I love you so much, my dearest."

"And I love you." She stroked my cheek again. "I asked when your trial was coming up. They told me soon. After Sylvia's death it may only be a formality. Perhaps."

"Yes," I said. "Perhaps. Or perhaps not. Perhaps they'll give me a long sentence."

"I don't think so."

"Because you don't want to think so."

"Yes," said Ruth. "That's right."

A gloomy silence fell between everything we said. I kissed her again, and we walked on, hand in hand.

"They let me see you alone. Only a guard is watching from a window. I think that's a good sign. They may decide there were extenuating circumstances, and you may be free sooner than you think. Otherwise they'd have sent a guard with me and not left us alone. And I'm not saying that just because I hope so."

"That's right," I said, and began to feel better. "I really think you are. And the judge said everything pointed to Sylvia's innocence."

"You see," said Ruth, and she was smiling again, I was too, and again her lips were trembling.

"Babs," I said. "How is she? I've known nothing about her for seven months, and it's driven me crazy."

"She's doing very well. Every now and then she has a 'bad' time, but right now things are very good. She has made progress. The muscular weakness on the left side is gone. She can write longer sentences, do some arithmetic, simple arithmetic. She can cook quite a few things, and her speech is much improved."

"And her eyes?"

"That hasn't changed, unfortunately. But she is very clever with her clay work, and she paints her pieces. She can dance to music now without falling down. At first she asked about you a lot, then, during one of her bad periods, she forgot all about you. But then she started asking for you again. The seven months haven't been seven months for her. Much less. Perhaps only seven days. She asked about you yesterday. I told her you were coming home soon."

"Home?"

"Yes. She considers the school her home."

"And the others?"

"The children are, of course, incapable of realizing what happens—all I can say is, thank God! The adults, naturally, know. The police questioned Hallein. But that all took place very discreetly, thanks to Sondersen. He is a real friend."

"Yes," I said. "And we're going to need real friends now."

We were walking slowly across the gravel path. "Today would be Babs's second birthday in Heroldsheid," I said. "Two years ago today we took her there on a bus. Do you remember?"

"Of course I remember!"

"The driver's name was Hausmeier."

"Still is."

"That was the day Otto broke a window, remember?"

"Of course."

"How is he?"

"Otto has done so well that he's been working in a machine shop the last three months. At a stamping machine. And he's living in a commune in Nürnberg."

"My God," I said, "how the time does fly. If something happens to me now, what will become of Babs?"

"I am there."

"And if something happens to you?"

"There will always be someone to look after Babs," said Ruth.

"Babs has been done out of her second birthday party," I said sadly. "She was so proud of her *two* birthdays. Most children have only one."

"She celebrated her second birthday, don't worry!"

"When?"

"With me. In the hospital, with her friends. With cocoa and a cake and candles and presents . . ."

"What friends?"

"Well, quite a few are still there. Do you remember Sammy, who called himself the Angel of Death?"

"He's still there?"

"And will be for a long time."

"No improvement?"

"Oh yes. But not enough. Pretzel—you remember, the psychologist—she celebrated with us, and Hallein came with Alois and Frau Bernstein. There were eight children."

"You're so good," I said.

"Nonsense! Don't say things like that!"

We walked on slowly. Ruth said, "Of course, now all the adults at Heroldsheid know who you really are. Nobody feels deceived or is angry about it. They all sympathize with you. I'm to bring you fondest greetings from everybody. I called them when I received permission to visit you, and they were so happy that we were going to see each other at last. Frau Grösser cried! She's baking a cake for you. You'll have it the day after tomorrow. She baked Babs's birthday cake too."

"But otherwise . . ." I started to say, but she interrupted me.

"Otherwise nobody at Heroldsheid knows what's going to happen next. Will reporters turn up? Will they respect Hallein's request not to waylay Babs or make a nuisance of themselves at the school? Up to now, no one has come. Perhaps the reporters are going to be merciful for a change."

"Why should they be? They never are!"

"Perhaps they won't find the school! We may be lucky for a change."

"Lucky?"

"They brought Babs to me in the hospital as soon as Sylvia's death was made public. Just in case. If reporters come, they won't find her at Heroldsheid. What will they do about Bracken?"

"Is he still here?"

"In the same prison as you. Has been for weeks. They don't know yet whether he'll be tried here or in the States. He's American, and he blackmailed Sylvia in the States."

"The animal!"

"The poor animal," said Ruth.

"And Sylvia?" I asked. "Where will she be buried?"

"In Hollywood. A gigantic funeral, the likes of which Hollywood has never seen! You can be sure of that. You have no idea how this trial is being exploited. Week after week Sylvia and Babs and you, or at least the two of you, are on the front page of a magazine. The scandal sheets are living off you! What you said that time in my apartment, about the rise in circulation of papers and magazines all over the world . . ."

"I remember."

"And you were right. Even more than you foresaw. Circulation has shot up in a way that's hard to believe. I heard that on television, which, by the way, is also making hay with the Moran case. You can't imagine, no one can who hasn't seen it happen, what advertising the Moran case has been for *The Chalk Circle!* The picture is still running in Nürnberg. Sold out every day. I haven't seen it yet. You have to reserve seats. And that's Nürnberg, a single city in Germany! And it's like that in every city all over the world. According to a statement

508

by Seven Stars, they're expecting a gross of four hundred million dollars!"

"Four hundred million dollars," I said softly.

"Joe Gintzburger is a clever man."

"He's a crook."

"That too. Naturally."

We were still walking hand in hand.

"How much visiting time did they give you?"

"They didn't say. They were very friendly. I'm practically sure, beloved, that your trial won't take long. Perhaps you'll get a suspended sentence."

"Perhaps." Suddenly I thought of something. " 'Confounded, we see the curtain down and nothing settled.' "

"That's from the Epilogue of *The Good Woman of Sechuan*. Brecht," said Ruth, looking at me astonished.

"Yes. And I just had to think of it. They have a wonderful library here. I read Brecht at night, when I couldn't sleep. Brecht and many other writers. The curtain down and ... and nothing settled. So many questions left open."

We walked on for a while silently. Then I asked, "Where is Joe?"

"Back in Hollywood."

"Then I can imagine what a production they'll make of Sylvia's funeral."

Ruth stopped. I did too.

"I spoke to Dr. Kassner when he was here," Ruth said. "We talked about Sylvia. Kassner said that from a psychological standpoint, Sylvia was a potential murderess. You see, that's the tragic aspect of it for him, the tragic result of his efforts to treat her successfully. He did the best he could. And he succeeded to the extent that she no longer broke down under the weight of her problems. Unfortunately she also reached a point where she was able to resolve her problems *actively*—in other words, act them out. Specifically the problem of Rettland."

"By murder?"

"Yes, by murder."

"Because she was *well* again?"

Ruth shook her head. "Listen, beloved. Sylvia wasn't really well, wouldn't have stayed well for any length of time. She was finished, broken, even if it may have looked in Berlin as if she had recovered. Kassner said she might have lasted through *Mission in Berlin*. Perhaps. Probably not. In any case, she would have collapsed again and never been able to make another picture, not with her guilt feelings."

I breathed deeply. "And Joe knew this!" I said. Suddenly everything was crystal clear to me.

"Kassner never mentioned it to him."

"Of course not! But Joe is a clever crook. In his lifetime he has seen many actors and actresses break down. He knew what was wrong with Sylvia. He didn't need a doctor to tell him. And I'm sure he made the best of a bad business. He squeezed as much money as he could out of a broken woman, and it turned out to be millions! He put on a last, gigantic spectacular with this pitiful wreck of a human being."

Ruth stared at me wide-eyed. "You really believe that?"

I nodded. "Yes. Now I can see exactly what his plan was, and what all the trial witnesses he could influence were planning. And that covers practically everyone involved, because all of them were dependent on him. For that shark, Sylvia was already dead, regardless of how much longer she might have lived, yes, even if they had acquitted her. Dead! Because he had no more use for her! Dead as an actress, as an object of value. But still to be exploited if he hurried. And he hurried!"

"My God!" Ruth was shaken.

"I know the industry! I know Joe! Believe me, dearest, that's the way it was. Joe's heart leaped with joy when Carmen Cruzeiro gave her venemous testimony, when I was arrested, when Bracken was exposed. His heart leaped with joy over everything that could make headlines! The trial was the last film Joe made with Sylvia! And he finagled a happy ending for himself, a happy ending he probably hadn't dared think of—no, that he probably had in mind all the time. I mean Sylvia's death. And he got it. And *that* was the greatest happy ending of his life!"

We walked on silently for a moment. "And he won't be punished for it?" asked Ruth.

"People like him aren't punished. Not in any ordinary fashion. Sometimes in an extraordinary way. But more often than not, not at all."

She looked at her watch. "I must get back to the hospital, beloved."

"When will you come again?"

"Tomorrow." And now she was smiling her wonderful smile. "The magistrate said I could visit you whenever I wanted to. And that's a good sign too. And oh . . . I almost

510

forgot . . . this is a present from Babs. She said I should give it to you just as soon as I saw you."

I took the small package and opened it. Babs had made a clay plate for me, the size of the palm of my hand, not exactly round, and not smooth, but it was a plate. No doubt about it. And Babs had smeared paint on it, red, blue, yellow and white spots, and thin green lines.

"Do you suppose they're flowers?"

"Yes. I think that's what they are," said Ruth. "Isn't it wonderful, what she can do?"

"Wonderful," I said, and could feel the tears rush to my eyes.

"She is making progress, dearest. I told you."

"Yes. Real progress."

"Of course it will take years before she reaches a point where she won't go under, when she will be able to live with the help of a healthy person. But she will *live*, dearest! She will live!"

"Yes."

"It doesn't matter whether she can stay in Heroldsheid or has to be moved somewhere else. It doesn't matter how many setbacks she has. She will always get a little bit better. She will never be perfectly all right, there can be no question of that. But she will be better. We just don't know how or when or where."

"No," I said. "That we don't know."

"But we know that she will never be alone again," said Ruth, looking at me seriously.

"That's right. She'll never be alone again," I said. I thought of Clarissa's farewell letter when she had begged me never to abandon Babs.

"I really must go now."

"Yes, beloved. And you'll come again tomorrow?"

"Certainly. Tomorrow."

We kissed. We clung to each other. Ruth smiled at me once more, then she walked away quickly down the gravel path. I watched her go. She turned around several times and waved. I thought I'd better go after her and lead her, because, with her idiosyncrasy, she was heading for the wrong door. I was about to shout and call her attention to her mistake when I realized all of a sudden that she wasn't going wrong at all! She walked past the wrong door, waved once more, then she was gone. For the first time since I had known her, Ruth had chosen the right direction.

I don't know how long I stood there in the shade. Suddenly I started, Babs's little plate in my hand. I had been looking at it for a long time, looking at the many colored spots and lines smeared on it. And I remembered a small plaque of thin gold that I had seen on the bookshelf wall of Ruth's apartment. The words . . .

Yes, I thought, they were flowers Babs had been trying to paint. A lot of small flowers. I put the little clay plate in my pocket carefully, and walked to the door that led back into the prison. It was quite cool now. Night was falling and my feet crunched on the gravel. I saw the high gray walls of the prison, with its many barred windows, and thought of the gold plaque and the words on it:

What are flowers for?
They are there so that they may bloom.